The Infrared Spectra of Complex Molecules

VOLUME TWO

Advances in Infrared Group Frequencies

The Infrared Spectra of Complex Molecules

VOLUME TWO

Advances in Infrared
Group Frequencies

L. J. BELLAMY

C.B.E., B.Sc., Ph.D.

SECOND EDITION

1980

CHAPMAN AND HALL

LONDON AND NEW YORK

150th Anniversary

First published 1968
by Methuen and Co. Ltd.,
Second edition 1980
Published by Chapman and Hall Ltd.,
11 New Fetter Lane, London EC4P 4EE
Published in the U.S.A. by
Chapman and Hall
in association with Methuen Inc.,
733 Third Avenue, New York, NY 10017
Typeset by John Wright & Sons Ltd.,
at the Stonebridge Press, Bristol
Printed in the United States of America

© 1968, 1980, L. J. Bellamy

ISBN 0 412 22350 3

British Library Cataloguing in Publication Data
Bellamy, Lionel John
    The infrared spectra of complex molecules:–
    2nd ed.
    Vol. 2: Advances in infrared group frequencies
    1. Molecular spectra
    2. Infra-red spectrometry
    3. Chemistry, Organic
    I. Title
    547'.1'28   QD272.S6   80-40094

ISBN 0-412-22350-3

Preface to the Second Edition

I have always regarded this book as being the completion of my earlier book, *The Infrared Spectra of Complex Molecules*. The latter sets out all the existing experimental facts on group frequencies in the infrared, but does not attempt to explain them. This present book is primarily concerned to explain why group frequencies move about in the way that they do following changes in substitution. I am therefore very glad that the publishers have decided that the two books should be regarded as Volumes 1 and 2 of a unified work on infrared group frequencies. Both aspects seem to me to be of equal importance. One cannot interpret an infrared spectrum without a good knowledge of the experimental facts, but too rigid an interpretation without any understanding of how these facts originate can lead to gross errors.

Time deals more severely with theories and with chemical mechanisms than it does with the results of experiment, so that this book after ten years has needed very extensive revision. I have rewritten about a third of the text, deleted about an equal amount, and have included about 450 new references from amongst the several thousand that it has been necessary to consult.

Some group frequencies, especially the XH stretching vibrations, are so free from coupling that they do afford a true measure of the bond strengths. A study of the factors which cause these frequencies to change is therefore a study of the mechanisms of chemistry itself. This is an area for which infrared has unique possibilities which have not as yet been fully exploited. A good example is the sizeable variations in the strengths of CH bonds in CH_3 and CH_2 groups which have been demonstrated by partial deuteration work. Hydrogen atoms which were previously thought to be equivalent have been shown to be not so, and bond energy differences in the CH bonds of methyl groups have been found to be as large as 13 k cal, in special cases. Two different mechanisms whereby such changes can occur have been shown to exist, mainly through a study of infrared group frequencies, and the results must influence current thinking on chemical mechanisms generally. Studies of this kind have also opened up new possibilities such as the estimation of bond lengths, bond angles, kinetic data and much else. There is scope for much more work in this field, and anyone who ventures into it will find that nearly all the experimental data he needs already exists, so that research of this kind is less tedious than would otherwise be the case, and it can be very rewarding, as I hope this book will show.

Contents

viii   Contents

1

Alkanes

1.1. Introduction

The standard correlations for saturated hydrocarbons are well established, and no new ones of major importance are now likely to come to light. Interest has therefore been concentrated either on the extension of the existing data and the development of specialized correlations for more limited situations or on the general improvement of our understanding of the underlying principles on which the correlations themselves are based.

So far as new correlations themselves are concerned, some advantage has been obtained from the higher-resolution instruments now becoming generally available, and correlations for such groups as Phenyl-CH_3, OCH_3 and NCH_3 are now available and appear to be capable of some further extension. A good deal of attention has also been directed to skeletal frequencies, particularly in alkyl benzenes and in groups such as the *sec*-butyl and *tert*-butoxy structures. Nevertheless, it is true that most of these correlations are based on specialist areas of study – hydrocarbons, alkyl aromatics, etc. – and will not be generally applicable elsewhere.

Significant advances have been made in our understanding of the nature of some of these group frequencies. The numbers and frequencies of all the complex coupled CH_2 rocking, twisting and wagging modes in longer-chain hydrocarbons have now been clearly worked out so that one can predict with reasonable precision all the bands likely to occur. Similarly, the factors which determine whether or not the $720 \, cm^{-1}$ CH_2 rocking mode will or will not split into two components, due to lattice interactions, are now thoroughly well understood. The realization that only certain types of crystallinity are likely to give rise to splitting of this band while others are not is of importance to those concerned with the study of crystalline/amorphous ratios in polymers and provides a good example of the significance of such fundamental studies to those concerned primarily with applications.

Recent studies on partially deuterated alkyl compounds have been particularly important, both in adding to our understanding of group frequency shifts, and in revealing the existence of interactions which were previously unsuspected but which are of considerable chemical importance. The demonstration by McKean *et al.* [71] that the uncoupled CH stretching frequency as derived from partial deuteration studies is a direct function of the CH bond length and of the dissociation energy enables us to identify frequency shifts with real changes in the hybridisation of the CH bonds and with changes in their chemical properties. There are minor exceptions to this generalisation, most of which are well understood, but it is remarkable that it covers the whole range of hybridisation states from alkanes to alkynes.

1.2. CH$_3$ stretching frequencies

(*a*) *The origins of changes in the* CH *stretching frequencies of methyl groups.* The methyl group has two fundamental CH stretching frequencies in molecules with C_{3V} symmetry, but this increases to three when the symmetry is C_S due to the removal of the degeneracy of the v_{as} vibration. At one time it was believed that there were large interactions between these stretching vibrations and the corresponding deformation modes. However partial, deuteration work has shown that such interactions are usually quite small and that there is good agreement between the mean CH stretch and the uncoupled frequency [74]. Any explanation of the changes of CH stretching frequencies must therefore be concerned with real chemical effects which change the hybridisation of the bonds.

There has been very little discussion in the literature of the origins of changes in CH stretching frequencies. Generally they are loosely attributed to alterations in the electronegativity of the adjacent atoms. Thus the high CH frequency of chloroform (3024 cm^{-1}) is attributed to the polar effects of the chlorine atoms. However, this does not stand up to detailed examination as the corresponding frequencies of bromoform and of iodoform are both higher than that of chloroform despite the lower electronegativities. In the methyl halides the CH stretch rises as the electronegativity of the halogen falls, and methyl iodide is found to absorb within a few wavenumbers of nitromethane. Perhaps the strongest evidence that electronegativity plays little part in determining the frequency is that replacement of three of the hydrogen atoms of methane by methyl groups lowers the frequency of the remaining CH bond by 98 cm^{-1} whereas replacement by three chlorine atoms raises it by 32 cm^{-1}. Both groups are more electronegative than hydrogen and both would therefore be expected to produce shifts in the same direction.

In studies on the CH stretching frequencies of methyl groups, using partial deuteration methods to eliminate any possible interference from coupling effects, McKean *et al.* [72] have been able to demonstrate that there is a good linear relationship between the frequency and the HCH bond angle over a very wide range of different compounds. Methyl groups attached to oxygen, nitrogen or fluorine do not follow this relationship, but these are known to be exceptional due to the lone pair interactions discussed in a later section. The otherwise general relation is in line with the previous findings of a relationship between vCH and rCH and confirms that the frequency is controlled by the hybridisation of the CH bond. It does not however give any indication of the mechanism responsible for the hybridisation changes. Any plot relating vCH to the percentage s character of the bonds must of course give a curve which rises steeply above 40% s. However, over that part which relates to angles between 105° and 115° the curvature is very small and the relationship is essentially linear as found.

Bellamy and Mayo [73] have sought to rationalise these findings as part of an overall explanation of the inequalities found in the individual CH bonds within a single methyl group. Such inequalities occur in many, but not of course all methyl groups and they are discussed in more detail in the following section. The explanation offered for the bond angle relationships found is in many ways parallel to the Gillespie–Nyholm approach which has been so successful in the interpretation of bond angle changes in inorganics, but it extends it by postulating interactions between the orbitals of bonds attached to adjacent atoms.

Gillespie and Nyholm pointed out that the electrons within each CH bond of methane will seek to get as far away from the electrons of the other CH bonds as possible. This leads directly to the tetrahedral arrangement. Similar considerations, after allowing for the effects of the lone pairs, enabled them to account satisfactorily for the observed bond angles of ammonia and of water. If one applies this principle to a molecule such as methyl chloride in which the C—Cl orbital is longer and more diffuse than the original CH orbital of methane, it will be seen that the repulsions between the individual CH bonds will be greater than those between CH and C—Cl. In consequence the HCH angles will open out and the hybridisation of the CH orbitals will change accordingly. The electronegativity of the substituent will play a minor role in determining the shape of the C—X orbital, but the C—X radius will be a much more important factor. It is due to the increasing size of the C—X radius that the CH stretching frequency rises in the methyl halides as one progresses from methyl fluoride to methyl iodide, as the repulsions between the adjacent CH bonds are progressively reduced, allowing the HCH angles to open out.

This accounts satisfactorily for those methyl compounds in which the HCH angles are greater than in methane, but there are a small number of cases, notably in the alkanes, in which these angles are reduced. In ethane for example the HCH angle is 107.5°, whilst in the methylene group of propane it is further reduced to 106.5°. Bellamy and Mayo [73] therefore suggest that orbital repulsions occur between C—H bonds on adjacent carbon atoms when they lie in the gauche configuration. If the combined effect of two gauche C—H bonds is greater than that of the original C—H of methane the HCH angle of the methyl group will close down as observed. The fact that such hydrogen atoms always do take a staggered rather than eclipsed conformation is clear evidence of some repulsive effect. This and related interactions are discussed more fully in the section which follows, but it is worth noting that this hypothesis would predict that the stretching frequencies on methyl groups joined to carbon atoms which do not carry hydrogen atoms or methyl groups should be somewhat higher than the frequency of methane itself (2992 cm^{-1}). This proves to be the case. The weighted mean CH stretching frequencies of such diverse compounds as CH_3COCl, CH_3COF, CH_3SO_2Cl and $CH_3SO_2NH_2$ are all close to 3000 cm^{-1}. It accounts also for one other unusual observation. Normally there is a close relationship between an XH stretching frequency and the corresponding bending mode. When an XH bond is lengthened the stretching frequency falls and the bending frequency rises. Both are the direct consequence of the increased p character of the link and there is a quantitative relation between the two. No such relationship is found between the behaviour of the CH stretch of methyl groups and the shifts of either the antisymmetric or the symmetric bend. It will be shown in the discussion in Section 1.5 that this behaviour is consistent with the postulate of orbital interactions.

Methyl groups in which the individual CH bonds are not the same

(a) *The effects of differing groups in the gauche position.* McKean and his collaborators have studied a very considerable number of alkyl compounds in which the individual CH bonds of the methyl group are non-equivalent [71, 74–82] and McKean [97] has written a comprehensive review of the available data. The effect is clearly shown through the use of CHD_2 groups when two, or even three different CH stretching bands appear due to the individual bonds. Even in propane there are small differences between the CH bonds of the methyl groups. The differences show up in the infrared but not in the NMR because the infrared can see the separate rotational isomers in which the individual CH bonds lie in different local environments. Some typical individual CH frequencies determined in this way are shown below:

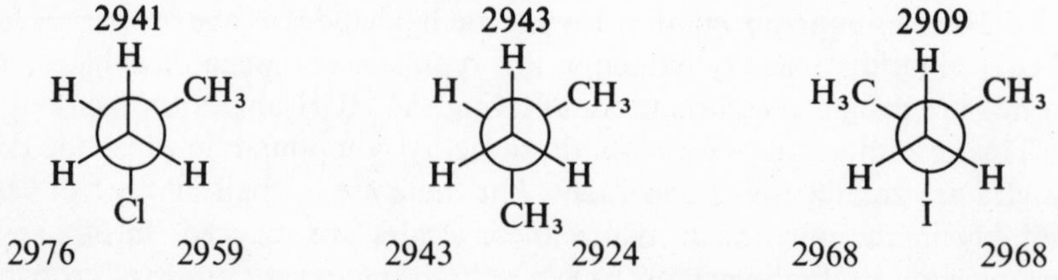

It will be seen that the CH frequency is dependent upon the local environment, and in particular on the nature of the atoms or groups which lie in the *gauche* position. McKean has studied this effect in alkanes, and in the ethyl, isopropyl and tertiary butyl halides, and has concluded that with respect to ethane, a *gauche* halogen atom raises the frequency by about 25 cm^{-1} (50 cm^{-1} for two *gauche* halogens), whilst a *gauche* methyl group lowers the frequency by about 32 cm^{-1} [77, 78]. These values show a good self-consistency throughout the series. McKean interprets these effects in terms of *trans* interactions with bonding pairs, similar in nature with those known to occur with lone pairs. However, there is a major difficulty in that the *gauche* effects of all the halogens appear to remain the same, despite the considerable variations in effective charge and in radius throughout the series. Such a result seems highly improbable either for a *trans* effect or for a local field interaction.

Bellamy and Mayo have therefore offered an alternative suggestion [73]. They propose that the interactions are largely limited to the orbitals of the CH bonds, which are reasonably close in space, and do not occur with the larger halogen atoms at longer distances. The frequency of a CH bond with two *gauche* halogen atoms remains close to that of methane which should be taken as the basis of assessment. The lowered frequencies of ethane then arise from the fact that each hydrogen atom is then affected by two others in the *gauche* position. The interaction with the *gauche* methyl group is assigned to a somewhat larger interaction between the CH orbits on the 1:3 atoms which lie nearly parallel to each other. There is an analogy for this in the well known 'rabbit ears effect' whereby conformations with parallel lone pairs on the 1:3 carbon are not allowed. A model of propane for example will show that whilst two hydrogen atoms of each methyl group lie *gauche* to a CH bond of the central methylene group, the third does not, and these two CH bonds lie in a near parallel arrangement. It is this difference which is responsible for the two separate CH stretching frequencies of the methyl group observed in partially deuterated methanes.

The earlier discussion on angle effects in methyl groups lists some of the supporting evidence for these ideas. However, there is some additional evidence:

(a) The CH stretching frequencies in the series $(CH_3)_4X$, are as follows

$X{=}C$ 2935 cm^{-1}, $X{=}Si$ 2939 cm^{-1}, $X{=}Ge$ 2954 cm^{-1}, $X{=}Sn$ 2960 cm^{-1}, $X{=}Pb$ 2978 cm^{-1}.

These values bear no relation to the polarity of the X atoms but they are consistent with a steady reduction in the CH interactions between adjacent methyl groups as these are moved further and further apart as the size of X increases.

(b) The hypothesis is consistent with the increased rotational barrier of propane as compared with ethane, and also with the observed HCH angles. In propane for example each of the CH bonds of the methylene group is *gauche* to four other CH bonds. Not only does their frequency fall to 2920 cm^{-1} but the HCH bond angle is reduced to $106.5°$.

(c) Precisely similar frequency effects can be seen in OH and NH bonds when these lie *gauche* to hydrogen atoms.

(d) Whenever such an effect is postulated it is observed to affect the frequencies of both of the CH bonds concerned. Thus the uncoupled aldehydic CH stretch of formaldehyde is 2813 cm^{-1} whereas that in acetaldehyde is 2770 cm^{-1}. This is attributed to orbital interaction with one of the CH bonds of the methyl group. Partial deuteration of the methyl group indeed shows that one CH bond has a frequency of 3002 cm^{-1} whereas the other two absorb at 2945 cm^{-1}. The former lies close to the oxygen atom and therefore absorbs close to methane, whilst the latter lie *gauche* to the aldehydic hydrogen and absorb close to ethane.

(e) Similar effects appear to occur in aromatics with interactions between the eclipsed CH bonds of the ring, and between these and attached methyl groups (see (b) below).

These interactions do not produce such large frequency shifts as do those which arise from *trans* lone pair effects. Nevertheless they can result in differences of as much as 50 cm^{-1} in the frequencies of the individual CH bonds in a methyl group, as for example in acetone. This approximates to a bond energy difference of 4–5 kcal, and these interactions are therefore of considerable importance in chemical kinetics.

(b) *Methyl groups attached to aromatic rings.* Toluene, the type compound, has been studied in detail by several workers [1–3] and compared with $C_6H_5CD_3$ and with $C_6D_5CD_3$. There is general agreement on the facts but not on the detailed assignments. This compound shows five bands as follows (the extinction coefficients being given in brackets as a guide to the relative intensities): 2970 cm^{-1} (16), 2946 cm^{-1} (20), 2916 cm^{-1} (34), 2869 cm^{-1} (16) and 2734 cm^{-1} (3). The band at 2916 cm^{-1} is the symmetrical stretching mode, and the weak band at 2734 the overtone of the symmetric methyl deformation ($2 \times \delta_S = 2758$). There is less agreement on the other assignments, but the most likely appear to be those of Josien, Fuson *et al.* [1, 4, 5, 6].

In toluene there is virtually free rotation of the methyl group, so that it is not possible to identify differences between the individual CH_3 bonds by partial deuteration. There is however evidence of interactions between these CH bonds and those of the CH groups on the ring at the *ortho* positions. Thus removal of these *ortho* hydrogens and their replacement by halogen or nitro groups raises the methyl stretching frequencies. In 2:4:6-trinitrotoluene for example the main bands occur at 3018, 2954 and 2916 cm^{-1}. At the same time there is a similar rise in the CH ring stretching frequencies, presumably as a result of the removal of the methyl interaction. In 1:3:5-trihalogenated benzenes, the main ring CH band is near 3100 cm^{-1}, as compared with 3053 in 1:3:5-trideuterobenzene, and to 3020 cm^{-1} in the corresponding trimethyl compound in which the methyl effect is maximised.

There have been extensive studies of variously substituted toluenes [1, 4, 5, 6], of methyl naphthalenes and anthracenes and of methylated polycyclic aromatics [7]. In general, the pattern of toluene is repeated with some intensity variations, particularly in the two higher-frequency bands.

Methylated heterocyclics have been less studied, but some data of Scrocco and Caglioti [8] on pyrrole derivatives show that the correlations listed above are obeyed. However, they failed to detect the ν_{a1} band in four out of eight compounds, presumably because of intensity variations.

(c) *Methoxy groups.* The study of compounds such as CCl_3COOMe [6, 9] and CD_3COOMe [10], in which the only hydrogen atoms present are in the methyl group, shows that the methoxy group has a pattern of five bands in the CH stretching region. However, the spectra are distinctive in that they contain a strong band in the 2845–2800 cm^{-1} range. It is sufficiently well removed and sufficiently intense for it to be valuable in identification. Several authors have noted the occurrence of this band, and Meakins *et al.* [11, 12], and also Nolin and Jones [10], have shown by deuteration studies that it is primarily associated with the O—CH_3 group. In aromatic methoxy derivatives [13] the band appears at essentially the same position as in esters (2845 cm^{-1}), but there is some further fall in the frequency of alkoxy materials which absorb in the region 2820–2810 cm^{-1}. At one time it was generally believed [1, 6, 9] that this band arose from a Fermi resonance interaction with the symmetric deformation mode, but partial deuteration studies have shown that this is in fact very limited [75], and that the low frequency arises from a different cause. McKean's studies on such compounds as CD_2HOCD_3 and $CD_2H\ OD$ have shown that two CH stretching bands appear in both cases. Two separate rotational isomers must therefore exist. These possibilities for methanol are illustrated below in a projection looking along the carbon oxygen bond. It will be seen that in one conformation the CH bond lies between the two oxygen

lone pairs, and that in the other it lies *trans* to one of them. It is this second conformation which is thought to be responsible for the lower CH stretching frequency, with the lone pair donating electrons into an anti-bonding orbital of the *trans* CH bond [83]. The phenomenon appears to be a general one and similar effects are observed in NCH_3 compounds (see below), and in some OH and NH compounds where a lone pair is available on the adjacent atom. There is also strong chemical evidence that a similar weakening of a C—C bond *trans* to a lone pair can occur, although this cannot be observed in the infrared [84–86]. The most surprising aspect of this interaction is not that it occurs, but the magnitude of the effect. In dimethyl ether the CH frequencies of the two isomers differ by 100 cm^{-1}, and as will be seen in trimethylamine the difference rises to 150 cm^{-1}. These correspond to dissociation energy differences between the individual CH bonds of the methyl group of about 9 and 13 kcal. The bonds are therefore weakened by about 10% as a result of this interaction. These studies therefore point the way to a hitherto unrecognised mechanism of chemistry, which in some situations could be of dominant importance in determining the course of a reaction.

The lone pair effect of oxygen is an entirely general one and occurs in compounds such as dimethylperoxide [91], methanol [75], methyl esters and similar materials. The resonance in esters reduces the availability of the lone pairs for donation so that the frequency rises to 2845 cm^{-1}. In ether complexes in which the lone pair is donated to an acceptor such as magnesium bromide the frequency rises still higher [92, 93].

(d) *N Methyl and* N(CH$_3$)$_2$. A comparison of the spectra of aniline and *N*-methylaniline [14] shows that the methyl group is again giving rise to multiple absorptions in the 3000–2800-cm^{-1} region. However, attention has been concentrated almost exclusively on the strong band at the lower end of this range, which seems to be most characteristic of this group. Hill and Meakins [14] first drew attention to this and pointed out that the position of the band varied, depending upon whether or not the CH$_3$ group was attached to *N*-Aryl or *N*-Alkyl groups, and also upon whether there were one or two methyl groups on the nitrogen atom. In this way these various possibilities can be differentiated. They suggested the following correlations:

C$_6$H$_5$·NCH$_3$ 2820–2810 cm^{-1}; alkyl or non-aromatic heterocyclic-N—CH$_3$ 2805–2780 cm^{-1}: C$_6$H$_5$·N(CH$_3$)$_2$ near 2800 cm^{-1} and the corresponding alkyl N(CH$_3$)$_2$ two bands 2825–2810 and 2775–2765 cm^{-1}.

Deuteration studies by Dalton, Hill and Meakins [12] on methyl aniline have confirmed the association of the 2814 cm^{-1} band with the methyl group. Independent work by Braunholtz et al. [15] and by Wright [16] led to similar conclusions, but with one important reservation. Braunholtz et al. noted that the band was absent in amides, in complexes with amines with metals, and in other compounds such as 1(H)-methylquinol-4-one, in which there is a substantial degree of delocalization of the lone-pair electrons of the nitrogen atom. It was at first thought that this low frequency band arose from a Fermi resonance interaction with the overtone of the deformation mode. However, Bohlmann [70] pointed out that a similar band appeared in compounds with a CH$_2$ group adjacent to a nitrogen atom, provided that the conformation was such that one of the CH bonds lay *trans* to the nitrogen lone pair. He therefore assigned this band to a weakened CH bond affected by donation from the *trans* lone pair. This assignment has been fully confirmed by partial deuteration studies by McKean et al. [71, 79, 84, 97], by the work of Ernstbrunner and Hudec [98], and by the findings of Graffeuil et al. [99], that the low frequency bands of the methyl groups of *cis* dimethylhydrazine are removed when this compound is complexed with BF$_3$. The complex formation is at the nitrogen atom which carries the methyl groups and the removal of its lone pair eliminates the trans interaction. The differences between the individual CH bonds of a methyl group of methylamine are very considerable, and are even greater in trimethylamine where the individual bands of the partially deuterated compound differ by 150 cm^{-1}. However, not all of this difference can be attributed to the lone pair effect, as some part of it is probably due to the weakening of the bond by the two *gauche* methyl groups in this second compound. Nevertheless the total difference corresponds to about 13 kcal and this clearly has important chemical implications. This low frequency band appears to be considerably intensified as a result of the interactions which weaken the bond, so that it can usually be seen clearly even in large molecules with few CH_3 groups of this kind.

This correlation is a valuable one, but must be used with discretion, paying due regard to the extent to which the nitrogen atom lone pairs are likely to be delocalized in the specific compound in question. Some studies of the CH_3-stretching frequencies of the methyl ammonium ion in compounds such as $CH_3NH_3^+$ Cl^-, $(CH_3)_3NH^+$ Cl^-, etc., have been given by Bellanato [17]. However, he worked in alkali halide discs and found that in each case the precise frequencies varied with the alkali halide chosen. These frequencies therefore have little application in correlation studies.

(*e*) *Methyl groups with other substituents.* Assignments for the multiple CH_3-stretching bands in compounds such as the methyl halides and in methyl cyanide have been given by Josien *et al.* [6, 9], and these have been amplified by McKean [71]. Compounds of this kind give only a single CH stretching band on partial deuteration. However, there are two separate types of bonds in compounds in which the methyl group is directly attached to the carbonyl group. One CH bond is eclipsed to the carbonyl group, and has a frequency near 3000 cm^{-1} whilst the other two are staggered with respect to the other carbonyl substituent. In acetaldehyde, these last two hydrogens are *gauche* to the aldehydic hydrogen atom and their frequency is therefore similar to ethane. This interaction does not lead to a sufficiently large shift to be useful for identification of this group from the frequencies. However, it does have a remarkable effect on the intensities. Unlike the lone pair interactions described above where the intensity increases, it is found that the CH stretching bands, both symmetric and antisymmetric, are weakened by a factor of about ten, whilst there is an intensity increase of about the same amount in the symmetrical deformation band. The weakening of the stretching bands is observed with some other substituents, such as CCl_3, NO_2, SCN, NCS, and I, but only with the carbonyl and the thiocyanate group is there such a large intensification of the deformation band. Higuchi *et al.* [88] have reported intensity values for the stretching and bending bands of a number of methyl compounds and have attempted to relate their results to the polarity of the substituents. However, there is no simple relationship between the intensities of these two absorptions and wide variations are observed.

Lone pair effects resulting in lowered CH stretching frequencies have been postulated for elements other than oxygen and nitrogen. It seems very probable that the low frequencies of methyl fluoride as compared with methyl chloride are primarily due to this. This is consistent with the fact that, along with oxygen and nitrogen, these values are exceptions to the frequency–angle relationship described by McKean [72]. There is less evidence that these effects extend widely into second and third row elements. The methyl stretching frequencies of dimethyl sulphide and dimethyl sulphoxide for example are similar. However, there is evidence of a rise in the stretching frequency of methyl phosphorus compounds when the phosphorus becomes pentavalent and the availability of the lone pair is removed. This is supported by NMR evidence for the presence of two rotational isomers in some $R-CH_3$ compounds [94].

(*f*) *The influence of polar groups not directly attached to the methyl group.* It is generally accepted that the effect of polar groups not directly attached to the methyl group can produce small upward shifts in vCH. Wiberley, Bunce and Bauer [18], for example, quote slightly higher-frequency ranges for methyl group stretching frequencies in oxygenated and sulphurated compounds as compared with those of the hydrocarbons. The most detailed and interesting study of this effect is due to Gotoh and Takenaka [19], who have measured v_{as} and v_s for the methyl group in alcohols, acids and bromides of various chain lengths. In all the straight-chain compounds both these frequencies decrease exponentially as the chain lengthens, attaining an exponential value at $N = 6$–7, which is the same as that of the parent hydrocarbons. The magnitude of the shifts can be assessed from the typical values given below:

	v_{as}	v_s
$CH_3 \cdot CH_2 \cdot COOH$	2986	2889
$CH_3 \cdot [CH_2]_2 \cdot COOH$	2970	2879
$CH_3 \cdot [CH_2]_3 \cdot COOH$	2964	2876
$CH_3 \cdot [CH_2]_4 \cdot COOH$	2961	2874
$CH_3 \cdot [CH_2]_5 \cdot COOH$	2960	2874
$CH_3 \cdot [CH_2]_{6-8} \cdot COOH$	2959	2873
$CH_3 \cdot [CH_2]_8 \cdot CH_3$	2959	2873

The biggest changes occur in the first members of the series, where the local environment of one of the methyl CH bonds changes from a *gauche* carbonyl group to a *gauche* CH_2. This would be expected to result in a fall in the frequency. Thereafter the changes are relatively small and it is difficult to decide whether these arise from small residual inductive effects or to minor changes in the local interactions, but it is noteworthy that the conformation of the chain appears to be more important than the polarity of the substituent groups.

Similar rises as compared with the hydrocarbons are shown by the other series. In branched-chain systems each methyl group is affected, depending upon the number of carbon atoms which separate it from the parent substituent. Gotoh and Takenaka [19] have derived the empirical relation $v - v_0 = Ae^{-BN}$. v_0 is the corresponding value for the saturated hydrocarbon, N is the number of carbon atoms in the chain and A, and B are constants for any one series. The constant A is a characteristic of the polarity of the substituent and B of the effectiveness of transmission of the inductive effect along the chain. This is controlled more by the configuration of the chain than by the type of polar group. In straight chains there is a diminution of the impact of the effect by about 0·45 for each intervening link between the polar substituent and the methyl group.

It is surprising to find that polar effects of this kind are relayed so far along the alkyl chain, but there is other evidence in support of this from intensity measurements which show that a polar substituent has an impact upon the intensity of adjacent methylene groups which attenuates slowly, but is still perceptible at the fourth carbon atom away from the polar substituent. Clearly, effects of this kind can invalidate determinations of chain lengths through intensity studies unless due allowance is made for them.

1.3. CH$_2$ stretching frequencies

Open chains. Gotoh and Takenaka [19] have studied the possibility of recognising CH$_2$ groups adjacent to polar atoms, but the problem is much more difficult than that presented by the terminal CH$_3$ group. It seems clear that, under high resolution, a detectable shift towards higher frequencies can be observed when polar groups are introduced into a hydrocarbon chain, but as these affect several adjacent CH$_2$ groups to different extents, the result cannot give precise correlations of much value. It is to be expected that the behaviour of CH$_2$ stretching frequencies will be closely parallel to those of the methyl group detailed above and that they will respond to substitution changes in the same ways and to a similar extent. Much less data are available, but Bohlmann [70] has shown that a CH$_2$ group adjacent to a nitrogen atom will show the 2800 cm^{-1} band provided the nitrogen lone pair lies trans to the CH bond, and Kreuger and Jan [89] have shown by deuteration methods that it is possible to differentiate between axial and equatorial CH bonds in cyclic imines. They have also detected the lone pair effect on the CH$_2$ group in propylamines [95]. A similar result must be expected for oxygen substitution. Similarly, the lower CH stretch of the methylene group of propane as compared with the methyl CH bonds can be attributed to interactions with the *gauche* methyl group, and this is supported by the closure of the HCH bond angle. It seems likely that there is a relationship between the CH$_2$ frequency and this angle, just as there is for the methyl group, but there are as yet insufficient data to establish this.

CH$_2$- *and* CH-*stretching frequencies in cyclic systems*

Markova *et al.* [21] have examined CH-stretching frequencies of cycloheptane and cyclopentane rings joined by CH$_2$ chains of different lengths. By measurements of the absorption coefficients, they find that the intensities of bands at 2947 and 2863 cm^{-1} are independent of the length of the connecting chain, while the intensity of a third band at 2915 cm^{-1} varies directly with chain length. They therefore ascribe the first pair of bands to the ring system and the last to the methylene chain. This correlation, however, is likely to be limited, as these values will certainly change if any polar substituents are introduced. Thus Boobyer [20] has shown that there are major intensity changes in the CH$_2$-stretching bands when carbonyl or exocyclic methylene groups are introduced into the ring. In addition, the intensity then becomes a function of the ring size, at least so far as the smaller rings are concerned. The absolute intensities per CH$_2$ group of cyclohexanone, cyclopentanone and cyclobutanone are 9000, 6300 and 4000 cm^2 mol^{-1}/l respectively.

Studies have also been reported on CH$_2$-stretching frequencies in cyclic hetero systems such as dioxane [22], and on CH frequencies in fluorinated cyclohexanones [23]. These again are of value only in limited specialist fields, but the latter does, for example, show that it is possible to differentiate between axial and equatorial hydrogen atoms in such systems.

One set of observations of particular theoretical interest concerns CH$_2$ groups in special environments in which hydrogen atoms from two separate methylene groups are brought together very close in space. Situations of this kind occur in certain fused bicycloheptane derivatives and in half-cage structures. Kivelson, Winstein, Bruck and Hansen [24] have examined some thirteen examples in which this situation occurs and compared them with other similar structures in which the opposition of the hydrogen atoms is removed. They find that these special environments lead to CH$_2$-stretching frequencies in the 3049–3018 cm^{-1} range, and they associate this with an increase in the CH-stretching force constants as a direct result of interaction between the opposed hydrogen atoms. This result must also be borne in mind when one is attempting to identify cyclopropane residues by virtue of their elevated CH-stretching frequencies. It is important to note that the conformations in these special compounds are very different from those other interactions between CH bonds described in Section 1.2(a) which result in a frequency fall. In the latter the orbitals of the CH bonds lie close enough to interact. In the special cases described by Kivelson et al. the protons themselves are thrust into near proximity and the resulting interaction is of a different kind.

A good deal of further work has been done on the CH-stretching frequencies of cyclopropane derivatives. A small number of compounds have come to light in which the usual 3060–3040 cm^{-1} correlation fails. These are either heavily substituted rings containing polar groups [25] or spiranes such as 7,7'-spirobis (bicyclo[4,1,0]-heptane) [26]. However, these are exceptional. Wiberley et al. [18] confirm the original correlation in some sixty cyclopropanes. Further data by Passivirta [27] and by Liebman and Gudzinowicz [28] support this. The latter workers make the significant distinction that cyclopropanes containing a CH$_2$ group absorb in the range 3077–3058 cm^{-1}, whereas those with a tertiary CH group absorb at 3012–3003 cm^{-1}. This correlation remains the most useful way in which cyclopropane residues can be detected, although some account should also be taken of the skeletal frequencies.

Finally, in the special field of steroids mention should be made of the high-resolution studies of Smith and Eddy [29]. They have observed changes in the vCH-stretching patterns which accompany minor structural changes; often these are no more than the appearance or otherwise of a small shoulder on the side of a major band; nevertheless, within the special context of the steroid group such factors can be significant, and some helpful correlations have been worked out which are, of course, applicable only within this field.

1.4. The symmetric methyl deformation frequency

(*a*) *Correlations.* The position of the CH$_3$ *sym*-deformation vibration is dependent almost entirely upon the nature of the element to which the methyl group is joined. This, and the characteristic splitting which occurs when more than one methyl group is joined to the same atom, makes this one of the most valuable correlations for diagnostic work. Recently, attempts have been made to extend the value of these correlations by studying the minor frequency shifts which occur when alterations are made in other substituents on the X atom. The results are set out in Table 1.1, which lists values for this frequency in a number of individual compounds, and also the frequency ranges which have been suggested for specific cases.

It will be seen that in the case of methyl groups joined to carbon atoms the observed shifts are indeed small. It is noteworthy, however, that methyl ketones show a low value for this absorption (1359 ± 5). This parallels the behaviour of methylene groups, where deformation vibrations also move to lower frequencies when they are adjacent to carbonyl compounds. However, the lowering is offset to some extent in acetates and in secondary (but not tertiary) amides. The rise of 10 cm^{-1} suggested for this vibration in ethoxy compounds is surprisingly large in view of the small changes brought about by other groups, and should perhaps be confirmed. In general, these effects are too small to find much application in correlation work, but they are, of course, of considerable theoretical interest.

With methyl oxygen compounds the results show that, as before, other substituents on the oxygen have little effect on the basic frequency. However, dimethoxyborane is an exception [34], and absorbs at 1493 cm^{-1}. This must indicate a major charge displacement on the oxygen atom and provides perhaps the most convincing evidence yet available of back-donation of electrons from the oxygen to the boron. The methyl nitrogen compounds have been the least studied, and this is a pity, because these are undoubtedly the most promising for correlation purposes. The effective nuclear charge on the nitrogen atom does vary appreciably with its environment, depending particularly upon the extent of delocalization of the lone-pair electrons. A corresponding shift of the *sym*-deformation mode might therefore be expected. The values for a few isolated compounds listed in the table certainly show a wide range of frequencies. Correlations have also been proposed [17, 40] for NMe groups in amino acid and amine hydrochlorides, although it is not clear whether these represent an anti-symmetric or symmetric CH_3 deformation or a combination of both. It is at least clear that this region is worthy of more intensive study in these instances.

(*b*). The values for methyl-group frequencies when the CH_3 is attached to other elements are included primarily to illustrate the discussion below. However, it is noteworthy that the characteristic interaction splitting which occurs when more than one methyl group is attached to the same atom persists in other elements also. The splitting of the symmetric methyl deformation in so many *gem*. dimethyl compounds has been discussed by Bellamy and Mayo [69] and by Horak and Pliva [90]. It would seem that this is largely a steric effect and that the splitting occurs only when the angle between the two methyl groups is sufficiently small to bring them into very close proximity. Thus, while the isopropyl group shows a clear-cut splitting, only a single band is shown in 1,1-dimethyl olefines in which the angle is opened out to 120°. Similarly, there is no splitting in $B(CH_3)_3$, even when account is taken of the Raman spectrum, but two bands appear in $(CH_3)_2B\overset{\overset{\displaystyle H}{\diagup\diagdown}}{\underset{\underset{\displaystyle H}{\diagdown\diagup}}{}}B(CH_3)_2$, in which the angle between the methyl groups is reduced. Linear compounds such as dimethyl mercury show no splitting, but two bands appear in the planar compound $(CH_3)_2Au\overset{\overset{\displaystyle I}{\diagup\diagdown}}{\underset{\underset{\displaystyle I}{\diagdown\diagup}}{}}Au(CH_3)_2$, in which the angle is again small. It is possible that the further development of this approach could lead to a useful method of detecting angle changes in suitably substituted co-ordination compounds.

(*c*) *Theories of the shift of* CH_3 *sym-deformation vibrations with changes in X*. Table 1.1 shows that this frequency has a unique value for every element, and it is therefore natural to inquire how this arises and what information these values give us on the nature of the C—X bonds. The frequencies are always a good deal higher than those of the corresponding C—X vibrations, and it is now generally accepted that there is little or no mechanical coupling between the two modes [35]. Coupling does, however, take place in the deuterated species in which the CD frequencies are lowered, and this is responsible for the low value for the CH/CD ratios which usually occur. In the absence of mass effects the most obvious alternative is to ascribe the whole of the shifts to changes in the hybridization in the orbits used by carbon in bonding to X, which must necessarily be accompanied by changes in the orbits used to bond with H, and so to changes in the frequency. There have therefore been a

Table 1.1. Selected literature values for the *sym*.CH$_3$ deformation frequency in various environments (cm^{-1})

Methyl-Carbon		Methyl-Other Elements	
CH$_3$–C	1370–1380	CH$_3$ F	1475
CH$_3$CN	1389	CH$_3$ Cl	1355
CH$_3$CF$_3$	1409	CH$_3$ Br	1305
CH$_3$CCl$_3$	1386	CH$_3$ I	1252
CH$_3$C≡CH	1382	(CH$_3$)$_2$ S	1325. 1315
CH$_3$NO$_2$	1397	(CH$_3$)$_2$ Se	1282
CH$_3$COOH	1381	(CH$_3$)$_2$ Zn	1185
C$_6$H$_5$CH$_2$	1381	(CH$_3$)$_2$ Hg	1205
[30] RCOCH$_3$	1359 ± 5	(CH$_3$)$_2$ Cd	1384 or 1129*
[31] C$_6$H$_5$OCH$_2$CH$_3$	1390	(CH$_3$)$_3$ P	1293. 1312
[33] ROCOCH$_3$	1375–1315	(CH$_3$)$_3$ As	1242. 1263
[32] CH$_3$CONHX	1373–1363	(CH$_3$)$_3$ SB	1194. 1213
[32] CH$_3$CON(CH$_3$)X	1356–1343	(CH$_3$)$_3$ B	1306
		(CH$_3$)$_3$ Bi	1147. 1165
Methyl–Oxygen		(CH$_3$)$_4$ Si	1250. 1263
CH$_3$OH	1455	(CH$_3$)$_4$ Ge	1240. 1247
[31] CH$_3$OC$_6$H$_5$	1438–1450	(CH$_3$)$_4$ Sn	1198. 1205
[30] CH$_3$OCOX	1439 ± 3	(CH$_3$)$_4$ Pb	1154. 1170
(CH$_3$O)$_2$ BH	1493		
[9] XCOOCH$_3$	1439 ± 5		
Methyl–Nitrogen			
CH$_3$NH$_2$	1426		
CH$_3$N$_3$	1417		
CH$_3$NCO	1377		
CH$_3$NC	1429		
((CH$_3$)$_2$N)$_2$	1460		
XNCH$_3$COCH$_3$	1384–1374		
XNCH$_3$COC$_6$H$_5$	1372–1353		
[40] CH$_3$NH$_3^+$·COO—	(Amino acid hydrochlorides)	(N.B. No distinction between δ_aCH$_3$ and δ_sCH$_3$.)	
[40 · 17] CH$_3$NH$^+$	1484 ± 5		
Amine-hydrochlorides	1470 ± 5		

* The assigned value of 1384 cm^{-1} seems to be so much out of line with the other data that it is tempting to consider the 1129-cm^{-1} band, which is also D-sensitive as the *sym*-CH$_3$ absorption.

number of attempts to relate the frequency shifts with the electronegativity of X. Wilmshurst [36], for example, related E (electronegativity) to v^2, and within a more limited series King and Crawford [35] relate it to the CH bending-force constants. However, a study of Table 1.1 shows that there is no universal relationship of this kind. The CH$_3$ deformation frequencies of CH$_3$Br and (CH$_3$)$_3$B are the same within 1 cm^{-1}, but it is certain that the electronegativity of bromine is greater than that of boron. Neither is the electronegativity of CH$_3$ (δ 1375 cm^{-1}) nor CCl$_3$ (δ 1389 cm^{-1}) likely to be greater than that of chlorine (δ 1355 cm^{-1}). Valid relations of this kind exist, as Sheppard [37] pointed out as long ago as 1955, only within any one group or any one row of the periodic table.

A further complication is the fact that force-constant correlations show that, although there is no mechanical coupling between δCH_3 and $\nu C—X$, there is nevertheless a cross-term in the potential-energy function which represents a repulsion force between X and the hydrogen atoms [35]. Calculations by Overend and Scherer [38], using Urey Bradley force fields, suggest that this force may well be considerable, amounting in the extreme case of CH_3F to 1·118 md/A, i.e. to about a quarter of the CH bond stretching force constants. While the precise magnitude of this value is doubtful, there can be little doubt that non-bonding interactions of this kind must be taken into account in any interpretation of the frequency shift.

The order of the CH_3 deformation frequencies as given by Table 1.1 is as follows:

$$F > O > N > CF_3 > CCl_3 > CH_3 > Cl > B > Br > P, \text{ etc.}$$

and although this is an unusual order, Bellamy [39] has pointed out that it has a direct parallel in the order of force constants for the HX-stretching frequencies themselves. There is a good smooth-curve relation between KHX and δCH_3X. The curvature is to be expected from a plot of force constants vs. frequencies, and would probably be found to vanish if reliable force constants for the CH_3X series were available and could be plotted directly against KHX. Now the values of KHX are thought to be controlled by the polarity of X and by its effective radius, and this implies that the radius of X is also a factor in determining the δCH_3 frequency. That this is indeed so is shown by a simple plot of δCH_3X vs. $rC—X$, when it is found that there are stepwise changes as one moves down the periodic table and corresponding to stepwise increases in the radius as each electron shell is completed.

The particularly interesting feature of the symmetric deformation frequencies is that they do not parallel the changes in the corresponding stretching modes. The latter have been shown (in the absence of any lone pair interactions) to be directly related to the HCH bond angles and so to the hybridisation of the CH orbitals. Normally deformation modes are similarly influenced, and a frequency fall in the stretching mode produces a proportionate rise in the corresponding deformation. In the case of the methyl group, the antisymmetric deformation seems to be almost indifferent to the nature of the substituent, whilst the symmetric mode parallels the behaviour of the corresponding XH compound rather than the hybridisation of the CH bonds. In the discussion of the stretching frequencies of CH_3X compounds it was concluded that hybridisation of the CH bonds was determined by the relative repulsions between the orbitals of the CH bonds and those of CX. In the latter case the orbital repulsion will be determined by the length of the CX bond and by the polarity of X insofar as it alters the orbital shape. These same two factors must operate in the deformation mode also, but it seems likely that the relative importance of each will be different in a vibration in which all three CH bonds are simultaneously bending towards the CX bond than will be the case when they are stretching away from it. Thus whilst the CH stretching frequencies of $SiCH_3$ compounds are only slightly perturbed from those of CCH_3 compounds, the corresponding symmetric deformation frequency falls by $115 \, cm^{-1}$ [39].

1.5. The CH_2 deformation frequency

The CH_2 deformation vibration occurs near $1465 \, cm^{-1}$ in hydrocarbons. Attempts have been made to relate the shifts of this band in methylene halides to the halogen electronegativities [45], but these have little practical application. Only one instance is known in which the displacement due to a polar substituent provides a useful correlation, and this is the case of acids, in which the methylene group is immediately adjacent to the COOH link. The CH_2 frequency then falls to $1420 \, cm^{-1}$. This correlation has been known for some time, but has now been elegantly substantiated by systematic deuteration studies in succinic acids [41]. It should, however, be noted that dimeric acids have a characteristic frequency of the COOH group which is near $1410 \, cm^{-1}$, and which may cause confusion. In the succinic acid series these absorptions can be differentiated by deuteration of the CH_2 groups when the $1410 \, cm^{-1}$ band remains and by deuteration of the COOH groups when the $1420 \, cm^{-1}$ band remains. Complete deuteration removes both bands. The $1410 \, cm^{-1}$ CH_2 deformation band has also been confirmed in compounds with the CH_2COX group when the complications arising from the COOH group are eliminated [96].

Some interesting observations have also been made on the conditions under which this band appears as a doublet. It has been known for some time that in long-chain hydrocarbons, such as polyethylene, two peaks appear at 1473 and $1464 \, cm^{-1}$, and this has been shown to be due to interchain forces. This has been confirmed by Novak [42], who has shown that only a single band appears at the melting point. However, a comparable effect, but with a different origin, appears to occur in many ring systems. Chiurdoglu et al. [43] have shown that the $1460 \, cm^{-1}$ band of monosubstituted cycloalcohols, chlorocyclanes and bromocyclanes is usually split into two components, $1450–1485 \, cm^{-1}$ and $1436–1450 \, cm^{-1}$. In these cases the splitting persists in dilute solution, and it cannot therefore be ascribed to interchain forces. Lere Porte et al. [100] have also studied the splitting of the CH_2 deformation band in cyclic systems and have also shown that the frequency varies with the conformation in hydroxylated and halogenated ethanes. The differences which are of the order of $20 \, cm^{-1}$ may well originate in *gauche* interactions between hydrogen atoms similar to those which cause changes in the CH stretching bands. Gunthard et al. [44] have also studied CH_2 deformations in cyclic systems of this kind. One useful correlation which may derive from a deformation or wagging mode is that observed by Mannion and Wang [60] for the $-C\equiv C-CH_2$-system. In hydrocarbons this invariably gives rise to a well-defined band in the

1335–1325 cm^{-1} range. As is to be expected from the nature of the mode concerned, the band is sensitive to polar substituents, and it moves outside these limits if a halogen or hydroxyl group is substituted directly on to the methylene group.

1.6. Skeletal vibrations

1.6.1. CH$_2$ wagging, twisting and rocking modes

None of these vibrations loosely classified in this way is a pure independent CH$_2$ motion, and all are coupled to various degrees. Coupling not only occurs between modes such as the rocking and twisting modes but there are also interactions between adjacent methylene groups which lead to multiple bands in all cases. The situation has been well reviewed by Sheppard [46]. For this reason the interest of organic chemists in these bands is usually limited to attempts to obtain a rough estimate of the chain length of a pure compound by reference to the numbers of bands arising primarily from one of these modes, and to the 720-cm^{-1} band, which is the terminal frequency of the rocking mode and which therefore appears consistently in all long-chain hydro-carbons with more than four methylene groups.

There has, however, been a notable advance in our understanding of the numbers and positions of these modes, of the extent to which coupling occurs, and of the actual motions of the individual atoms involved. This is the work of Snyder and Schachtschneider [47–49], who have made a full vibrational analysis of all the n-paraffins from C$_3$H$_8$ to n-C$_{19}$H$_{40}$. The whole of the data so obtained has then been fed into a computer programmed to adjust a set of force constants common to the series, to give the best least-squares fit. In this way it has been possible to obtain force-constants values which will reproduce all the observed frequencies in any one molecule to within 0·25 per cent. This does provide good grounds for the belief that the assignments suggested for these molecules, and indeed for polyethylene itself, are soundly based. It is certain that the introduction of polar groups will result in some substantial changes, although there is evidence that some at least of these correlations will remain valid. The methods originally suggested by Jones [57] for the assessment of chain length in polymethylene compounds, based on the array of wagging and twisting modes in the 1400–1100 cm^{-1} region, were developed on long-chain alcohols and acids rather than on the hydrocarbons, and the well-known 720-cm^{-1} rocking band, of course, persists in almost all structures with more than four (CH$_2$) groups. This new approach therefore represents a beginning from which we may hope to see the unravelling of this very difficult and hitherto intractable region not only in the parent straight-chain hydrocarbons but also in branched chains and in materials with polar substituents. Preliminary application of the derived-force constants to branched hydrocarbons has given very encouraging results, which suggest that the transferability of force constants may well extend to this series. Thus this method has been very successfully applied to the computation of the vibrational frequencies of isotactic polypropylene [61, 62]. It is to be expected that differences in the stereoregularity of polymers will lead to characteristic changes in the spectra, and these have been extensively studied in the case of polypropylene [63–67]. It is possible, not only to identify each specific form, but also to estimate the proportion of the isotactic polymer present.

The 720-cm^{-1} band of long-chain hydrocarbons represents the low-frequency limit of the array of CH_2 rocking modes, and this accounts for its constancy in position in long-chain compounds. Hawkes and Neale [50] have published an interesting graphical presentation of the variation in frequency of this band with changes in chain length in alkyl benzenes. This shows very clearly, as do the results of Snyder and Schachtschneider [48], that the frequency is invariant in chains longer than four methylene groups. Hawkes does draw attention, however, to the danger of the indiscriminate use of this correlation in aromatic hydrocarbons, some of which show aromatic absorption bands close to this frequency.

This band has been used for many years as a means of estimating through intensity studies the approximate chain length or degree of branching. It is particularly useful for hydrocarbons with alicyclic end-groups, as the methylene groups of the latter do not absorb in this region [51, 52]. However, the greatest interest in this band springs from the fact that in crystalline hydrocarbons it is split into a doublet due to interchain interactions between the methylene groups. This feature has been adopted for such purposes as the estimation of the degree of crystallinity in polyethylene and has been studied intensively. Studies on individual crystalline paraffins show that a small proportion of the even-numbered series have only a single band. This occurs in C_{16}, C_{22} and C_{24} paraffins, and has been traced to the fact that these particular compounds do not crystallize in the usual orthorhombic form, in which the adjacent methylene chains are suitably oriented for lattice interaction [53, 54, 55]. However, the C_{24} compound can be obtained in the orthorhombic form, and splitting then occurs [55]. Single bands have been found in substituted materials such as long-chain esters, 1-monoglycerides and triglycerides [54]. These all crystallize in hexagonal forms, in which the chains in each sub-cell tend towards equivalence, in consequence there is effectively one chain per unit cell and only one absorption band. Similar considerations of crystal structure determine whether or not the band will split in carboxylic acids and compounds with other polar substituents. These effects must be taken into account in assessing the likely validity of the results of crystallinity estimations based on the splitting of this band. In general, orthorhombic and monoclinic crystalline paraffins contain two chains per unit cell and show doubling, whereas triclinic crystals contain only one unit and give therefore only a single band. The situation is made more complex by the observation that the triclinic C_{24} hydrocarbon changes over to the orthorhombic form at room temperature, when mixed with other hydrocarbons [53].

Some assignments for CH_2 rocking modes within the limited series of polyethylene glycols have been suggested by White and Lovell [56] which have application within this special class. From their nature, however, it is not to be expected that they can be used in situations in which the molecular environment of the methylene groups is not the same.

1.6.2. Other skeletal modes

(a) iso-*Propyl,* sec *and* tert-*butyl and* tert-*butoxy groups*

It is well recognized that the correlations for skeletal vibrations of these groups [(CH$_3$)$_3$C· 1250 ± 5 and 1250–1200 cm^{-1}; (CH$_3$)$_2$CH·1170 ± 5, 1170–1140 cm^{-1}] are strictly limited to hydrocarbon systems and cannot be expected to apply in other instances. Hawkes and Neale [50] have studied their applicability to alkyl benzenes. In general, the correlations were obeyed, although they failed to detect the second (lower-frequency) band of the iso-propyl group in three out of four examples. In iso-propyl benzene itself the higher-frequency band was displaced to 1183 cm^{-1}. Even with this relatively minor change in substitution therefore, there is need to exercise caution in the use of these correlations.

Specialist correlations for the *sec*-butyl group attached to aromatic rings have been suggested by Putman [58], who finds these weak bands at 957 ± 2 cm^{-1}, 995 ± 3 cm^{-1} and 1016 ± 1 cm^{-1} in a number of alkyl benzenes in which this group was attached to the rings. The bands were not present in other alkyl-substituted compounds and were not due to ring vibrations. It would, however, be very unwise to apply these correlations outside this very limited area.

Somewhat similar correlations have been suggested for the *tert*-butoxy group by Ory [59], although due to the isolating effect of the O atom these are likely to be more generally applicable. In a series of thirty-one *tert*-butoxy derivatives, bands were found in the ranges 1200–1155 cm^{-1}, 1040–1000 cm^{-1}, 920–820 cm^{-1} and 770–720 cm^{-1}. The lowest frequency is ascribed to the skeletal symmetric vibration of the *tert*-butyl group, and that at 920–820 cm^{-1} to another skeletal mode. The 1000-cm^{-1} band is assigned to a C—C vibration, and that at 1200–1155 cm^{-1} to the C—O stretch. These two must be mixed to some extent, as is shown by the fact that in esters both bands occur at lower frequencies (1175–1155 and 1018–1000 cm^{-1}) than in the others which absorb in the higher-frequency ends of the listed ranges. The presence of a number of skeletal bands, each in the appropriate ranges, does afford a useful indication that the group in question is present. However, the inverse is not necessarily true. In titanium *tert*-butoxide, for example, in which the alkyl groups are in an abnormal environment, only the bands at 1004 and 797 cm^{-1} are seen.

(b) Cyclopropane rings

The appearance of the skeletal cyclopropane frequencies near 1020 cm^{-1} and near 860 cm^{-1} has now been studied in a considerably larger number of compounds than before [25–28]. As is to be expected, these are very much less reliable than the CH-stretching modes, and many instances have come to light in which reliance on these bands alone would lead to misidentifications. Paasivirta [27], for example, reports a number of instances in which these correlations fail, and Rothchild [68] has shown that the correlation is largely fortuitous. Thus the 'characteristic' band in C_3H_5CN originates in a CH_2-wagging mode, whereas in C_3H_5Br it originates in the CH_2 twist. Nevertheless, the bands do appear in a relatively high proportion of the cyclopropane systems studied, particularly in those in which the ring is not fused or heavily substituted, so that they do offer some small measure of confirmatory evidence for identifications made elsewhere.

Bibliography

1. Fuson, Garrigou-Lagrange and Josien, *Spectrochim. Acta,* 1960, **16**, 106.
2. Wilmshurst and Bernstein, *Can. J. Chem.,* 1957, **35**, 911.
3. Kovner and Peregudov, *Optika. Spectroskopija,* 1958, **5**, 134.
4. Fuson, Josien, Deschamps, Garrigou-Lagrange and Forel, *Bull. Soc. Chim. Fr.,* 1959, 93.
5. Force, Fuson and Josien, *J. Opt. Soc. Amer.,* 1960, (50), 1228.
6. Josien, Fuson, Deschamps and Forel, *C. R. Acad. Sci. (Paris),* 1958, **246**, 1992.
7. Badger and Moritz, *Spectrochim. Acta,* 1959, **17**, 672.
8. Scrocco and Caglioti, *R. C. Accad. Lincei,* 1958, (24), 429.
9. Deschamps, Forel, Fuson and Josien, *Bull. Soc. Chim. Fr.,* 1959, 88.
10. Nolin and Jones, *Can. J. Chem.,* 1956, **34**, 1382.
11. Henbest, Meakins, Nichols and Wagland, *J. Chem. Soc.,* 1957, 1462.
12. Dalton, Hill and Meakins, *J. Chem. Soc.,* 1960, 2927.
13. Katritzky and Coats, *J. Chem. Soc.,* 1959, 2062.
14. Hill and Meakins, *J. Chem. Soc.,* 1958, 760.
15. Braunholtz, Ebsworth, Mann and Sheppard, *J. Chem. Soc.,* 1958, 2780.
16. Wright, *J. Org. Chem.,* 1959, **24**, 1362.
17. Bellanato, *Spectrochim. Acta,* 1960, **16**, 1344.
18. Wiberley, Bunce and Bauer, *Analyt. Chem.,* 1960, **32**, 217.
19. Gotoh and Takenaka, *Bull. Inst. Chem. Res., Kyoto Univ.,* 1961, **39**, 202.
20. Boobyer, *Spectrochim. Acta,* 1967, **23A**, 321.
21. Markova, Bazulin and Plate, *Optics and Spectroscopy,* 1960, **8**, 260.
22. Tarte, *Bull. Soc. Chim. Belg.,* 1961, **70**, 43.
23. Steele and Whiffen, *Tetrahedron,* 1958, (3), 181.
24. Kivelson, Winstein, Bruck and Hansen, *J. Amer. Chem. Soc.,* 1961, **83**, 2938.
25. Allen, Davis, Humphlett and Stewart, *J. Org. Chem.,* 1957, **22**, 1291.
26. Moore and Ward, *J. Org. Chem.,* 1960, **25**, 2073.

27. Pasaivirta, *Suomen, Kem.*, 1958, **115**, 3113.
28. Liebman and Gudzinowicz, *Analyt. Chem.*, 1961, **33**, 931.
29. Smith and Eddy, *Analyt. Chem.*, 1959, **31**, 1539.
30. Katritzky, Monro, Beard, Dearnaley and Earl, *J. Chem. Soc.*, 1958, 2182.
31. Katritzky and Coates, *J. Chem. Soc.*, 1959, 2062.
32. Katritzky and Jones, *J. Chem. Soc.*, 1959, 2067.
33. Jones and Cole, *J. Amer. Chem. Soc.*, 1952, **74**, 5648.
34. Lehmann, Onak and Shapiro, *J. Chem. Phys.*, 1959, **30**, 1215.
35. King and Crawford, *J. Mol. Spectroscopy*, 1960, **5**, 421.
36. Wilmshurst, *J. Chem. Phys.*, 1957, **26**, 426.
37. Sheppard, *Trans. Faraday Soc.*, 1955, **21**, 1465.
38. Overend and Scherer, *J. Chem. Phys.*, 1960, **33**, 446.
39. Bellamy, in *Spectroscopy*, ed. Wells, Institute of Petroleum, 1962, p. 205.
40. Watson, *Spectrochim. Acta*, 1960, **16**, 1322.
41. Shimanouchi, Tsuboi, Takenishi and Iwata, *Spectrochim. Acta*, 1960, **16**, 1328.
42. Novak, *Bull. Acad. Sci. U.S.S.R. Phys. Ser.*, 1958, **22**, 1114.
43. Chiurdoglu, Proost and Tursch, *Bull. Soc. Chim. Belg.*, 1958, **67**, 198.
44. Bürer and Gunthard, *Helv. Chim. Acta*, 1960, **43**, 1487.
45. Wilmshurst, *Can. J. Chem.*, 1957, **35**, 937.
46. Sheppard, in *Advances in Spectroscopy*, Vol. I, Interscience, New York, 1959, p. 288.
47. Snyder, *J. Mol. Spectroscopy*, 1960, **4**, 411.
48. Snyder and Schachtschneider, *Spectrochim. Acta*, 1963, **19**, 85.
49. Schachtschneider and Snyder, *Spectrochim. Acta*, 1963, **19**, 117.
50. Hawkes and Neale, *Spectrochim. Acta*, 1960, **16**, 673.
51. Glebovskaja, Maksimov and Petrov, *J. Analyt. Chem. Moscow*, 1959, **14**, 478.
52. Glebovskaja and Maksimov, *Bull. Acad. Sci. U.S.S.R. Phys. Ser.*, 1959, **23**, 1194.
53. Martin, Johnson and O'Neal, *Spectrochim. Acta*, 1958, **12**, 12.
54. Chapman, *J. Chem. Soc.*, 1957, 4489.
55. Holland and Neilsen, *J. Mol. Spectroscopy*, 1962, **8**, 383.
56. White and Lovell, *J. Polymer. Sci.*, 1959, **41**, 369.
57. Jones and Sandorfy, in *Chemical Applications of Spectroscopy*, Ed. West, Interscience, New York, 1956, p. 346.
58. Putman, *J. Chem. Soc.*, 1960, 2934.
59. Ory, *Analyt. Chem.*, 1960, **32**, 509.
60. Mannion and Wang, *Spectrochim. Acta*, 1961, **17**, 990.
61. Schachtschneider and Snyder, *Spectrochim. Acta*, 1964, **20**, 853.
62. Schachtschneider and Snyder, *Spectrochim. Acta*, 1965, **21**, 1527.
63. Peraldo and Cambini, *Spectrochim. Acta*, 1965, **21**, 1509.
64. Zerbi, Gussoni and Ciampelli, *Spectrochim. Acta*, 1967, **23A**, 301.
65. Koenig, Wolfram and Grasselli, *Spectrochim. Acta*, 1966, **22**, 1233.
66. Liang, Lytton and Boone, *J. Polymer Sci.*, 1960, **44**, 144; **47**, 139; 1961, **54**, 523.
67. Macdonald and Ward, *Polymer*, 1961, **2**, 341.
68. Rothchild, *J. Chem. Phys.*, 1966, **44**, 1712.
69. Bellamy and Mayo, International Conference on Molecular Spectroscopy, Madrid, 1967.
70. Bohlmann *Chem. Ber.*, 1958, **91**, 2157.
71. McKean, Duncan and Batt, *Spectrochim. Acta*, 1973, **29A**, 1037.
72. McKean, *J. Mol. Structure*, 1976, **34**, 181.
73. Bellamy and Mayo, to be published.
74. McKean, *Spectrochim. Acta*, 1973, **29A**, 1559.
75. Mallinson and McKean, *Spectrochim. Acta*, 1974, **39A**, 1133.
76. McKean, *Spectrochim. Acta*, 1975, **31A**, 861.

77. McKean, Saur, Travert and Lavalley, *Spectrochim. Acta,* 1975, **31A**, 1713.
78. McKean, Biedermann and Burger, *Spectrochim. Acta,* 1974, **30A**, 845.
79. McKean, *Chem. Commun.,* 1971, 1373.
80. McKean and Laurie, *J. Mol. Structure,* 1975, **27**, 317.
81. McKean and Ellis *J. Mol. Structure,* 1975, **29**, 81.
82. McKean, *Spectrochim. Acta,* 1975, **31A**, 1167.
83. Hamlou, Okude and Nakagerwe, *Tetrahedron letters,* 1969, 2553.
84. Deslongchamps, *Tetrahedron,* 1975, **31**, 2463.
85. Deslongchamps, Lebreux and Taillefer, *Can. J. Chem.,* 1973, **51**, 1665.
86. Deslongchamps, Atlani, Fiehel, Malaval and Moreau, *Can. J. Chem.,* 1974, **52**, 3651.
87. Allan, McKean, Perchard and Josien, *Spectrochim. Acta,* 1971, **27A**, 1409.
88. Higuchi, Kuno, Tanaka and Kamada, *Spectrochim. Acta,* 1972, **28A**, 1335.
89. Kreuger and Jan, *Can. J. Chem.,* 1970, **48**, 3236.
90. Horak and Pliva, *Coll. Czech. Chem. Comm.,* 1969, **25**, 1679.
91. Christie, *Spectrochim. Acta,* 1971, **27A**, 463.
92. Kress and Guillermet, *Spectrochim. Acta,* 1973, **29A**, 1713.
93. Deroualt, Le Calve and Forel, *Spectrochim. Acta,* 1972, **28A**, 359.
94. Cowley, Dewar and Jackson, *J. Amer. Chem. Soc.,* 1968, **90**, 4185.
95. Kreuger and Jan, *Can. J. Chem.,* 1970, **48**, 3227.
96. Frankiss and Kynaston, *Spectrochim. Acta,* 1975, **31A**, 661.
97. McKean, *Chemical Society Reviews,* 1978, **7**, 399.
98. Ernstbrunner and Hudec, *J. Mol. Structure,* 1973, **17**, 249.
99. Graffeuil, Labarre, Leibovici and Taillandier, *J. Mol. Structure,* 1973, **15**, 367.
100. Lere Porte, Petrissana and Gromb, *J. Mol. Structure,* 1976, **34**, 55.

2

Alkenes and Vibrations of C=N and N=N Links

2.1. The C=C stretching frequency

A good deal of new data has accumulated on the positions of C=C absorptions in different chemical environments, so that we are now in a better position to discuss the various factors which control the frequency shifts. But it is clear that, in this instance, both chemical and physical factors are important, and much remains to be done to determine the relative impacts of each. These two factors can be simply defined as follows. Chemical effects arise from alterations in the electron distribution within the bond which follow the replacement of one substituent by another. There is therefore a change in bond character which is reflected in an altered force constant and a shift in the vibrational frequency. However, the vibrational frequency can also be affected by factors such as substituent mass, bond-angle changes and vibrational coupling. These are purely physical effects, and they do not correspond to any change in the force constant of the bond, except insofar as angle changes may affect the hybridization. In many situations both types of effect are in operation. In conjugated systems, for example, the force constant of the bond is lowered as compared with the non-conjugated case, due to the delocalization of the π electrons. This leads to a shift to lower frequencies. However, there is now an increased possibility of vibrational coupling between the two C=C links, which will modify the frequency, although in itself it does not alter the force constants.

Some of the most informative studies in this field have been those concerned with the effects of bond-angle changes and of ring strain, and these will therefore be considered first, as they illustrate very well the substantial impact of physical effects, and the difficulties which arise in disentangling them from the chemical effects which occur simultaneously.

2.1.1. Bond-angle effects

Hydrocarbons

It has been known for many years that the frequencies of endocyclic C=C bonds fall with increasing ring strain, whereas those of exocyclic bonds rise. This is illustrated by the data in Table 2.1. These shifts may arise either from chemical effects due to changes in the hybridization of the carbon orbits engaged in σ bond formation or from kinetic-energy effects which will also become increasingly important as the bond angles close down below 120°. Both will in fact affect the frequency, but at one time it was generally believed that the hybridization changes were the predominant factor. As the bond angles close down, towards 90° the carbon–carbon orbits of the ring take on more *p* character, and with endocyclic double bonds one would therefore predict a systematic frequency fall due to the lengthening of the C=C bonds. This must be accompanied by a corresponding rise in the =CH stretching frequencies, as these take on proportionately more *s* character. The inverse would be predicted for the exocyclic double bonds, as is in fact found. However, a detailed comparison of the data now available suggests that the impact of this effect may well be much less than has hitherto been supposed.

Some idea of the magnitude of changes due to hybridization should be obtainable from measurements on the corresponding CH stretching frequencies, which can fairly be regarded as uninfluenced by mass effects and as a realistic measure of the force constants. In fact, the CH frequencies of cycloalkanes are not much altered by bond-angle changes, and it is only in the three-membered ring system that the frequency rises sufficiently to give any useful differentiation. This appears to be true also of the =CH stretching frequencies of cycloalkenes which have been compiled by Wiberg and Nist [1]. These systems show symmetric (A_1) and antisymmetric (B_1) stretching bands, and unfortunately some of the more important B_1 frequencies are not known. Nevertheless, the small shifts of the A_1 bands are difficult to reconcile with the substantial changes of the C=C frequencies if one assumes that both have a common origin. Further, there is no parallel in the CH stretching frequencies for the remarkable drop of the C=C frequency of cyclobutene [2] as compared with the five- and three-membered ring systems. Indeed, this last phenomenon is difficult to account for on any simple picture of hybridization change, but, as will be seen, is readily explicable in terms of physical effects. As will be seen in Chapter 5, polarity measurements on carbonyl frequencies in strained ring systems also show that there is little change in the electron distribution within the carbonyl link as a result of strain and that a very large proportion of the observed shifts must be attributed to physical effects.

The most interesting and convincing demonstration of the dominance of angle effects in determining C=C frequencies comes from the simple mechanical model experiments carried out by Colthup [3]. In these models the atomic nuclei are represented by weights which are individually supported on long threads; they are connected by helical springs which represent the interatomic distances. The stiffness of the springs is so adjusted that those representing double bonds are twice as stiff as the others. When this model is set up at a given series of interatomic angles, and is connected by a loose coupling to an eccentric on a variable-speed motor, it can be made to perform the normal modes of vibration. Only when the frequency of the eccentric oscillation matches one of the natural vibrational frequencies does the model vibrate. In this way the impact of angle changes can be effectively studied in isolation from other factors.

We will consider first the results in unsubstituted systems. In these it was observed that the attachment of springs and balls corresponding to hydrogen atoms made little or no difference to the $C=C$ frequencies. This is in accord with the idea that during the vibration of the $C=C$ link the attached hydrogens move with the carbon atoms so that no compression of the CH

links is involved and there is no effective coupling. Simple theory predicts that kinetic coupling effects will be at a minimum in cyclobutene (I), in which the vibration of the double bond does not involve any extension or compression of the C—C single bonds. However, as the ring angle opens out to greater than 90° (as in II), the vibration of the double bond can occur only at the expense of the compression of the single bonds, because, unlike the hydrogen atom, the single-bond carbon atoms do not move appreciably during this vibration. The effect will be to raise the frequency, as is found in practice. Equally, a reduction of the angle to less than 90° (III) involves an extension of the C—C bonds during the $C=C$ vibration. This restraining force again raises the $C=C$ frequency. These predictions are fully borne out by the experimental observations, and Colthup has been able to reproduce the various frequencies of Table 2.1 simply by making the appropriate angle changes and without any alterations in the stiffness of the springs themselves. Thus he finds a value of 1560 cm^{-1} for cyclobutene, 1640 cm^{-1} for cyclopropene and 1660 cm^{-1} for cyclohexene. The ability to reproduce the otherwise anomalous frequency of cyclobutene is particularly pleasing and provides strong support for the validity of the model. The effects of ring strain on exocyclic double bonds are likewise reproduced with good precision. Again the decisive factor is the

Table 2.1. C=C frequencies and ring strain (cm^{-1})

Ring or chain	$\begin{array}{c}HH\\ \diagdown\!\diagup\\ C{=}C\\ \diagup\diagdown\\ CC\end{array}$	$\begin{array}{c}HCH_3\\ \diagdown\!\diagup\\ C{=}C\\ \diagup\diagdown\\ CC\end{array}$	$\begin{array}{c}H_3CCH_3\\ \diagdown\!\diagup\\ C{=}C\\ \diagup\diagdown\\ CC\end{array}$	$\begin{array}{c}FF\\ \diagdown\!\diagup\\ C{=}C\\ \diagup\diagdown\\ F_2CCF_2\end{array}$	Exocyclic $\begin{array}{c}C\\ \diagdown\\ C{=}CH_2\\ \diagup\\ C\end{array}$
Chain *cis*	1661 ⎫	1681 ⎫	1672	1733 ⎫	1661
Chain *trans*	1676 ⎭				
Three-membered ring	1641	1782	1890	1938	1780
Four-membered ring	1566	1640	1685	1789	1678
Five-membered ring	1611	1658	1686	1754	1657
Six-membered ring	1649	1678	1685	1740	1651
Seven-membered ring	1651	1673	—	—	
Eight-membered ring	1653	—	—	—	

$\begin{array}{c}C\\ \|\\ C\\ \diagup\diagdown\\ CC\end{array}$ bond angle, and in consequence the C=C frequencies rise as the ring strain is increased and the angle closes.

The incidence of angle effects is well shown in Fig 2.1. Ethylene, substituted with two alkyl groups, either at the 1,1 or (*cis*) 1,2 positions, absorbs at 1661 cm^{-1}. If one assumes from this that the two cases are reasonably equivalent it is possible, on the basis of the data in Table 2.1, to plot the variations of the C=C stretching frequencies of endo and exocyclic un- saturated compounds, against the bond angle α, over a very wide range of

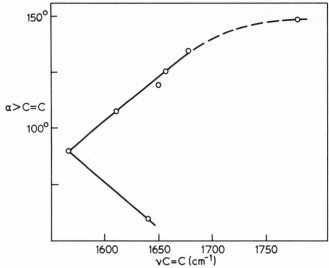

Figure 2.1. Variations of νC=C in endo and exocyclic bonds with C—C—C angle

values. The result is shown in the figure. As expected, the minimum value of vC=C occurs at an angle of 90°. It is also interesting to find that the frequencies for angles of 60° and 120° are essentially the same. This is reasonable, as it implies the same amount of work is done when a C—C bond at a given angle is either extended or compressed.

Similar considerations apply to substituted ring systems. The replacement of a hydrogen atom on the double bond by a methyl group introduces a new C—C link which must likewise be compressed if the bond angle is greater than 90° and extended if the angle is less. In consequence, there is a significant rise in all the C=C frequencies on substitution, which are faithfully reproduced by the model. In the case of 1,2-dimethylcyclobutene (II), for example [4] the C=C bond is now in essentially the same situation as in the open-chain system (V) in that there is no coupling with the C—C ring bonds or with the CH bonds in the open chain. The restraining forces originate only in the C—C bonds of the alkyl groups, and one can predict that these will be similar, although the frequency of the cyclobutene derivative should be a little higher, as the bond angle is larger. In fact, 1,2-dimethylcyclobutene absorbs at 1685 cm^{-1} and *cis*-but-2-ene at 1661 cm^{-1}. This is very satisfactory, and it would certainly be difficult to account for this very large shift on substitution of cyclobutene purely in terms of real changes in the force constants. Similar effects account for the remarkable leap in the C=C frequency of cyclopropene (1640 cm^{-1}) to 1782 cm^{-1} in the 1-methyl derivative, and to 1890 cm^{-1} in the 1,2-dimethyl derivative [5, 6, 87].

The introduction of a single methyl group as a substituent raises vC=C[7]. With two methyl groups the situation is complicated by the fact that there are also adjustments occurring in the bond angles due to the steric repulsions. Thus the C=C frequencies of 1,2-dimethyl derivatives of four-, five- and six-membered rings are all similar, presumably because the decrease in ring angle is partly offset by an increase in the angle which the non-cyclic substituents make with the double bond. It can therefore be stated with confidence that a very large part of the frequency shifts in strained ring systems have their origins in physical effects and do not correspond to significant changes in the C=C force constants. However, as will be seen, it must not be supposed that the substitution of a hydrogen atom by an alkyl group has no effect whatever upon the electron density distribution within the double bond, and in special cases the impact of the two effects can be measured independently.

The substitution of a methyl, or certain other groups at the 3 position in four-, five- or six-membered ring olefines, has the effect of doubling the vC=C band, as a second weaker absorption now appears about 35 cm^{-1} above the normal band [74–77]. This new band vanishes when the substitution is symmetrical, as in 3,5-dimethylcyclopentene, and it is also absent in larger rings. Thus it does not appear in 3-methylcycloheptene. Pinchas *et al.* [74–76] attribute this extra band to coupling of the C=C and C—C vibrations. In 3-dimethyl cyclopropene the frequency rises slightly to 1656 cm^{-1} [88] whilst in the corresponding difluoro compound it falls to 1597 cm^{-1} [89]. This is probably due to a real change of force constant, but it does serve to confirm that the exceptional value of 1938 cm^{-1} found for the tetra fluoro compound (see below) is due to physical rather than to chemical factors.

2.1.2. Fluorinated hydrocarbons (rings)

It is well known that the C=C frequencies of perfluoro hydrocarbons are exceptionally high. Those of the cyclic series also conform to this pattern but show the further apparent anomaly pointed out by Miller [8] that the C=C frequency of endocyclic double bonds rises with increase of ring strain (Table 2.1). This contrasts with the normal behaviour where they fall. Thus cyclobutene absorbs at 1566 cm^{-1}, but perfluorocyclobutene at 1789 cm^{-1}. It is difficult to imagine that flourine substitution will not result in a marked change in the C=C force constant due to its strong inductive effect. Nevertheless, the high frequencies can be rationalized simply in physical terms alone, and these can also account for the reversal of the direction of shift with ring strain. Thus a rise in the C=C frequency on fluorine substitution is to be expected because K C—F is significantly greater than K C—C and the work done during the C=C vibration in compressing the substituent bonds will be increased. So far as the ring system is concerned, we have already noted that the C=C frequency is insensitive to ring strain in the 1,2-dimethylcycloalk-1-enes, and have attributed this to the fact that any diminution of ring angle is offset by an increase in the angle of the substituent. Thus on going from dimethylcyclohexane to dimethylcyclobutene the ring angles close from 120° to 90°, but the angles the substituents make with the double bond increase from 120° to 135°. If this latter effect produces enough interaction in hydrocarbons to counterbalance the change in ring angle it is to be expected that in fluorocarbons the balance will be tilted in the other direction. The C—F force constants are higher than those of C—C bonds, so that the effect of an angle change from 120° to 135° will be significantly greater. As the force constants of the ring single bonds remain much the same, the result must be that C=C frequencies will be higher in small ring systems than in large. The fact that the observed facts can be qualitatively explained in this way does not, however, allow one to presume that there is a quantitative relationship and that the whole of the shifts are due solely to this. As will be seen later, there is significant evidence that force-constant changes also occur on fluorine substitution, as is to be expected from chemical considerations. Unfortunately Colthup's models have not been extended to the special cases of fluorine substitution, and the results of any such work would be of the greatest interest. However, the data on variously fluorinated cyclopropenes strongly support the view that the physical effect is the dominant term. Thus 3:3-di-fluoro*cyclo*propene absorbs at 1597 cm^{-1} [89], the 1:3:3-trifluoro derivative at 1792 cm^{-1}, and the tetrafluoro compound at 1938 cm^{-1} [91]. Mixed halogen substitution has also been studied and the results are in line with what would be expected from the changes in the C—X bond strengths. 1:3:3-trifluoro*cyclo*propene absorbs at 1863 cm^{-1} [91] and the corresponding 2-bromo derivative at 1844 cm^{-1} [92]. The presence of the weaker C—X bond therefore lowers the frequency below that of 1:2-dimethyl*cyclo*propene (1890 cm^{-1}).

2.1.3. Oxygenated ring systems

By analogy with the case of fluorine it is to be expected that oxygen substitution will also have a major impact on C=C frequencies, because of the high force-constants of C—O single bonds. There is some evidence for a frequency rise in a small number of cases, but in general the effects are relatively small. It is difficult to decide how far this is to be attributed to a purely chemical effect. Some delocalization of the π electrons of the double bond is to be expected on the attachment of any oxygen atom, and this would lead to a fall in vC=C. However, this would also lead to a considerable increase in the stiffness of the C—O link, so that there would be a corresponding rise in frequency due to coupling. If physical factors are predominant one might therefore expect an overall frequency rise similar to that given by fluorine, and this is not observed. Also the fact that in vinyl ethers the out-of-plane CH deformation frequencies are greatly displaced, points to the fact that a significant rearrangement of the force field has occurred in these cases. It therefore seems too early to draw any specific conclusions as to the origins of the effects so far observed.

The experimental facts are as follows. The substitution of a single OR group in ethylene lowers vC=C slightly (1618 cm^{-1}), whereas a CH$_2$ group raises it. Two OR groups on the same carbon atom as in ketene acetals [9] give a small frequency rise (1635 cm^{-1}), but this is again less than in the corresponding dimethyl compound (1661 cm^{-1}). In cyclic systems such as benzofurans [10] vC=C is 1635–1616 cm^{-1}, but 1,2-dimethoxycyclohex-1-ene absorbs at 1698 cm^{-1}. Although high, this last value is not much different from the corresponding 1,2-dimethyl derivative (1685 cm^{-1}). Often, however, when the oxygen atoms themselves form part of a closed ring appreciably higher values are found for vC=C. Miller [8] has examined a number of 1,2-dioxocyclohexenes in which the oxygen atoms are part of a six-membered ring. Here the frequency rises to 1721–1709 cm^{-1}, but it must be remembered that these are fused ring systems which from experience in C=C systems can be expected to be abnormal. This is emphasized by the results for the corresponding five-ring oxygen systems. Here vC=C rises to 1745 cm^{-1}, and it is important to note that this is in the wrong direction for a shift purely derived from angle changes. On passing from a six-membered oxygenated ring to a five-membered one the $\overset{O}{\diagdown}C=C\overset{O}{\diagup}$ angles must diminish, and this should lead to a frequency fall which is not found. However, in vinylene carbonate the C=C frequency is at 1627 cm^{-1} which is only marginally greater than the value for cyclopentene [93]. Similarly the C=C frequencies of diketene [11, 94] and of 3-methylene oxetane [95] are equal at 1693 cm^{-1}. Here the exocyclic methylene group is attached to a ring oxygen but the frequency is only 15 cm^{-1} higher than that of methylene cyclobutane.

It is therefore too early to form any decisive views on the factors operating to alter this frequency, but the fact that (OR) substituents are so very different in their behaviour from (F), itself implies that force-constant changes must make a significant contribution in addition to the more direct physical effects.

2.1.4. Conjugation effects in rings

Some interesting new data have become available on conjugation effects in strained ring systems. The results show a number of very interesting anomalies which still await an adequate explanation. Thus conjugation, as in 1,2-dimethylenecyclopentane [12], has only a small effect, lowering C=C by only 7 cm^{-1}. It is difficult to see why this should be so, as the bonds must be coplanar. The corresponding 1,2-dimethylenecyclobutane [13], in contrast, does show a significant fall in frequency (to 1626 cm^{-1}) as compared with the mono-methylene derivative (1678 cm^{-1}). But in tetramethylencyclobutane the frequency again rises to 1662 cm^{-1} [96]. The non-conjugated 1,3-dimethylenebutane [14] also shows some frequency fall to 1660 cm^{-1}, which may reflect some interaction across the ring. In three-membered ring systems the effect of conjugation actually results in a frequency rise. Methylene*cyclo*propane absorbs at 1780 cm^{-1} and trimethylene*cyclo*propane at 1800 cm^{-1} [97]. The reasons for this are not understood. With *endo/exo* conjugation, conjugation often produces a splitting about the mean frequencies rather than a frequency fall.

1-Methyl-3-methylenecyclobutene [14] has two bands at 1672 and 1598 cm^{-1} whereas the expected values for the two separate (unconjugated bonds) are 1640 cm^{-1} and 1678 cm^{-1}. 1-Phenyl-3-methylenecyclobutene [15] is similar, absorbing at 1680 and near 1600 cm^{-1}. However, a further anomaly appears in 3-methylene-cyclobutene [14] and in 3,3-dimethyl-4-methylenecyclobutene [14], as these show only a single absorption at 1680 cm^{-1} which presumably originates in the exocyclic double bond. No absorption at all is shown in the 1600-cm^{-1} region, where the endocyclic bond absorption might be expected to occur.

Some anomalies also seem to occur in the intensities of exocyclic C=C links. These should be relatively intense bands, as are those of vinylidene derivatives, and most of the compounds listed above fall in this class. However, in 1-methyleneindene [16] the C=C intensity is very low, so that this bond cannot be differentiated from those of the aromatic ring. This is remarkable in that conjugation usually intensifies this particular absorption.

Some useful spectral data on fully conjugated large ring systems have been given by Sondheimer *et al.* [17], although as these show no great strain, the findings are essentially normal. Conjugation of endocyclic double bonds with carbonyl groups in cyclohexenes has been studied by Noack [18]. This work was primarily concerned to explain the doubling of the carbonyl frequency in many compounds of this type, and has shown that this is due to Fermi resonance interactions with overtones of bands near 900 cm^{-1}. The C=C bands, however, were clearly differentiated from the carbonyl absorption by the fact that they failed to show significant solvent shifts, and their positions show some interesting features. Thus cyclohex-2-enone absorbs at 1618 cm^{-1}, showing a fall of 31 cm^{-1}, as compared with cyclohexene. A methyl group in the 2-position raises this frequency, as expected, to 1640 cm^{-1}. The shift as compared with 2-methylcyclohexene being 38 cm^{-1}. The 3-methylcyclohex-2-enone is similar, absorbing at 1632 cm^{-1}. However, the 2,3-dimethyl derivative does not show the further upward jump which would be expected, and this also absorbs at 1624 cm^{-1}. (Conjugation shift compared with corresponding cyclohexene 51 cm^{-1}.) Here again no obvious explanation suggests itself, and the observation serves to underline the hazards of attempting to define the position of this particular band in a given environment. The results on conjugated three-membered rings are particularly interesting. One would at first sight expect to find very little coupling between the C=O and C=C bonds of *cyclo*propenones because these bonds are at right angles to each other. However, in 1:2-disubstituted *cyclo*propenones, the two strong bands at 1850 and 1650 cm^{-1} do not correspond to the carbonyl and olefine bonds as might be expected, but to in phase and out of phase motions of both so that the contribution of either is about 50% in both [98]. However, in *cyclo*propenone itself, the uncoupled C=C frequency is considerably reduced by the replacement of the alkyl substituents by hydrogen. The coupling is reduced accordingly and the observed bands at 1840 and 1483 cm^{-1} correspond reasonably closely to true C=O and C=C vibrations. The exceptionally low value for the C=C stretch is not fully understood.

2.1.5. Fused ring systems

Fusion of a second ring to a cyclic olefine does not alter the C=C frequency significantly unless it introduces additional strain. *Cyclo*pentene and dihydro-di*cyclo*pentadiene absorb at 1614 and 1611 cm^{-1} respectively. However in bi*cyclo* (2:2:1-)hept-2-ene and in the corresponding 2:5-diene, the C=C in the five-membered rings absorbs at 1568 and 1575 cm^{-1} respectively. These values are close to those which would be expected from a four- rather than a five-membered ring. Similarly di*cyclo*pentadiene shows two bands, one at 1611 cm^{-1} corresponds to the unstrained ring and the other at 1568 cm^{-1} to the strained ring of the same size [99]. Six-membered rings behave similarly, *cyclo*hexene absorbing at 1656 cm^{-1} and bi*cyclo*(2:2:2-)oct-2-ene at 1614 cm^{-1}. These effects cannot be attributed to angle changes such as were used to explain the normal changes of C=C frequencies with ring size. Geometry changes may well play some part but there is some evidence of changes in the reactivities of these strained ring double bonds which may imply that real force-constant changes are also involved. The fact that shifts produced as a result of strain from fused rings correspond almost exactly to the effects of a reduction by one in the ring size is especially interesting in that it parallels precisely the behaviour of carbonyl groups in strained rings. Here it is well established that the fusion of a second ring to a cyclic carbonyl compound causes the carbonyl frequency to rise to the value of the next smallest cyclic ring. No data on the corresponding exocyclic methylene compounds in fused systems appear to be available but these must be expected to behave like the carbonyl and to rise in frequency as a result of ring fusion.

2.2. C=C frequencies in open chains

In most open-chain systems the olefinic bond angles remain close to 120°, so that the angle effects discussed above become constant. However, when there are two large substituents on the same carbon atom steric effects will be likely to open the angle and lower the C=C frequency. Rea [19] reports this as a general phenomenon in his Raman study of olefines, and other examples are provided by Petrov *et al.* [20] (vinyl acetylenes) and by the straightforward example of 2-methylpropene and 2-*tert*-butylpropene, which absorb at 1661 cm^{-1} and 1639 cm^{-1} respectively. Similarly, it is known from microwave measurements that the FCF angle of perfluoroethylene is closed down to 110°, and this must make some contribution to the raised frequencies discussed below.

In general, however, the origins of shifts in C=C systems in open chains must be looked for elsewhere. The most obvious physical effect is that of mass, and data from the deuteration experiments are now available which show the importance of this factor for hydrogen atoms [21–23]. The replacement of a hydrogen atom which moves during the C=C vibration by a carbon atom which effectively does not, clearly tends to raise the frequency, and accounts in part for the systematic changes in vC=C with increasing substitution. However, this is by no means the only effect, and the chemical effects of the substituents in changing the C=C force constants also play some part. This is shown, for example, by the work of Baker and Shulgin [23] and Kuhn [78] and Grundy [79] who measured the variations of vOH in compounds in which OH groups were hydrogen bonded to the π cloud of the multiple bond. Variations of vOH from 64 to 127 cm^{-1} were found, depending on the type and degree of substitution at the double bond, the larger shifts occurring with the more heavily substituted olefines. Similarly, Bellamy and Williams [24] have shown that, despite the obvious impact of mass effects, there is a smooth-curve relationship between vC═C and the heats of hydrogenation of many simple hydrocarbons.

The impact of mass effects other than that of deuterium/hydrogen substitution is difficult to evaluate. Calculations of the normal type suggest that a frequency rise of about 50–60 cm^{-1} would occur on replacing one of the hydrogen atoms of ethylene by an alkyl group, and that further substitution would give further increases. Further increases in the mass would, however, have only marginal effects. In practice, rises of the expected order of magnitude are found in some cyclic systems (cyclobutene 1566 cm^{-1}, 1,2-dimethylcyclobutene 1685 m^{-1}), but not in open chains. In the latter the normal rise is limited to about 10 cm^{-1} for each methyl group introduced (see Table 2.2). The reasons for this are not clear, but it is likely that the discrepancy arises due to the neglect of the bending terms in the calculations. In open chains the C═C bond may be able to achieve its normal amplitude without having to do the full amount of work that would be expected from the compression of the C—C bonds linking it to the substituents. It could do so by opening the C—C═C angle during the vibration. In cyclic rings the restraining forces against this are much greater, and these therefore show the full mass effect.

It is also very difficult to decide how far the changes in vC═C that follow the introduction of an element other than carbon at the double bond originate in force-constant effects or are associated with real changes in the strength of the

Table 2.2. C═C frequencies in open-chain systems. Effects of halogen substitution

R₁	$CH_2{=}CHR_1$	$CH_2{=}C(R_1)_2$	$R_2{=}F$	$R_2{-}R_1$	$R_2{=}H$	$R_1{-}CH{=}CH{-}R_1$	$CHCH_3{=}C(R_1)_2$
			$CF_2{=}C\genfrac{}{}{0pt}{}{R_1}{R_2}$				
H	1623*	1623*	1788	1728	1728	1623*	1648
D			1774	1692	1706		
F	1650	1728	1872*	1872*	1788		
Cl	1610	1620	1792	1747	1750	cis 1590 trans 1653	
Br	1605	1593	1788	1718	1742		
I	1593						
Ch_3	1648	1661				cis 1661 trans 1676	1681
CF_3			1797	1751		1700 (cis)	
OCH_3	1618	1639					1675
Hg, Sn, P, Zn (vinyl)ₙ[37]	ρ1580						
Sn, Ge, Si, As, Hg (per F vinyl)ₙ[32]			1730–1710				
B(vinyl)₃	1605	1695					
SCH_3[35, 36]	1586						1605

* Raman value.

C=C bond itself. The fact that other frequencies, such as the CH_2 out-of-plane bands, are also altered shows that there are substantial changes in the molecular force field. However, the shifts of the bending bands do not parallel those of $\nu C=C$, and it is likely that the latter is affected by a combination of several factors.

The prediction of C=C frequencies in specific molecules is still extremely difficult. However, a good deal of useful factual data has accumulated, which is discussed below, and is in part summarized in Table 2.2.

2.2.1. The effects of attachment of elements other than carbon

(a) *Vinyl ethers*

A substantial number of vinyl ethers have been examined by various workers [25–29], and detailed analyses of the individual spectra have been attempted [27–29]. There is general agreement that the C=C absorption appears as a doublet with band centres near 1612 cm^{-1} and 1635 cm^{-1}. This is due to rotational isomerism about the C—O bond, and the two bands accordingly show variations in their relative intensities with temperature. In the special case of the compound [25] $CH_2=CH\cdot O\cdot CH_2\cdot CHFCl$ rotation is apparently inhibited by the CFCl group, and only a single band is shown. In other instances three bands appear. These occur commonly in vinyl ethers with alkyl groups terminating in CH_2OH groups. The presence of the third band has been ascribed [29] to changes in the degree of coupling of the $\nu C=C$ vibration in one rotational form as compared with the other. This is possible if there are significant differences in the force fields of the two forms, but in view of the fact that three bands have been most commonly found with this special series, it may well be that hydrogen-bonding effects of the π clouds of the olefinic bond are involved. Nevertheless, the possibility that Fermi resonance effects will accompany rotational isomerism to give multiple absorptions is quite possible in some instances.

(b) *Other elements*

The values for $\nu C=C$ when attached to various elements are listed in Table 2.3. Only very limited data are available on N—C=C systems, and that quoted is based on vinyl lactams [30], and may be abnormal due to the adjacent carbonyl group. However, in the absence of perturbing groups of this kind the $\nu C=C$ frequencies in the compounds listed can be expected to fall within about $\pm 5 \text{ cm}^{-1}$ of the values given for vinyl substituents. Somewhat higher frequencies may arise from increased alkyl substitution on the double bond in accordance with the general principles outlined earlier. Some very extensive tables of C=C Raman frequencies are given by Dollish, Fateley and Bentley [99] which illustrate well the effects of various substitution changes.

Whilst alkyl substitution at the double bond raises the frequency by small increments, almost all other elements except fluorine, lower it. In vinyl chloride the frequency falls to 1620 cm^{-1}, and this falls further with progressive chlorine substitution to a value of 1571 cm^{-1} in tetrachloroethylene. The corresponding reductions in the bromo derivatives are somewhat greater. All these changes are consistent with the weaker C—X bonds (as compared with C—C) and with the reduction of the work required to stretch the C=C bond. However, the magnitudes of the changes are not quantitatively related to the C—X bond strengths and other factors are almost certainly involved. One such factor must be the facility with which back donation can occur into vacant d orbitals on the element in question. In the cases of silicon, germanium and tin, Raman measurements [31] of frequency and intensity suggest that this last factor does cause a change in the shape of the π electron cloud, and hence of the polarizability elipsoid. Similar effects are to be expected in some of the other elements listed. The C=C band is at 1607 cm^{-1} [86] in trivinyl boron; the corresponding perfluoro compound [32] (Table 2.2) absorbs at 1695 cm^{-1}. This compares with $1730–1710 \text{ cm}^{-1}$ for perfluoro vinyl silicon or germanium. The boron compound therefore has the lower frequency in the vinyl series, but the higher frequency in the perfluoro compounds. This is clearly the result of complex interactions.

Very much less is known of metal–olefinic frequencies in compounds other than the vinyl series. However, the *cis* and *trans* forms of propenyl lithium [33, 38] have been studied and shown to absorb at 1623 and 1645 cm^{-1} respectively. The corresponding pentapropenyl stibines [34] absorb at 1606 and 1607 cm^{-1}. These values confirm the expected small rise associated with further substitution on the ethylene bond.

2.2.2. Fluorine substitution in open chains

The behaviour of C=C frequencies on fluorine substitution is strictly parallel to the cases of the cyclic systems which have already been discussed in full. There is a rise of about 150 cm^{-1} on passing from the hydrogen series to the perfluoro-vinyl derivatives, and this persists in compounds such as perfluoro-vinyl mercury, etc. It is remarkable here that the valency state of the substituent element does not have more effect in influencing the frequency, as the extent of back-donation from the double bonds would be expected to vary with the number of vinyl groups available to contribute to the vacant orbitals. This does not appear to be the case, and it seems doubtful whether the whole of the 100 cm^{-1} difference between $CF_3 \cdot CF=CF_2$ and $B(CF=CF_2)_3$ can be attributed to donation effects. It may be that the small B atom enforces angle-opening effects on the C—F bonds which would significantly affect the frequency. The very high C=C frequencies of highly fluorinated olefines must originate primarily in the increased force constants of the C—F bonds as compared with C—C, but this cannot be the complete explanation. In vinylidene fluoride the FCF angle is closed down from the expected 120° to 110°. This will of course accentuate the force constant effect but the fact that it occurs indicates that considerable hybridisation changes must be taking place within the C=C bond which must also be reflected in the frequency.

Certainly the position is complex, and one single simple explanation will not suffice to deal with the whole of the data now available.

2.2.3. Conjugation effects on double bonds in open chains

(*a*) s-cis *and* s-trans *αβ-unsaturated ketones*

Several groups have studied the differentiation [18, 39–41, 100] of these two isomers, and some relatively simple rules are now available. A preliminary indication of the structure can be obtained from the separation of the vCO and >C=C bands. In s-*trans* compounds this is usually less than 60 cm^{-1}, whereas in s-*cis* compounds the separation is greater than this. Thus 3-methylcyclohexen-2-one (s-*trans*) has vCO 1680 cm^{-1} and vC=C 1641 cm^{-1}, and mesityl oxide (s-*cis*) has vCO 1692 cm^{-1} and vC=C 1619 cm^{-1}. Further identification is possible through the comparison of the relative intensities of the two bands, and of the changes that occur on passing from carbon tetrachloride to chloroform solutions [41]. In the s-*trans* compounds the carbonyl bands are always much stronger than the C=C absorptions (usually about twice the intensity), while in the s-*cis* series the olefinic bands are considerably stronger than in the *trans*. These intensity differences are increased in chloroform solution. In this solvent vC=C in the *cis* compounds is much intensified and is shifted by 3–6 cm^{-1} to lower frequencies. In the *trans* compounds the intensity change relative to that of vCO is very much smaller and there is no frequency shift. With other types of conjugation the intensity ratio and the band separation become rather less reliable as diagnostics. In unsaturated acid halides [101] for example the ratio of intensities ranges from 38.4 to 1.97, but the latter is for a compound believed to occur in the *cis* conformation. The most detailed studies of the band splitting and of its significance are due to Taylor [102] who concludes that the two bands are more properly described as out of phase and in phase modes of the CO—C=C system. He points out that the mean of both frequencies is similar in both conformations and deduces from this that there is no essential difference in the degree of conjugation. The difference is due only to the greater degree of vibrational coupling in the *cis* conformers. In conformity with this the lower frequency band (in phase) gains intensity as the higher frequency band approaches, in both conformers. He concludes that a simple plot of vC=C versus vC=O (or in phase versus out of phase frequencies) is the best method of differentiating between the *cis* and *trans* forms. These differences have been ascribed to the fact that there is a greater degree of vibrational coupling between vCO and vC=C in the s-*cis* compounds [41]. There are closely related problems in the identification of the C=C band in enamino ketones which have been discussed by Dabrowski [83] and by Smith and Taylor [103, 104].

(b) Conjugation with other double bonds

Within special classes of compounds it may be possible to make use of the C=C stretching frequencies to determine the configurations of the separate double bonds [42]. Thus in compounds of the type R·CH=CH·CH=CH·CO·X there is a progressive fall in both the C=C stretching frequencies as one goes from the *trans/trans* through the *trans/cis* to the *cis/cis* form. Typical values are as follows: *trans/trans* 1649 and 1624 cm^{-1}, *trans/cis* 1643 and 1606 cm^{-1}, and *cis/cis* 1633 and 1594 cm^{-1}. However, the total data in this field are still limited, and the method must be applied with caution.

(c) Conjugation with triple bonds

A great body of information on the vinyl acetylenes has been built up by Russian workers [20, 43–45], but beyond the fact that the C=C frequency usually falls between 1620 and 1610 cm^{-1}, there is little new in group frequencies. Conjugation with both triple bonds and carbonyl groups has been studied by Wailes [42], and conjugation with nitriles by Heilmann and Bonnier [46] and by Miller [80]. In the latter cases vC=C is displaced by 20–40 cm^{-1} below its normal position, the precise amount depending upon the degree of substitution of the olefinic bond. Thus, fumaronitrile absorbs at 1611 cm^{-1}, maleonitrile at 1577 cm^{-1} and tetracyanoethylene has a Raman band [80] at 1603 cm^{-1}. The rise in this last compound, despite the increase in the conjugation, is not unexpected, as C=C frequencies rise with the degree of substitution, for the reasons already given. This effect offsets the additional conjugation. Conjugation with isocyanate groups appears to have little effect, presumably because the possibilities of further delocalization of the π electrons are small. Thus vinylidene di-isocyanate absorbs at 1668 cm^{-1} [81].

2.2.4. The effects of π cloud interactions

It is now generally accepted that olefines are capable of participating in hydrogen bonding through the interaction of their π clouds with the acidic hydrogen atom. These interactions can be quite strong, and δvOH values for phenol in association with olefines have been found as high as 110 cm^{-1}. The OH frequency shifts are found to vary systematically with the degree of substitution at the double bond, showing that some real changes in the electron distribution do occur as the hydrogen atoms are replaced by alkyl groups. However, although a certain amount of information is available on the OH frequency shifts of donors such as phenol [23, 47, 48, 78, 79], there is little in the literature on the effects of hydrogen bonding on the C=C frequencies themselves. These must be presumed to be very small.

π-cloud interactions of a somewhat similar kind are involved in the formation of certain inorganic coordination compounds such as $[Pt(C_2H_4)_2Cl_2]Cl_2)$. In these the interaction is, of course, much stronger, and there is now a marked fall in the C=C frequency. This now occurs in the 1500–1530-cm^{-1} region. The original assignment by Chatt and Duncanson [49] has been questioned by Babushkin et $al.$ [50], who prefer to associate the 1500-cm^{-1} band with a CH_2 deformation absorption. However, the detailed assignments of Adams and Chatt [52], Powell and Sheppard [51] and Jonassen and Kirsch [53] leave little doubt that the original assignment is correct. The most convincing evidence is the observation that the band persists in complexes such as ($PtCl_2(cis$-but-2-ene)$_2$) which do not contain a methylene group.

2.2.5. Deuterium substitution

This has been studied in detail by Hoffmann [54]. The result is invariably to lower the C=C frequency by 10–20 cm^{-1}. Thus cis-hex-3-ene absorbs at 1658 cm^{-1}, and this falls to 1643 and then to 1634 cm^{-1} as the hydrogen atoms at the double bond are successively replaced by deuterium. Similarly, the 1640 cm^{-1} band of hex-1-ene falls to 1625 if a deuterium atom is substituted at the 1-position, and to 1620 if the deuterium is at the 2-position. Deuterium at both the 1 and 2 positions lowers the frequency further to 1603 cm^{-1}. These differences are almost certainly due to some degree of coupling between the C=C and CD stretching vibrations. The increase in mass makes it less easy for the deuterium atom to ride along with the C=C stretch, and some greater compression of the CD bond is therefore involved in the olefinic stretching mode.

2.3. CH stretching vibrations of olefines

The CH stretching frequencies of olefines occur in narrowly defined regions. The CH_2= group has a characteristic band in the 3095–3070 cm^{-1} range, due to the antisymmetric stretch. The corresponding symmetric stretch occurs in the 2990–2980 cm^{-1} range where it is obscured by alkyl CH bands. The CH= group has a characteristic absorption in the 3040–3000 cm^{-1} region. Both are intrinsically weak compared with the corresponding methylene absorptions [82]. Even in the Raman spectrum the intensities of the CH stretches of $trans$ or trisubstituted olefines are low, although the bands are of medium intensity in the cis isomers.

The frequencies are almost certainly determined wholly by the hybridis-ation of the CH bonds and by the minor changes in its s or p character which result from substituent changes. This is well shown by some studies by Duncan [105] on vinyl compounds. Measurements on the symmetric and antisymmetric stretching frequencies of the $CH_2=$ group in a range of compounds have shown that the separation of the two is a function of the HCH bond angle as determined by microwave measurements. The mean frequency will vary similarly but the separation is a more sensitive function of the angle. It is to be expected that the coupling between these two modes will vary with this angle, becoming maximised at 180° and being zero at 90°. The fact that the band frequency moves up and the band separation increases can only be due to an increase in the s character of the CH orbitals, and this is of course also angle related.

Whilst this relation is clearly a useful and sensitive technique for studies of angle change, it must be used with discretion and is probably unsuited for accurate measurements with unsymmetrical substituents. This has been made apparent by some detailed partial deuteration studies on ethylenic CH bands by McKean. These indicate that in many unsymmetrically substituted olefines, there are intrinsic differences in the individual uncoupled CH frequencies of the $CH_2=$ group. This will contribute to the band separation, independently of the HCH bond angle, and so will lead to error in the angle measurement.

McKean's studies [106] cover a wide range of halogenated ethylenes in which all the olefinic hydrogens except one are replaced by deuterium. In this way he obtains uncoupled frequencies and is able to determine how these change with both the nature of the X substituent and with the position of that hydrogen in relation to the X substituent. McKean measures a series of S values, S_{cis}, S_{trans} and S_x. These represent the differences between the observed uncoupled frequencies of a vinyl X compound and those of ethylene. The same values can be derived indirectly from the differences between X_3 and X_2 substituted compounds, and the good measure of agreement achieved is an indication that these effects are essentially additive. The CH frequencies, as with the alkanes are a direct measure of the CH bond length and therefore reflect changes in the hybridisation of the CH orbits of the various CH bonds. How far these changes are brought about by electron donation or withdrawal effects operating along the bonds, or by orbital repulsions similar to those proposed for the alkanes (see Chapter 1), or both, is yet to be determined. McKean suggests that there is a strong *trans* interaction which changes considerably with the nature of the halogen, and such an effect is of course well recognised in NMR studies. The particularly interesting feature of these results is that the individual CH stretching frequencies of the CH_2 of a vinyl group are not always the same, indicating different bond lengths and differences in the individual hybridisations of the CH bonds. These cannot be brought about wholly by changes produced by X in the orbitals used by the CH_2 carbon in the $C=C$ bond which would affect both CH bonds to an equal extent. Some directional or spacial factors must be of importance and the further study of isolated CH frequencies of this kind could well open the way to a better understanding of this basic mechanism of chemistry. Some examples illustrating the variations in individual isolated CH frequencies measured by McKean are given below:

$$3057\ \text{H} \diagdown \quad \diagup \text{H}\ 3085 \qquad\qquad 3100\ \text{H} \diagdown \quad \diagup \text{H}\ 3080$$
$$\text{C}=\text{C}$$
$$3074\ \text{H} \diagup \quad \diagdown \text{Br} \qquad\qquad 3087\ \text{H} \diagup \quad \diagdown \text{F}$$

$$\text{H} \diagdown \quad \diagup \text{Br} \qquad \text{H} \diagdown \quad \diagup \text{H} \qquad \text{H} \diagdown \quad \diagup \text{I} \qquad \text{H} \diagdown \quad \diagup \text{I}$$
$$\text{C}=\text{C} \qquad\qquad \text{C}=\text{C} \qquad\qquad \text{C}=\text{C} \qquad\qquad \text{C}=\text{C}$$
$$\text{Br} \diagup \quad \diagdown \text{H} \qquad \text{Br} \diagup \quad \diagdown \text{Br} \qquad \text{I} \diagup \quad \diagdown \text{H} \qquad \text{I} \diagup \quad \diagdown \text{H}$$
$$\quad 3102 \qquad\qquad\quad 3080 \qquad\qquad\quad 3100 \qquad\qquad\quad 3050$$

CH frequencies (isolated) cm^{-1}

A different mechanism is responsible for the abnormally low CH stretching frequencies of aldehydes and of some $CH_2{=}N{-}$ compounds, which absorb well below the values which would be expected from the sp_2 hybridisation. In these cases Bellamy and Mayo [119] have shown that back donation from the *trans* lone pair on the oxygen atom is responsible for the weakening of the CH bonds. In complexes with BF_3 the aldehyde CH stretch rises substantially [120].

2.3.1. In-plane CH deformations in alkenes

(a) Vinyl and vinylidene compounds

The scissoring vibration of the terminal $={CH_2}$ group occurs near 1420 cm^{-1} in hydrocarbons. The position of this band in compounds with other elements at the double bond is listed in Table 2.3 and some extensive tables listing the position of this band in the Raman spectra of many compounds are given by Dollish *et al.* [107]. It will be seen that the band position is not particularly sensitive to substitution, at least as far as a single substituent is concerned. However, in vinylidene compounds with two polar substituents the frequency falls sharply [56]. Thus in vinylidene bromide this band appears at 1372 cm^{-1} and at 1357 cm^{-1} in vinylidene fluoride. Copious data are available on the location of this band in the vinylacetylenes [43–45], but here it seems to be essentially unaltered by conjugation.

Neither this band nor the corresponding $={CH}$ bending mode (also listed in Table 2.3) constitutes a very good group frequency. Although their origins are satisfactorily established by deuteration studies [54–56[, both are fairly extensively coupled with the C=C stretching mode. However, it should not be forgotten that the in-plane $={CH_2}$ band occurs near 1420 cm^{-1}, if only

Table 2.3. X—CH=CH$_2$ frequencies

Element	—CH=CH$_2$	CH *in-plane vibrations*		CH *out-of-plane vibrations*	
C	1645	1295	1415	995	910
O	1615	1321	*	965	815
N[30]	1625			970	840
S[35, 36]	1580	1285	1430	960	870
Si[31]	1595	1272	1409	1009	950
Ge[31]	1594	1263	1400		
Sn[31, 37]	1588	1267	1392	1000	948
P[37]	1595	1248	1397	982 or 1020	948 or 918
Zn[37]	1565	1258	1390	990	952
Hg[37]	1588	1255	1398	1008	945
F	1650			c 925	863
Cl	1610			938	894
Br	1605			936	898
I	1593			943	905
D				1000	943

* The position of this frequency is uncertain and is variously assigned as 1370–1390, 1400–1419 or near 1481 cm^{-1}

because of the danger of confusion with the bending mode of the CH$_2$ group in the CH$_2$CO structure.

(b) Cis *and* trans *disubstituted ethylenes*

The differences that are reported to occur between the in-plane bending frequencies of *cis* and *trans* disubstituted ethylenes have been more fully investigated. Deuteration studies, and a number of new measurements [54], confirm that *cis* olefines usually absorb in the range 1420–1385 cm^{-1} whereas the corresponding band in the *trans* compound appears between 1310–1280 cm^{-1}. This difference is confirmed by many Raman measurements where the in-plane deformation can be identified with more certainty due to its considerable intensity in both isomers. However, here again there is extensive coupling, and the band positions are not sufficiently reliable for diagnostic purposes. This is well shown by the calculations of Majanac [57], who has assessed the factors controlling these frequencies and concluded that comparisons between one spectrum and another, in this region, are valid only if the two compounds have similar substituents at both ends of the double bond, and have similar force fields. The dangers of over-simplification are well shown by the data on propenylstibines [34] (CH$_3$CH=CH)$_3$Sb, etc., which show no significant differences between the spectra of the *cis* and *trans* forms at all frequencies above 1100 cm^{-1}, although there are minor intensity variations. Even the C=C frequencies, which are normally different for *cis* and *trans* structures, occur within 1 cm^{-1} of each other in these compounds.

2.3.2. CH out-of-plane deformation vibrations

These very important bands have been extensively studied by Potts and Nyquist [58], who have given extensive tables showing the frequency variations with structural change. In addition, there have been groups of papers on vinyl ethers [26–29], vinyl sulphides [35], and many studies of individual molecules, such as vinyl fluoride [59, 60] and vinyl bromide [61]. Force-field studies on the vinylidene halides are also available [56]. These, together with some extensive unpublished data of Philpotts, provide the basis of Table 2.4. In this table a representative set of frequency data is given to illustrate the way the frequencies vary with structure. Some additional data on vinyl compounds will also be found in Table 2.3, and in the tables given by Colthup and Orloff [108]. Intensity data in hydrocarbons have been given by Wexler [82], and for polar compounds by Colthup and Orloff [108].

In all but the tertiary $-CH=C\hspace{-0.3em}\diagdown$ group, a number of different out-of-plane deformation modes are possible. However, as the absorptions are always strong, it is reasonable to suppose that a substantial dipole moment change is involved, and this enables the individual modes to be identified in nearly every case. Thus in the $CH_2=C\hspace{-0.3em}\diagdown$ group the band near 900 cm^{-1} must originate in a vibration in which the two hydrogen atoms wag together above and below the C=C plane. The alternative mode, in which they deform on opposite sides of this plane, would involve little or no dipole moment change. Similarly, in the disubstituted *cis* and *trans* ethylenes the two hydrogen atoms must move together on the same side of the double bond. In the *trans* compounds this has been described as a twisting mode, as it involves changes in the torsional angles of the CH= planes. The band near 1000 cm^{-1} in vinyl compounds was at one time classified as a CH deformation of the lone hydrogen atom, as it vanished in vinylidene compounds in which this hydrogen is substituted. However, a normal coordinate analysis of the vinyl halides has suggested that the motion is primarily one in which the two hydrogen atoms at opposite ends of the double bond deform together on the same side of the C=C plane, while the third hydrogen atom takes the opposite direction. The mode is therefore very similar to the twisting mode of *trans*-disubstituted ethylenes described above. The idea is supported by the close parallelism between the behaviour of this band with changes in the substituents and that of the 965-cm^{-1} band of *trans*-ethylene compounds. This description, which is due to Potts and Nyquist [58], will therefore be used in the discussion below. It recieves some measure of confirmation from the calculations of Colthup and Orloff [108] who have used this designation of the frequency to calculate reasonably good values for this absorption using molecular orbital techniques.

Little that is new has appeared on the CH bending modes of trisubstituted ethylenes. The numbers of compounds of this type which have been studied outside the hydrocarbon series is relatively small, and the band is in any case a good deal less intense than those from olefinic double bonds less heavily

Table 2.4. δCH out-of-plane vibrations of substituted ethylenes

R_1	R—CH=CH$_2$		R$_1$—CH$_2$—CH=CH$_2$		CH$_2$=C⟨$^{R_1}_{R_2}$						R$_1$—CH=CH—R$_2$ *trans*		
	Twist	*Wag*	*Twist*	*Wag*	CH$_3$	R$_1$	Cl	CH$_2$R$_1$	CH$_3$	C$_6$H$_5$	C$_6$H$_5$	Cl	CH$_2$R$_1$
CH_3	986	908	988	908	887	887	875	887	964		959	926	964
Cl	938	894	983	929	875	867	867	891	926		930–942	892	931
Br	936	898	981	924		877		896					935
$C\equiv N$	972V	955V	982	926	930	959	916		953		962	920	
C_6H_5	989	906	989–915	912–915	890		877		959		958	930–942	
$COOH$	982	970			947		933		966		976		
$COOR$	982	961			939		925		968		976		
$RCOO$	950	873	987	920–925, 930–940	869				948				
$CH_2=CH$	1011	907	995	910	889								
CH_3O	960	813	991	921	795								
CHO	984	963		921					964		972		
I	943	905	982	918									
$N=C=S$	939	896	984	922			897						
C_6H_5-O	944	851	989–995	912–915									
COR	962s	955–962			930						972		
$CH_3-CH=CH$	984–993	896											
$CH_2=C(CH_3)$	1061	902											
OEt	987					711							

substituted. The frequency range, even within the hydrocarbons, is larger than in the other classes, so that it is to be expected that polar substituents will have a considerable effect.

The situation on the *cis* disubstituted ethylenes is also unsatisfactory. This is not so much due to the lack of data as to the wide variations found in the frequency positions, and in the relative intensities of the bands. It remains true that in many *cis* disubstituted ethylenes a moderately strong band appears near 700 cm^{-1}, as for example in *cis* CHF=CHF (756 cm^{-1}) (deuterated compound 597 cm^{-1}) [65]. However, in many other cases no strong or medium intensity band can be identified in this region, so that one must conclude that this is not a worth-while group frequency for general purposes.

In contrast to this, there has been a good deal of effort devoted to the vinyl, vinylidene and *trans* disubstituted ethylene frequencies, which has increased our understanding and widened the field of application of the group frequencies. The vibrations are essentially uncoupled in this series, and the frequencies should therefore be directly dependent on the chemical forces (induction, resonance, etc.) that determine the electron densities in the CH bonds. However, despite this, there is no relationship whatever between the two separate CH out-of-plane bending modes of vinyl compounds (i.e. the CH twist and the CH$_2$ wag). Each seems to vary independently of the other. Nor is there any relation between either and the C=C stretching mode. The reasons for such a result are discussed below, but it is not irrational if one considers some of the chemical effects as arising from interactions across space rather than along the bonds.

In any event, the effects of individual substituents on any one mode do appear to be at least partly additive, so that while we cannot yet claim fully to understand the origins of some of the shifts, it is at least possible to make reasonably good predictions of the likely position of these absorptions in any given structure.

A number of typical frequencies with various substituents are given in Tables 2.3 and 2.4, and these are discussed below.

2.3.3. CH out-of-plane twisting vibrations

(a) Vinyl compounds (the 990 cm^{-1} band)

In straight-chain hydrocarbons this band appears in the normal range 986–992 cm^{-1}. There is a small upward shift with branching at the α carbon atom [58], so that 3-methylbut-1-ene absorbs at 996 cm^{-1}, and 3,3,3-trimethylprop-1-ene at 999 cm^{-1}. The band is little affected by conjugation of the double bond, so that styrene absorbs in the normal hydrocarbon range. There is a small upward shift in a few cases, such as penta-1,3-diene (1001 cm^{-1}), but this is not general, and 3-methylbuta-1,3-diene absorbs at 987 cm^{-1}. A series of compounds in which the vinyl link was directly attached to a carbonyl group were also found to absorb in the 992–982-cm^{-1} range.

Conjugation with an acetylenic bond lowers the frequency a little (vinyl-acetylene 972 cm^{-1}), but the nitrile group is more effective in this, and the frequency then falls to 960 cm^{-1}. The direct attachment of the N=C=S or S=C=N group is particularly effective, and the frequency falls to 939 cm^{-1}.

Polar groups at the α-carbon atom have only a very small effect, so that the monohalogenated propenes, for example, absorb only a few cm^{-1} below the normal values. Even α-trifluoromethyl substitution lowers the band only to 979 cm^{-1}. The effects are more marked when elements other than carbon are attached at the double bond. Elements of low electronegativity give a small frequency rise (Si, Hg, etc., 1000 cm^{-1}), but polar elements lower the position. With nitrogen the band is near 970 cm^{-1}, and with sulphur [35] near 960 cm^{-1}. In vinyl ethers the band is doubled due to rotational isomerism [27, 62] and bands appear near 960 and 940 cm^{-1}. Only a single band appears in vinyl esters, and this occurs near 950–935 cm^{-1}. Halogens produce a more marked effect, as can be seen from the table. The lowest frequency at which this band has been assigned is 925 cm^{-1} in vinyl fluoride.

The origins of these shifts have been discussed by Potts and Nyquist [58]. They deduce from the fact that conjugation has little effect upon the frequency that resonance effects are unimportant, and they therefore assign the whole of the shifts to the impact of inductive effects. In support of this they have shown that there is a reasonably good smooth curve relationship between the positions of the CH twisting bands and the pK values of the acids XCH$_2$COOH, where X is the substituent of the vinyl group. Some degree of correlation also exists between these frequencies and the Taft σ^* values or the σ' values of Roberts and Moreland. However, both correlations show some discrepancies. The points for nitrile, and for branched-chain alkyl groups both lie well off the pK plot, while some of the σ^* values, notably that for CH$_3$O, are well out of line. The correlation would also predict a substantially greater effect for CF$_3$ groups (high σ^* value) than is actually observed.

Nevertheless, these correlations do provide a remarkably good rule-of-thumb guide to the likely position of this band in a given structure, even though other factors than simple induction along the bonds may be operating in some cases. Another approach is that of Colthup and Orloff [108] who have calculated these frequencies for both vinyl and *trans* disubstituted ethylenes, using molecular orbital techniques. These must be treated with some reservations as they involve the use of the normal coordinates which are themselves derived from frequency measurements, and also require the use of scaling factors. Nevertheless they have shown that it is possible to derive frequencies within 10 cm^{-1} of those observed by calculations on the total energy change during the twisting mode. They are therefore of value in both prediction and in the differentiation of isomers. However this technique does not throw any clear light on the mechanism whereby the dipole moment and energy changes are brought about. In this connection Bellamy [63] has drawn attention to the present unsatisfactory position in the assessment of the relative impacts of the inductive effects of substituents by various physical methods. An assessment, based on electronegativity values, which is used to demonstrate correlations with inductive effects in cases such as the P═O stretching vibration, gives an entirely different order of effectiveness to that from the Taft σ^* values or pK values. Iodine, for example, has the same electronegativity as carbon, so that on this basis the frequency in vinyl iodide should be similar to that in hydrocarbons. In fact, the frequency shift is even greater than that of vinyl ethers. The pK scale does show a higher inductive coefficient for iodine than for carbon, but this in its turn proves to be unsatisfactory in other situations.

This has led to the suggestion that inductive effects, as measured by chemists using physical methods, are in fact a composite of forces working along the bonds and those working across intramolecular space. The latter will vary in their impact with the molecular geometry so that different types of molecules will appear to show different relative orders of effectiveness of the substituents in induction. Dewar [64] has even suggested that inductive effects have no real existence and that all the effects previously attributed to this cause should now be assigned to intramolecular field effects. Certainly the fact that the vinyl ethers show two CH twisting frequencies is good evidence that the forces operating along the bonds are insufficient to account for the facts completely. Nevertheless, it would be premature, to say the least, to suppose that normal inductive forces are absent. For the present it can be said that the frequencies depend almost entirely on the chemical effects of the substituents, and that these probably operate by more than one mechanism.

(b) *The* CH *out-of-plane twisting mode in* trans *disubstituted ethylenes* (*the 965 cm^{-1} band*)

This mode is so similar to that of the vinyl group discussed above that it is most conveniently dealt with here. In hydrocarbons it falls in the narrow range 967–958 cm^{-1}, and like the vinyl absorption, it is unaltered by conjugation with a single double bond, carbonyl or phenyl group. More surprisingly, even the nitro group has little effect, so that the compound [58] $C_6H_5CH═CHNO_2$ absorbs at 965 cm^{-1}. Conjugation at both ends of the double bond raises the frequency by only a few wave numbers. However, unlike the vinyl group there is a cumulative effect as more and more double bonds are involved. This can lead to significant shifts, and in extreme cases the frequency can rise as high as 1000 cm^{-1}.

As before, polar groups on the α-carbon atom have only slight effects, and the major effects arise when elements other than carbon are attached to the double bond. Chlorine, oxygen and bromine atoms all produce a lowering of about 35 cm^{-1}, and this is doubled when the substituent is present at both ends of the double bond. Thus, *trans*-$CH_3 \cdot CH═CHCl$ absorbs at 926 cm^{-1} and $Cl \cdot CH═CH \cdot Cl$ at 892 cm^{-1}. In the corresponding difluoro compound the band is at [65] 874 cm^{-1}. This additivity of the effects provides a sound rational basis for the prediction of the frequency positions. Electropositive substituents are reported as raising this frequency, and certainly the value of 960 cm^{-1} found for Cl·CH=CH·B(OH)$_2$ suggests that the boron atom is effectively countering the influence of the chlorine. On the other hand, the propenyl stibines show [34] this absorption in the normal range, so that more data are required before any final conclusions can be drawn on this point. Nevertheless, the parallel with the vinyl CH twist vibration is sufficiently close to support the view that both frequencies are controlled primarily by chemical factors, and that resonance effects play little or no part in these. The failure of the nitro group (which by any standards is a strongly inductive group) to produce a frequency shift must be attributed to some counterbalancing effect operating in the opposite direction, and indirectly reinforces the suggestion that something more than simple induction along the bonds is operating in some cases. As in the cases of the vinyl compounds some useful predictions of the frequency positions are possible through the method of Colthup and Orloff [108].

2.3.4. The CH$_2$= wagging mode

This absorption is common to both vinyl and vinylidene groups. The data for each class are given separately below, followed by a discussion of the causative factors which are applicable to both.

(a) *Vinyl compounds* (*the* 900-*cm*$^{-1}$ *band*) (data from ref. [58])

This band is very stable in position in hydrocarbons, appearing always within the range 912–905 cm^{-1}. It is insensitive to direct conjugation by double bonds, so that the band appears at the normal position in styrene and in 1,3-butadiene. In allenes a similar band appears at 860 cm^{-1} which originates in a comparable mode. However, the behaviour of this band with other types of conjugation or on substitution with polar elements appears to be extremely erratic. Sufficient data have now accumulated to allow a reasonably reliable prediction of the absorption position in any given structure, but the reasons why one electronegative group (CF$_3$) should raise the frequency by 60 cm^{-1} whereas another (fluorine) should lower it by 42 cm^{-1} are very much less clear. The essential facts are as follows:

(*i*) Conjugation with carbonyl groups raises the frequency to 960–970 cm^{-1}, so does conjugation with the nitrile group. The influence of the latter can even be relayed through an intervening double bond which would otherwise be ineffective. Thus, in the compound NC·CH=CH·CH=CH$_2$ the CH$_2$ wagging band is raised to 927 cm^{-1}. In contrast, conjugation with N=C=S or S=C=N has only a small lowering effect (896–898 cm^{-1}).

(*ii*) Polar groups on the α-carbon atom raise δCH_2. Oxygen or halogen atoms in the CH_2X group attached to the double bond raise this frequency to the 920–930-cm^{-1} region, and further substitution leads to still higher values. The $CH_2Cl\cdot$ group produces a frequency of 929 cm^{-1}, while the $CHCl_2$ group raises this to 937 cm^{-1}. Here again there is some degree of additivity. A small frequency rise is also shown when a double bond is attached to the α-carbon atom, so that the compound $CH_2=CH—CH_2—CH=CH_2$ absorbs at 910 and 920 cm^{-1}. Halogen substituents at the *ortho* position in styrene also raise the frequency by 15–20 cm^{-1}.

(*iii*) Halogens substituted directly on the double bond lower δCH_2, but only by a small amount. The values for the vinyl halides are given in the table, and only in vinyl fluoride is there any substantial frequency fall. However, elements of low electronegativity, such as silicon, tin, phosphorus and mercury, all cause the frequency to rise into the 950-cm^{-1} region [58, 73].

(*iv*) The most dramatic effects follow oxygen substitution. In vinyl ethers the band appears in the range 810–820 cm^{-1}, usually in the form of a doublet due to rotational isomerism. In vinyl esters, in which the resonance effects of the ether oxygen atom are reduced by the influence of the carbonyl group, the band appears between 870 and 850 cm^{-1}. Higher values still are obtained in esters of halogenated acids, so that in $CF_3COOCH=CH_2$ the CH_2 deformation band is almost restored to its original value, and appears at 890 cm^{-1}.

(*v*) Data on nitrogen substitution are limited to cyclic systems, but the general pattern is similar to that of oxygen, with the deformation band appearing in the 830–840 cm^{-1} region.

(*vi*) *Vinylidene compounds*. The factors which control the CH_2 deformation frequency in vinylidene compounds seem to be the same as operate in the vinyl series, and the effects of individual substituents are approximately additive. Thus, all those groups which raise δCH_2 in vinyl compounds do so to similar extents in the vinylidene series. CH_2Cl groups raise the frequency by 15–20 cm^{-1}, carbonyl groups by 40–60 cm^{-1} and nitrile groups by 40 cm^{-1}. Two nitrile groups, as in vinylidene cyanide, produce twice the effect, and this compound absorbs at 985 cm^{-1}. Similarly, substituents which lower the vinyl frequency do so to similar extents in this series also. Halogens (except fluorine) show only small shifts to lower frequencies. In vinylidene chloride the two chlorine atoms produce a total shift of only 20 cm^{-1}, but in the difluoride there is a substantial frequency fall to 804 cm^{-1}. Even with oxygen the effect of two substituents is roughly double that of one, so that the large effects observed in vinly ethers become even greater in this series. A compound such as vinylidene (bis) diethyl ether absorbs at 711 cm^{-1}.

This simple additivity is extremely useful in the prediction of frequencies. The resultant for any given two substituents is usually very closely the same as the sum of the separate shifts of the two individually substituted vinyl compounds. We are now in a good position to predict the band position in both vinyl and vinylidene compounds, and although this varies very widely

$(1000-700 \text{ cm}^{-1})$, the frequencies for any given class of compound remain very close to the expected values. An alternative approach to the prediction of these frequencies in both vinyl and vinylidene compounds is through the correlation found by Colthup and Orloff [108] between the observed values and the electron density on the CH_2 carbon atom as computed by molecular orbital techniques. Although the CNDO/2 method must be used with some reservations the linearity achieved in a plot of observed frequencies and total electron density is remarkable. These authors quote the following linear correlation $w_q = 6802.16 - 973.42q_c$ where w_q is the calculated $=CH_2$ wag wavenumber and q_c is the total electron density on the $=CH_2$ carbon atom calculated by the CNDO/2 method.

The effects of ring strain on exocyclic methylene groups have also been considered and shown to be very small indeed. Bellamy [63] lists a number of examples of this type, but even in methylene cyclopropane the δCH_2 band is at 892 cm^{-1}, very close to the normal hydrocarbon range.

(b) The origins of the frequency shifts of the $\delta CH_2 =$ wagging modes

The behaviour of the $CH_2=$ wagging frequencies with alterations in the substituents is totally different from that of the corresponding CH twisting modes, even though, in the vinyl series, one of the two hydrogen atoms involved is the same in both cases, and is executing a very similar out-of-plane movement. Thus, substituents such as CO, Si, CH_2F and CH_2O, which have only very small effects on twisting frequencies, give rise to substantial shifts in the wagging vibrations. Conversely, substituents such as the halogens, iodine, bromine, etc., have only a small effect on the wagging frequencies but a large effect on the twisting absorption. The directions of shift are also erratic, and the electronegative CF_3 group produces an upward shift in the wagging absorption, whereas fluorine itself moves the frequency downwards. The approximate positions of this band in vinyl compounds with various types of substituent are as follows:

$SiCl_3 > CF_3 > CO > SiR_2 > CH_2Cl > CH_2O > CH_3 > I > Br > Cl > OCO=$
975   965   963   950   929   921   908   905 898 894 870

$SR > F > NR_2 > OR$
870   863 840 810 cm^{-1}

The clear distinction from the behaviour of the twisting vibrations, and the fact that there are such large shifts from elements such as oxygen and nitrogen which are capable of taking part in resonance, and small ones from elements such as chloride which have only a limited capacity in this respect, point strongly to the likelihood that resonance effects are the dominant factor in determining the position of this absorption. Potts and Nyquist [58] believe that the frequency is wholly determined in this way, and have sought for correlations with physical properties which measure the degree of resonance. One such parameter is the difference between the Hammett σ values for *para* substituents and the Roberts and Moreland σ' values for inductive effects. This gives some measure of resonance which is akin to Taft σ_R values. A plot of these values against δCH_2 frequencies gives a reasonably good smooth curve relation, although the agreement for the lower-frequency points is rather better than for the higher frequencies, where there is a sizeable scatter. An alternative measure of resonance, which these authors suggest correlates rather more effectively, is the actual percentage of *meta* substitution products resulting from the nitration of X phenyl compounds. The yields rather than the rates are used as the measure of resonance, and the agreement is certainly rather better for the higher-frequency compounds. No test of this correlation is possible for compounds with δCH_2 values lower than 905 cm^{-1} as all such compounds have substituents which lead to 100 per cent *ortho/para* nitration products when present in an aromatic ring. Colthup and Orloff [108] have explored the possibility that only resonance factors are involved by calculating the π electron densities at the $=CH_2$ carbon by the Hückel molecular orbital method. However, they find that there is only a limited relationship between the values obtained and the observed frequencies. There appears to be a reasonably good linear relationship for electron donors but no overall correlation. They do however find a good fit with the total electron density derived from CNDO/2 calculations. This includes all factors influencing the electron density including the geometry so that it is clear that resonance alone is not the only factor involved.

The failure of conjugation effects to influence the δCH_2 frequency suggests that it is possible to have a substantial delocalization of the π cloud without effecting any major change in the orbitals which control the length and polarity of the CH bonds. This has led Bellamy [63] to suggest that the direct field effect between the substituent and the CH_2 group was a primary mechanism for the frequency shifts.

There is some support from the fact that vinyl ethers show two δCH_2 bands corresponding to two different rotational forms. This in itself indicates that the molecular geometry, as well as the nature of the substituents, plays a part in determining the precise position of these bands. Geometric differences of this kind also show up in the electron density calculations of Colthup and Orloff [108] and support the idea that interaction effects across space play some part in the frequency shift. So also does the observation that axial and equatorial OR substituents at the 2 position in 1-methylene-cyclohexane give different δCH_2 frequencies. The field-effect approach also offers the best possibility of explaining the fact that a double bond or an iodine atom attached to the α carbon atom will alter the group frequency, whereas it is unchanged if they are directly substituted on the double bond itself [63].

The true interpretation of the origins of the frequency shifts shown by this absorption are therefore still in some doubt, and it is probably the case that the true explanation lies somewhere between the two alternative theories that have been discussed.

The fact that the δCH_2 frequencies of $XCH=CH_2$ compounds appear to correlate well with the CH out-of-plane vibrations of the corresponding $XC\equiv CH$ compounds [85] is interesting, but does not, at this stage, throw any new light on the origins of the shifts. It can, however, be used for the prediction of one of these frequencies where the other is known.

Although studies of this kind are often indecisive, they are important in that they are helping us towards a better understanding of the behaviour of group frequencies and a more rational utilization of them. However, perhaps even more important is the light they may throw on the transmission of substituent effects in organic molecules. It is to be hoped that this last area, which is still largely neglected by organic and physical chemists, will be more thoroughly explored in the next few years.

(c) *Intensities*

Colthup and Orloff [108] have measured the integrated intensities of the $=CH_2$ wagging band in a variety of compounds with polar and with alkyl compounds. Their results for the latter agree reasonably well with the earlier measurements of Wexler [82] and show that the intensities for variously substituted alkyl compounds show little variation. However, there is considerable variation in the polar compounds. The intensity is found to decrease as the frequency increases. This is attributed to the fact that a decrease in the electron density on the carbon atom will result in a corresponding decrease in the dipole moment change during the vibration. As the former has already been shown to vary inversely with the frequency the intensity behaviour must also follow this pattern.

2.4. The C=N stretching frequency

The C=N absorption is not always strong in the infrared, and much of the more precise data we have are derived from combinations of infrared and Raman work. Absorption occurs in much the same region as the C=C band, and like this it shows relatively minor alterations with changes of structure. Some of the main types of C=N absorptions are listed below, and the results are summarised in Table 2.5.

(a) *Oximes, aldoximes and ketoximes*

These have been studied by a number of workers [109–111]. With alkyl substitution, both types absorb in the 1665–1650 cm^{-1} range. This corresponds to solutions in which the oximes are associated, and there are changes in these frequencies corresponding to polarity changes in the C=N bond as the strength of the association alters. The different frequencies of the two crystalline forms of benzaldoxime are attributed to this cause. However, whilst the earlier Raman workers suggested that strong association lowered the C=N frequency, there is some recent evidence that the shift is in the opposite direction. Thus Geiseler *et al.* [111] have shown that in decanaldoxime, in the *anti* form, the C=N band is at 1648 cm^{-1} in the monomer and at 1660 cm^{-1} in the associated form. The *syn* isomer shows similar behaviour with slightly different frequencies (monomer 1643 cm^{-1}, associated 1653 cm^{-1}). Aryloximes absorb in the 1620 cm^{-1} region.

(b) Hydrazones, semicarbazones and thiosemicarbazones

The infrared spectra of hydrazones have been studied by Wiley and Irick [67], and a thorough review of both infrared and Raman data is given by Kitaev *et al.* [112]. The Raman data on semicarbazones and thiosemicarbazones are reviewed by Raevskii *et al.* [113]. In the infrared the bands are often weak and in aromatics they are difficult to disentangle from the aromatic bands in the same region. Alkyl derivatives of all three types absorb in the 1650 cm^{-1} region. Aryl substitution at the carbon atom lowers this value to about 1625 cm^{-1} as does substitution at the nitrogen atom. Formaldehyde dimethyl hydrazone is exceptional in giving the very low frequency of 1584 cm^{-1} [114].

(c) Imines and amidines

Alkylaldimines absorb in the 1675–1665 cm^{-1} region, and this falls by 10–20 cm^{-1} on aryl substitution at either end of the double bond. Less data are available on ketinimes, but derivatives of diphenylketimine absorb near 1620 cm^{-1}. In the amidines, multiple C=N bands are often found. These arise from the existence of *N* mono substituted amidines in the *syn* and *anti* forms, and, in the case of *N* disubstituted amidines in which only the *syn* form occurs, to the formation of cyclic dimers. In polar solvents the monomer form gives rise to absorption in the 1630–1620 cm^{-1} region, but in solvents such as hexane the band is at 1590 cm^{-1} or less due to the dimer. In liquids, both bands appear.

(d) Azines

The infrared and Raman data available on alkyl azines have been summarised by Dollish *et al.* [115]. In methanalazine the antisymmetric C=N band occurs at 1637 cm^{-1}, and in acetone azine at 1648 cm^{-1} [116]. In general, aldazines and ketazines are characterized by a strong infrared band in the 1665–1635 cm^{-1} range. Araldehyde azines have been studied by Nyquist *et al.* [117]. In some 20 compounds they find the antisymmetric C=N band in the range 1637–1636 cm^{-1}, where it occurs with medium to strong intensity.

These general results are collected together in Table 2.5.

Individual values in this table refer to specific compounds, but where ranges are quoted they relate to the generic family. A range listed under CH_3 refers to all alkyl derivatives, and one under C_6H_5 to all substituted aromatics. The data, although limited, are sufficient to allow the general trends to be distinguished.

Table 2.5. $\nu C{=}N$ in cm^{-1} in compounds

$$\begin{array}{c} X \\ {}^{\diagdown} \\ {}_{Y}{}^{\diagup}C{=}N{\diagdown}Z \end{array}$$

X	CH₃ (Y)		C₆H₅ (Y)		H (Y)		NHCH₃ (Y)		N(CH₃)₂ (Y)		OH (Y)	
	CH₃	C₆H₅	CH₃	C₆H₅	CH₃	C₆H₅	CH₃	C₆H₅	CH₃	C₆H₅	CH₃	C₆H₅
H	1675–1665	1654	1637				1612		1647		1660–1650	1645
			1621				1604		1634		1652	1614
CH₃	1662–1649	1650	1640		1646	1632	1635		1652		1684	1640
		1640			1640	1620	1625		1625		1652	1620
C₆H₅	1650–1640		1640		1632						1640	
					1620						1620	
NHCH₃	1685	1651	1627									
N(CH₃)₂		1621	1597									
SCH₃		1622	1611									
OCH₃			1665		1655–1650	1655–1645						

The impact of aromatic conjugation at either the carbon or nitrogen atom is clear cut, and is well brought out in the table. The effects of conjugation with olefinic bonds are much more complex, as there is then extensive $C{=}C/C{=}N$ interaction. The final frequencies cannot then be properly identified with either bond. Changes in the substituents at either the carbon or nitrogen atoms can lead to sizeable frequency shifts, which are in many ways parallel to the effects the same substituents produce on the $C{=}C$ link, and which are at least in part related to the changes in the force constants of the X—C or X—N links. Replacement of a hydrogen atom on the double bond by carbon usually (but not always) gives a frequency rise of 10–20 cm^{-1}. As with the $C{=}C$ stretching mode, this shift is very much smaller than would be expected from the calculated mass effect. Sulphur substitution lowers the frequency, and this is consistent with the low force constants of C—S or N—S links. With oxygen substitution the frequency rises. This may well be due to the larger force constant of the C—O or O—N bond, but the behaviour is an interesting contrast to that of the $C{=}C$ link, where oxygen substitution causes the frequency to fall. The frequency rises whichever end of the bond the oxygen is attached, but the shift on attachment to nitrogen (as in the oximes) is usually slightly greater than if the oxygen is attached to the carbon atom. The frequency falls with nitrogen substitution at the $C{=}N$ bond, the largest shift occurring with the NR_2 group, which is the most basic. In these cases at least, resonance clearly predominates over other effects. The spectra of oximes illustrated by Hadzi [84] suggest that there may well be significant differences in the intensities of νC=N in corresponding *syn* and *anti* forms, but no measurements have been reported on this.

Further work will need to be done, particularly with halogen-substituted C=N bonds, before any final conclusions can be drawn on the factors affecting this frequency. νC=N seems to be sensitive to resonance effects, to changes in the force constants of the attached bonds and possibly also to inductive forces. Which of these will predominate in a given situation we have not sufficient data to judge.

The data on C=N frequencies in cyclic systems remain in a confused state. Meyers [69] has tabulated data on this band in Δ^1-pyrrolines and Δ^2-thiazolines. The frequency falls as usual on conjugation, but the range for alkyl-substituted compounds (1653–1639 cm^{-1}) is not very different from that of open-chain compounds. A few six-membered ring systems such as Δ^1-tetrahydropiperidines have been examined [70], and these absorb at slightly higher frequencies (1675–1660 cm^{-1}). However, the recorded value for an exocyclic C=N band in a five-membered ring is only 1666 cm^{-1}, which suggests that angle changes at the double bond C=N carbon atom may be less important than in the olefines. In the latter a similar change from an endocyclic five-membered ring system to an exocyclic arrangement would produce a frequency shift of about 50 cm^{-1}. However, the various C=N values are not all recorded under similar conditions, and the C=N frequency shows some sensitivity to changes of phase, so that it is too early to draw any final conclusions.

The values of νC=N in other heterocyclic systems such as indoles and indolines have been given by Katritzky and Ambler [70] and Katritzky and Taylor [118] in comprehensive reviews of the infrared spectra of heterocyclics, and these should be consulted for further data and references in this area.

2.5. The N=N stretching frequency

The group frequencies of the azo compounds are largely of academic interest. The N=N band appears in the same region as aromatic absorptions, and as it is weak, it is very difficult to identify. As these constitute the largest group of stable N=N compounds, the use of the frequencies for diagnosis must be limited. There has been some controversy on whether this mode should be assigned to bands at 1600 or 1450 cm^{-1}, but this has been resolved by some elegant work of Luttke *et al.* [71]. Using N^{15} substitution they have been able to show that in aromatic azo compounds in the *trans* configuration, the N=N band occurs between 1440 and 1410 cm^{-1}. The higher value is that of *trans*-azobenzene, and the frequency falls when electron donors are substituted in the ring. The p-hydroxy compound absorbs at 1416 cm^{-1} and the p-amino at 1418 cm^{-1}. With an NH group attached, the frequency falls to 1416 cm^{-1}, but the absorption is then more properly ascribed to the *as* mode of the

N$=$N—NH system. A second band due to the symmetric stretching mode is also observed at 1202 cm^{-1}, and this is likewise sensitive to isotopic substitution of the nitrogen atoms. In the ion $(C_6H_5 \cdot N=N=N \cdot C_6H_5)^+$ these frequencies fall to 1362 and 1209 cm^{-1}, probably indicating that the chain is bent.

cis-Azobenzene absorbs at 1511 cm^{-1}. The reason for this very significant rise as compared with the *trans* isomer is not known. Nor is it understood why the *trans* aromatic azo-compounds absorb at so much lower frequencies than *trans*-azomethane, in which νN$=$N occurs at 1576 cm^{-1} (Raman data).

Morgan has given some further data on the N$=$N frequencies of some aryl azo naphthols [72]. These show N$=$N bands near 1450 cm^{-1}, but they are of little use for identification purposes.

Bibliography

1. Wiberg and Nist, *J. Amer. Chem. Soc.*, 1961, **83**, 1226.
2. Lord and Rea, *J. Amer. Chem. Soc.*, 1957, **79**, 2401.
3. Colthup, *J. Chem. Education*, 1961, **38**, 394.
4. Criegel and Louis, *Chem. Ber.*, 1957, **90**, 417.
5. Doering and Mole, *Tetrahedron*, 1960, **10**, 65.
6. Breslow and Hover, *J. Amer. Chem. Soc.*, 1960, **82**, 2644.
7. Sverdlov and Krainov, *Optics and Spectroscopy*, 1959, **6**, 214.
8. Miller, *J. Org. Chem.*, 1960, **25**, 1279.
9. McElvain and Starn, *J. Amer. Chem. Soc.*, 1955, **77**, 4571.
10. Briggs and Colebrook, *J. Chem. Soc.*, 1960, 2458.
11. Miller and Carlson, *J. Amer. Chem. Soc.*, 1957, **79**, 3995.
12. Blomquist, Wolinsky, Meinwald and Longone, *J. Amer. Chem. Soc.*, 1956, **78**, 6057.
13. Blomquist and Verdol, *J. Amer. Chem. Soc.*, 1955, **77**, 1806.
14. Caserio, Parker, Piccolini and Roberts, *J. Amer. Chem. Soc.*, 1958, **80**. 5507.
15. Applequist and Roberts, *J. Amer. Chem. Soc.*, 1956, **78**, 4012.
16. Wood, Elofson and Saunders, *Analyt. Chem.*, 1958, **30**, 1339.
17. Sondheimer, Wolovsky and Amiel, *J. Amer. Chem. Soc.*, 1962, **84**, 274.
18. Noack, *Spectrochim. Acta*, 1962, **18**, 692.
19. Rea, *Analyt. Chem.*, 1960, **32**, 1638.
20. Petrov, Kupin, Jakovleva and Mingaleva, *J. Gen. Chem. Moscow*, 1959, **29**, 3732.
21. Hoffmann, *Liebigs Annalen.*, 1958, **618**, 276.
22. Dalton, Ellington and Meakins, *J. Chem. Soc.*, 1960, 3681.
23. Baker and Shulgin, *J. Amer. Chem. Soc.*, 1959, **81**, 4524.
24. Bellamy and Williams, *J. Chem. Soc.*, 1958, 2463.
25. Brey and Tarrant, *J. Amer. Chem. Soc.*, 1957, **79**, 6533.
26. Sorygin, Skurina, Sostakovskij and Graceva, *Bull. Aca. Sci. U.S.S.R. Ser. Chim.*, 1961, 3011.
27. Mikawa, *Bull. Chem. Soc., Japan*, 1956, **24**, 110.
28. Popov, Abdreev and Kajan, *Optics and Spectroscopy*, 1962, **12**, 37.
29. Popov and Kajan, *Optics and Spectroscopy*, 1962, **12**, 194.
30. Sorygin, Skurina, Sostakovskij, Sidel'Kovskeja and Zelenskaja, *Nachr. Akad. Wiss, Ud.S.S.R. Ser. Chim.*, 1959, 2208.
31. Mironov, Egorov and Petrov, *Bull. Akad. Sci. U.S.S.R.*, 1959, 1400.
32. Stafford and Stone, *Spectrochim. Acta*, 1961, **17**, 412.

33. Nesmejanov, Borisov and Novikova, *C.R. Acad. Sci. U.S.S.R.*, 1958, **119**, 712; *Bull. Akad. Sci. U.S.S.R. Chem. Ser.*, 1959, **7**, 1216.
34. Borisov, Novikova and Cumaeskij, *C.R. Akad. Sci. U.S.S.R.*, 1961, **136**, 129.
35. Boonsrta and Rinzcina, *Rec. Trav, Chim. Pays. Bas.*, 1960, **79**, 962.
36. Popov and Kajan, *Optics and Spectroscopy*, 1961, **11**, 730.
37. Kaesz and Stone, *Spectrochim. Acta*, 1959, 360.
38. Allinger and Herman, *J. Org. Chem.*, 1961, 1040.
39. Mecke and Noack, *Spectrochim. Acta*, 1958, **12**, 391; *Chem. Ber.*, 1960, **93**, 210.
40. Noack and Jones, *Can. J. Chem.*, 1961, **39**, 2201.
41. Noack, *Spectrochim. Acta*, 1962, **18**, 697, 1625.
42. Wailes, *Austral. J. Chem.*, 1959, **19**, 173.
43. Petrov, Kolesova and Porfireva, *J. Gen. Chem. Moscow*, 1957, **27**, 2081.
44. Petrov and Semenov, *J. Gen. Chem. Moscow*, 1957, **27**, 2941; 1958, **28**, 71.
45. Petrov, Porfireva and Semenov, *J. Gen. Chem. Moscow*, 1957, **27**, 1167.
46. Heilmann and Bonnier, *C.R. Acad. Sci. France*, 1959, **248**, 2595.
47. West, *J. Amer. Chem. Soc.*, 1959, **81**, 1614.
48. Oki and Iwamura, *Bull. Chem. Soc. Japan*, 1959, **32**, 567.
49. Chatt and Duncanson, *J. Chem. Soc.*, 1953, 2939.
50. Babushkin, Gribov and Hellman, *Russ. J. Inorgan. Chem.*, 1959, **4**, 695.
51. Powell and Sheppard, *Spectrochim. Acta*, 1958, **13**, 69; *J. Chem. Soc.*, 1960, 2519.
52. Adams and Chatt, *Chem. and Ind.*, 1960, 149.
53. Jonassen and Kirsch, *J. Amer. Chem. Soc.*, 1957, **79**, 1279.
54. Hoffmann, *Annalen*, 1958, **618**, 276.
55. Mironev, Egorov and Petrov, *Bull. Akad. Sci. U.S.S.R.*, 1959, 1400.
56. Overend and Scherer, *J. Chem. Phys.*, 1960, **32**, 1720.
57. Majanac, *Optics and Spectroscopy*, 1958, **5**, 369.
58. Potts and Nyquist, *Spectrochim. Acta*, 1959, **15**, 679.
59. Bak and Christensen, *Spectrochim. Acta*, 1958, **12**, 355.
60. Scherer and Potts, *J. Chem. Phys.*, 1959, **31**, 1691.
61. Scherer and Potts, *J. Chem. Phys.*, 1959, **30**, 1527.
62. Kirmann and Chancel, *Bull. Soc. Chim. France*, 1954, 1338.
63. Bellamy, in *Spectroscopy*, ed. Wells, Institute of Petroleum, London, 1962, p. 205.
64. Dewar and Grisdale, *J. Amer. Chem. Soc.*, 1962, **84**, 3548.
65. Craig and Entemann, *J. Chem. Phys.*, 1962, **36**, 243.
66. Cross and Whitham, *J. Chem. Soc.*, 1961, 1650.
67. Wiley and Irick, *J. Org. Chem.*, 1959, **24**, 1925.
68. Clougherty, Sousa and Wyman, *J. Org. Chem.*, 1957, **22**, 462.
69. Meyers, *J. Org. Chem.*, 1959, **24**, 1233.
70. Katritzky and Ambler, in *Physical Methods in Heterocyclic Chemistry*, Academic Press, 1963, pp. 161 *et seq.*
71. Kubler, Luttke and Weckherlin, *Zeit. Electrochem.*, 1960, **64**, 650.
72. Morgan, *J. Chem. Soc.*, 1961, 2151.
73. Henry and Noltes, *J. Amer. Chem. Soc.*, 1960, **82**, 555.
74. Pinchas, Gil Av, Shabati and Altmann, *Spectrochim. Acta*, 1965, **21**, 783.
75. Pinchas, Shabati, Herling and Gil Av, *J. Inst. Petroleum*, 1959, **45**, 311.
76. Shabati, Pinchas, Herling, Greener and Gil Av, *J. Inst. Petroleum*, 1962, **48**, 13.
77. Henbest, Meakins, Nicholls and Wilson, *J. Chem. Soc.*, 1957, 997.
78. Kuhn and Bowman, *Spectrochim. Acta*, 1967, **23A**, 189.
79. Grundy and Morris, *Spectrochim. Acta*, 1964, **20**, 695.
80. Miller, Sala, Devlin, Overend, Lippert, Luder, Moser and Varchmin, *Spectrochim. Acta*, 1964, **20**, 1233.
81. Carlson, *Spectrochim. Acta*, 1964, **20**, 1781.
82. Wexler, *Spectrochim. Acta*, 1965, **21**, 1725.

83. Dabrowski, Kamienska Trela, *Spectrochim. Aeta*, 1966, **22**, 211.
84. Hadzi and Premru, *Spectrochim. Acta*, 1967, **23A**, 35.
85. Moritz, *Spectrochim. Acta*, 1967, **23A**, 167.
86. Good and Ritter, *J. Chem. and Engineering Data*, 1962, **7**, 416.
87. Mitchell and Merritt, *Spectrochim. Acta*, 1969, **25A**, 1881.
88. Mitchell, Dorkon and Merritt, *J. Mol. Spectroscopy*, 1968, **26**, 197.
89. Quoted in [90].
90. Craig, Alpern and Parkin, *Spectrochim. Acta*, 1971, **31A**, 1463.
91. Gamaggi and Gazzo, *J. Chem. Soc. (C)*, 1970, 178.
92. McGlineley, Reynoldson and Stone, *Chem. Comm.*, 1970, 1264.
93. Dorris, Boggs, Danti and Alpeter, *J. Chem. Phys.*, 1967, **46**, 1191.
94. Durig and Morrissey, *J. Chem. Phys.*, 1966, **45**, 1269.
95. Durig and Willis, *Spectrochim. Acta*, 1966, **22**, 1299.
96. Miller, Brown and Rhee, *Spectrochim. Acta*, 1972, **28A**, 1467.
97. Rhee and Miller, *Spectrochim. Acta* 1971, **27A**, 1.
98. Tuazon, Finseth and Miller, *Spectrochim. Acta* 1975, **31A**, 1137.
99. Dollish, Fateley and Bentley, *Characteristic Raman Frequencies of Organic Compounds*. Wiley/Interscience, New York 1973, p. 97.
100. Faulk and Fay, *J. Org. Chem.* 1970, **35**, 364.
101. Al-Jallo and Jalhoon, *Spectrochim. Acta*, 1975, **31A**, 265.
102. Taylor, *Spectrochim. Acta*, 1976, **32A**, 1471.
103. Smith and Taylor, *Spectrochim. Acta*, 1976, **32A**, 1477.
104. Smith and Taylor, *Spectrochim. Acta*, 1976, **32A**, 1489.
105. Duncan, *Spectrochim Acta*, 1970, **26A**, 429.
106. McKean, *Spectrochim. Acta*, 1975, **31A**, 1167.
107. Reference 99, pp 72–75.
108. Colthup and Orloff, *Spectrochim. Acta*, 1971, **27A**, 1299.
109. Harris and Bush, *J. Chem. Phys.*, 1972, **56**, 6147.
110. Reference [99], page 134.
111. Geiseler, Luck and Fruwert, *Spectrochim. Acta*, 1975, **31A**, 789.
112. Kitaev, Buzykin and Troepol skaya, *Russ. Chem. Rev*, 1970, **39**, 441.
113. Raevskii, Shagidullin and Kitaev, *Doklady Acad. Sci. USSR*, 1966, **170**, 853.
114. Harris, Glenn and Knight, *Spectrochim. Acta*, 1975, **31A**, II.
115. Reference [99] page 139.
116. Harris, Yang and Wilcox, *Spectrochim. Acta*, 1975, **31A**, 1981.
117. Nyquist, Peters and Budde, *Spectrochim. Acta*, 1978, **34A**, 503.
118. Katritzky and Taylor in *Physical Methods in Heterocyclic Chemistry* Vol 4. Ed Katritzky, Academic Press New York, 1971.
119. Bellamy and Mayo, *J. Phys Chem.*, 1976, **80**, 1217.
120. Liquier, Tailandier and Leibovici, *J. Mol. Structure*, 1972, **12**, 241.

3

X=Y=Z Systems and Triple Bonds

3.1. Introduction, multiple bond systems

The various types of multiple bond are most conveniently grouped together with the triple bonds, not only because they occur in much the same frequency ranges but also because there is often some degree of overlap between the two. Thus in isothiocyanates RNCS there is some degree of resonance between the two canonical forms R—$\overset{+}{N}$≡C—$\overset{-}{S}$ and R—N=C=S and there has been a good deal of argument as to which of the two predominate.

The linear X=Y=Z systems form a special class in which vibrational interactions play a major part in determining the final frequencies. The simplest cases are those in which X is the same as Z, as in CO_2, CS_2, etc., and these have, of course, been exhaustively studied. These compounds show a single absorption in the infrared which corresponds to a stretching motion, and this is at a much higher frequency than would be expected from the bond order of the links involved. It is important that the organic chemist should realize that this is not due to a real increase in the bond order, but rather to a coupling phenomenon in which the molecule executes symmetric and anti-symmetric stretching vibrations about the central atom Y. The symmetric mode is forbidden for linear molecules in the infrared, but can be observed in the Raman spectrum. It occurs at a much lower frequency than the corresponding anti-symmetric vibration, and it is the mean of these two frequencies, and not that of the anti-symmetric mode alone, that bears some relation to the bond orders of the links.

With systems in which X differs from Z, symmetry rules allow the appearance of both frequencies in the infrared, although the symmetric band is usually weak if the molecule is linear. The extent to which coupling now occurs depends very much on the bond angles and on the values of the theoretical unperturbed frequencies of the X=Y and Y=Z bonds. If these frequencies are close together the situation is analogous to that in carbon dioxide and pseudo anti-symmetric and symmetric bands appear with their frequencies widely separated. As the original uncoupled frequencies become more widely separated (i.e. as the X and Z elements differ in character), the interaction effects become smaller, so that in the ultimate case (which is never fully realized) we would have simple uncoupled vibrations of the two separate halves of the system. This would lead to a frequency fall in the original infrared active stretching band, because its high frequency originated in coupling effects and not in a real increase in bond order. As will be seen from later sections of this chapter, this apparently obvious situation needs to be stressed because of the frequency with which chemists have misinterpreted the significance of shifts of this kind.

With non-linear $X=Y=Z$ systems the position is very different. If the $X=Y$ and $Y=Z$ bonds were at right angles to each other, the mechanical coupling would fall to zero and seperate bands from each of the individual bonds would appear. Consequently as the $X=Y=Z$ bond angle closes from $180°$ towards $90°$ the separation of the symmetric and antisymmetric bands is reduced. In carbon dioxide this separation is 1006 cm^{-1}, and in most other linear systems it is in the $900–1000$ cm^{-1} region. However, in NO_2 with a bond angle of $134°$, the separation is reduced to 300 cm^{-1}, in SO_2 with an angle of $119°$ to 172 cm^{-1}, and in the nitrite ion (angle $115°$) to 67 cm^{-1}. Such non-linear systems are considered separately in later chapters.

The individual frequencies of a variety of $X=Y=Z$ links are listed in Table 3.1, and are discussed in detail below. Much new qualitative data are available, and quantitative intensity studies have been made in some cases. In addition, the impact of solvent effects has been more widely studied, and promises to provide additional diagnostic help, in that the directions of frequency shifts in proton-donating solvents are different in some cases from others

3.2. Isothiocyanates, R—N=C=S

Qualitative data have been supplied by Ham and Willis [1], Caldow and Thompson [2], Svatek *et al.* [3], Foffani *et al.* [4], Lieber *et al.* [5], Kniseley *et al.* [99] and Kristian *et al.* (aryl isothiocyanates) [95]. Some quantitative measurements on band intensities are included in references [1] and [3]. In addition, some isothiocyanates of boron have been studied by Lappert [6] and by Sowerby [7], while there have been numerous studies on various types of coordination compound containing the isothiocyanate link. These last will be referred to in more detail later.

The data on the high-frequency stretching vibration of organic iso-thiocyanates which are assembled in Table 3.1 are largely a composite of the information in references [1–4]. There is some measure of disagreement between the various authors, which is probably due to the fact that the band is never single. It is usually a doublet, but sometimes this carries an additional shoulder. This makes it difficult to assign a precise value to the real

Table 3.1(a). X=Y=Z, C≡N and N≡C groups with alkyl substituents

R	NCS	SCN	NCO	CN	NC	NNN	NCN	CCC	δCH_2 (allenes)
Methyl	2106	2141	2288	2255	2183	2104		1961	858
Ethyl	2092	2155	2280	2249	2160		2138		
n-Propyl	2085	2156		2253					
n-Butyl	2088	2155	2273	2254	2146	2083	2138	1945	848
n-Amyl			2274	2248					
Isopropyl	2093	2153	2270		2140		2128		
sec-Butyl		2156	2262				2128		
tert-Butyl	2085				2134				
Benzyl	2100	2141	2265	2253	2146	2088	2140		
Allyl	2084			2253					
Vinyl				2230					
Cyclohexyl	2100		2255		2138		2130		
CH₂Cl				2260					
CHCl₂				2259					
CCl₃				2249					
Cl				2214				1960	
Br				2200				1960	875
F				2290					
I				2175				1970	
(CH₃)₂N		2137		2222					
CH₃NH		2139		2237					
CF₃				2271				2000 ⎫ 1970 ⎭	
Na	2020			2080					
OCH₃				2232				1970	
COOH								1900 ⎫ 1930 ⎭	850

Table 3.1(b). X=Y=Z, C≡N and N≡C groups with aryl substituents

R	NCS	SCN	NCO	CN	NC	NNN	NCN
α-Naphthyl	2080		2275	2222			2100 ⎫ 2152 ⎭
β-Naphthyl	2080		2267	2227	2122		
Phenyl	2060	2170	2267	2229	2123	2144	
Para-OCH₃	2080		2250	2226	2125		2120 ⎫ 2142 ⎭
"　OC₂H₅	2087		2274				
"　Cl	2052		2275	2236	2116		
"　Br	2050		2269	2237		2110	
"　NO₂	2045	2174	2269	2238	2116	2114	
"　NH₂	2105	2166		2221			
"　CH₃			2280	2229	2125	2092	2120 ⎫ 2145 ⎭
Meta-CH₃			2266	2229			
"　NO₂			2272	2240	2120		
"　Cl				2231		2096	
Ortho-CH₃			2273	2229	2122		
"　Cl	2090			2236	2166	2088	

unperturbed fundamental, but the effect is not a common one with $X{=}Y{=}Z$ links (the thiocyanates, for example, show a single strong absorption), and it is therefore a valuable feature in identification. Ham and Willis [1] report that there are sufficient differences between the band shapes of aryl and alkyl isothiocyanates to enable the two to be differentiated, and they suggest also that the former shows the greater number of bands. However, this finding is not wholly borne out by the data in references [2] and [3]. The origins of the multiple bands are generally agreed to be Fermi resonance interactions, with overtones or combination bands arising from lower-frequency fundamentals. The bands concerned have been identified in some cases [1], and the interpretation is confirmed by the behaviour of the multiple peaks in various solvents [2, 3, 97].

In all cases the solvent effects are the same. One of the principal bands near 2100 cm^{-1} moves to higher frequencies on passing from carbon tetrachloride solution to chloroform, while the other moves to lower frequencies. The shift of the main band can be as much as 50 cm^{-1} between these two solvents [2], and this affords a useful diagnostic for the νNCS band itself, which has been used in the selection of the data in the table. This solvent sensitivity also provides a simple means of differentiation from the organic thiocyanates which show little change in different media. The values given in the table refer to the frequencies in inert solvents, and it should be noted that the vapour-phase values are not higher than these but actually lower. It will be seen from the tables that aromatic isothiocyanates absorb at lower frequencies than alkyl derivatives, and that electron-attracting substituents at the *para* position tend to give somewhat lower values. This is an interesting point of difference from the thiocyanates, in which electron-attracting substituents tend to raise the frequency [4]. A similar dichotomy is found with nitriles and isonitriles.

Attachment of the isothiocyanate group to boron instead of carbon lowers the frequency considerably. Boron tri-isothiocyanate [7] absorbs at 2020 cm^{-1}, thiocyanic acid itself at 1980 cm^{-1} [9] and the purely ionic form (in which SCN^- becomes identical with NCS^-) in the range 2080–2000 cm^{-1} [8]. However, the frequencies of these latter two groups cannot be compared directly with those of the organic compounds because of the mass effect. In the organic materials the single bond C—N link is compressed during the anti-symmetric motion of the NCS bonds. This causes the frequency to appear at a higher value than in the ion or in the acid, where little or no work is required for this purpose. In just the same way the frequencies of alkyl nitriles are higher than those of the ions or of HCN itself. The true significance of the frequency shifts that follow changes in the substituents is not easy to determine. Apart from the complications introduced by Fermi resonance, the directions of shift are liable to change, depending on the relative proportions of the two possible canonical forms $R{-}N{=}C{=}S$ and $R{-}\overset{+}{N}{\equiv}C{-}\bar{S}$, as indicated above.

The position of the symmetric stretching absorption should be of some help in this, but unfortunately the bands are weak and their identification uncertain. Lieber assigns this band at 1050 cm^{-1} in alkyl isothiocyanates [5], and Ham and Willis [1] put it at 927 cm^{-1} in aromatic derivatives. In HNCS it is at [9] 850 cm^{-1}. These clearly indicate an appreciably shorter C=S bond than would be expected from the structure R—N≡C—S, so that it seems fairly certain that the covalent form makes the major real contribution. This is confirmed by x-ray data on the bond lengths. On the other hand, Ham and Willis [1] assign this mode at 673 cm^{-1} in methyl isothiocyanate, and this is supported by Stevenson [10]. If the true frequency range is as great as these differences would suggest, it makes it entirely unrealistic to discuss the smaller frequency changes that occur in various types of coordination compound. However, it seems more probable that the earlier assignments are correct, especially as Lewis *et al.* [11] find this band at 820 cm^{-1} in coordination compounds with the metal linked directly to the NCS group. The corresponding value for the metal-SCN group is appreciably lower (near 700 cm^{-1}), and this provides a useful method for determining the point of attachment of the SCN ion. These results have been confirmed by Pecile *et al.* [16].

Nevertheless, the frequency range of the *sym*-NCS vibration is considerable, even if one excludes some of the extreme values. This suggests that considerable variations are possible in the proportions of the two canonical forms. This is borne out by the sensitivity of this band to solvent effects. Not only is the frequency raised by proton donors, such as chloroform, which associate with the sulphur atom but it is also raised when the hydrogen atom of HNCS is bonded to a proton acceptor. Anything which increases the polarity of the system therefore raises this frequency.

The anti-symmetric mode has also been studied in compounds in which the NCS group acts as a bridging unit and is coordinated at both ends [12]. The frequency range is then higher than either isothiocyanates or thiocyanates. However, it is not necessary to seek any chemical interpretation of this observation, as the increased restrictions imposed on the movements of the nitrogen and sulphur atoms will automatically lead to a frequency rise. The observed range is 2185–2150 cm^{-1}.

Intensity studies on the 2080 cm^{-1} band have already been mentioned [1, 2]. The band is extremely strong, and despite the difficulties in assessing the intensities of split peaks, there is good agreement among the various workers that it is of the order of 10–20 mol^{-1} l.cm^2 intensity units. This is many times the intensity of the nitrile band, but is similar to the values given by other multiple groups, such as N=C=O and N=C=N. Ham and Willis [1] regard this as further evidence that the covalent type of structure predominates. The intensity of the corresponding band in the NCS— ion is, of course, very difficult to measure accurately in the solid state, but it appears to be about five times less intense than the organic isothiocyanates.

3.3. Thiocyanates, RS—C≡N

The situation with this group is a good deal clearer than in the isothiocyanates. Only a single high-frequency band is shown which has a relatively low intensity compared with many other X=Y=Z systems, and in organic derivatives the frequency ($2156\text{--}2140\ cm^{-1}$) is sufficiently above that of isothiocyanates to enable a clear distinction to be made. New data on thiocyanate frequencies are given in references [1, 2, 4, 5, 13, 14, and 97–98], and much of this is summarized in Table 3.1. It will be seen that the frequency range is relatively narrow. Aromatic compounds absorb at slightly higher frequencies than the alkyl compounds ($2175\text{--}2160\ cm^{-1}$), and electron-attracting substituents in the *para* position give a small frequency rise [4]. Presumably this reflects a reduction in the already small contribution from the polar $R\text{—}\overset{+}{S}\text{=}C\text{=}\overset{-}{N}$ form.

A low frequency band is found near $680\ cm^{-1}$ and is generally agreed to be largely a C—S stretching mode rather than a symmetric SCN vibration. This C—S band is often multiple due to rotational isomerism. The thiocyanates, as a whole, can therefore be regarded as existing very largely in the non-polar R—S—C≡N form. This is fully supported by the insensitivity to solvent effects of the main absorption at $2150\ cm^{-1}$, which is in strong contrast to the behaviour of the isocyanates [97, 98].

There has been a substantial amount of work on the thiocyanate ion in coordination compounds. The position of the high-frequency band in relation to the type of salt is discussed by Tramer [15], and by Pecile *et al.* [16, 17], and other data will be found in references [8, 11 and 14]. In purely ionic compounds there is, of course, no difference between the thiocyanate and isothiocyanate ions, but the point of attachment in coordination compounds can be readily determined from the position of the lower-frequency bands.

3.4. Isocyanates, RNCO

The high-frequency anti-symmetric stretching absorption occurs at a higher value than that of any other X=Y=Z system, and falls more in the range associated with triple bonds. From these it is readily differentiated by its very great intensity, which is similar to that of the isothiocyanates. The band is usually single, but sometimes shows signs of shoulders, and is a little broader ($25\text{--}30\ cm^{-1}$ half-bandwidth) than the corresponding bands of thiocyanates. Ham and Willis [1] attribute the increased bandwidth to a Fermi resonance effect similar to that of the isothiocyanates, but which is insufficient to split the band into a clearly resolved doublet.

The data on isocyanates in Table 3.1 are based in part on the older work of Davison and Hoyer. Some new data from references [1] and [100], however, are also included. This absorption has been discussed by Derkosch *et al.* [18], and the special cases of $Si(NCO)_4$, $Ge(NCO)_4$ and $Pb(NCO)_4$ have been dealt with by Miller *et al.* [19, 20]. Even in the silicon derivative, which is tetrahedral and has a linear Si—N=C=O system, the frequency is very little affected (2284 cm⁻¹) by the p_π—d_π bonding which almost certainly occurs, while in the germanium compound the frequency is somewhat reduced but is still close to the normal values of carbon compounds (Ge(NCO)$_4$ 2247 cm⁻¹). This and the data assembled in Table 3.1 indicate that this frequency is almost wholly insensitive either to the nature of the atom to which the group is joined or to the nature of any substituents it carries. No data are available on the effects of proton donors on this absorption, but the close agreement between the values reported for the liquid and solid states would suggest that solvent effects are likely to be small. This would be entirely consistent with the formulation of these compounds in the covalent form R—N=C=O, with little or no contribution from polar structures. Some data on the near-infrared spectra of the compounds have been reported by David [96].

3.5. Azides, R—N=N=N

The limited amount of data in Table 3.1 is derived wholly from the papers of Lieber *et al.* [21, 22, 23]. They confirm the appearance of a strong band in the 2160–2088 cm⁻¹ range, and a second weaker band between 1250 and 1290 cm⁻¹. The appearance of this symmetric band must indicate that the N=N=N link in organic azides is non-symmetric, and there is some x-ray evidence that the bond lengths of the N=N links are unequal in methyl azide (1.24 Å and 1.10 Å). The main anti-symmetric absorption is usually single and sharp, but appears as a doublet in a few instances, such as in benzazide and some of its nitro derivatives, and in compounds such as $CH_3OCH_2N_3$ and $CH_3SCH_2N_3$. Hetero atoms of this kind appear to affect the frequency somewhat. Azido ethers absorb near 2120 cm⁻¹, azido thioethers at 2100 cm⁻¹ and azido methylamines near 2095 cm⁻¹. Although the differences are not large, they are probably significant when one remembers that the changes are occurring at the α-carbon atom and not in the atom directly attached to the azide group. Some additional data on organic azides are available in the paper by Sejnker *et al.* [106].

In the purely ionic salts, in which the N=N links become equal in length (I.15 A) and in which the symmetric stretching band vanishes, the main absorption is near 2030 cm⁻¹ which is the position of this band in ammonium azide. Fujita and his colleagues [24] have reported some coordination complexes with azide links which absorb at higher frequencies than the ionic forms. Thus $Cr(NH_3)_5N_3I_2$ absorbs at 2094 cm⁻¹ and the corresponding cobalt compound at 2047 cm⁻¹. They suggest that this indicates a greater degree of covalency in the azide group. In view of the values obtained for the organic compounds, this is probably a reasonable conclusion, but it should be recognized that the rise in this frequency does not, *per se,* prove that the proportion of the covalent form has increased. In this connexion, Rao and

Hahl [25] have quoted a range of 2040–2140 cm^{-1} for ionic azides without giving values for the individual compounds. However, the materials studied include the α and β forms of lead azide, which may well have some degree of covalency, so that the high frequencies may be accounted for in this way. Other inorganic complex azides studied are the series $X_2Zn(N_3)_4$ where X is potassium, rubidium and caesium. Multiple bands occur in the 2110–2050 cm^{-1} region in these compounds due to factor group splitting [107].

3.6. Carbodi-imides, R—N=C=N—R

Compounds of this kind are rare and have received little attention. However, Meakins and Moss [26] have reported on a number of them, and these values are given in Table 3.1. The infrared and Raman data on others have been reviewed by Mogul [108]. The anti-symmetric stretching band is again very intense, being comparable with that of the isocyanates and isothiocyanates. It is single with alkyl substituents, but doubles in the aryl derivatives. The reasons for this are not fully established, but by analogy with the iso-thiocyanates it is likely that Fermi resonance is again responsible, in this case with some overtone band of the aromatic residue. Only symmetrically substituted compounds have been studied, and these are too few to enable any conclusions to be drawn on the stability of the frequency or on the nature of any substituents which might cause frequency shifts. However, it is to be expected that the frequency range will be a narrow one, and values much outside those listed in the table are unlikely.

3.7. Diazo compounds, R—CH=$\overset{+}{N}$=$\overset{-}{N}$

The earlier studies on diazo compounds were very largely concerned with aromatic diazo compounds, in which high frequencies occur corresponding to the form $C_6H_5 \cdot N \equiv \overset{+}{N}Cl$—. These bands are sensitive to the nature of ring substituents [30] but insensitive to the nature of the anion. Some new data on compounds of this kind have been given by Kazicyna et al. [27]. These confirm the earlier assignments and place the N≡N stretching band between 2230 and 2300 cm^{-1}, depending upon the nature of the ring substituents. These workers find somewhat lower frequencies in metal complexes of the type $C_6H_5N_2ClSbCl_3$ but not in $C_6H_5N_2BF_4$. They conclude that in the diazo chloride a lone pair of electrons remains on the terminal nitrogen atom, which is available for coordination with a metal but not with the borofluoride, in which no suitable vacant bonding orbital is available.

A limited amount of data is now available on aliphatic diazo compounds. Yates et al. [28] have studied both these and carbonyl diazo compounds, and the latter have been studied also by Fahr [29]. In alkyl diazo compounds there is a much greater contribution from the structure R—CH=$\overset{+}{N}$=$\overset{-}{N}$, and regardless of whether the R group is aryl or alkyl, the main absorption appears in the 2050–2035 cm^{-1} range. Conjugation with a triple bond appears to raise the frequency as diazopropyne absorbs at 2069 cm^{-1}. With disubstitution there is a small further frequency fall to 2030–2000 cm^{-1}. This is a little unexpected, as the mass effect might have been expected to operate in the opposite direction. However, it is difficult to predict the impact of such effects on the splitting of the *as* and *s* modes, and it is this that primarily determines the observed values.

The compound $C_6H_5CH_2 \cdot CH=\overset{+}{N}=N \cdot C_6H_5$ absorbs at 2020 cm^{-1} showing that the covalent structure predominates in diazo compounds that are not salts. Keto-diazo-compounds [28, 29, 110] of the form $RCOCHN_2$ and $RCOCRN_2$ show some degree of resonance between the carbonyl and diazo links. This leads to lower carbonyl frequencies, but to higher values for the azido bond, which now has some triple bond character. Values of 2100–2080 cm^{-1} are given by monosubstituted derivatives and of 2075–2050 cm^{-1} for the disubstituted compounds.

3.8. Allenes, $R_2C=C=CR_2$

3.8.1. The C=C=C stretching vibration (as)

The linear allenes are excellent examples of a strongly coupled vibrational system. The three carbon atoms vibrate in symmetric and anti-symmetric modes, giving two bands which are well separated. Only the latter is observed in the infrared. The coupling dominates all other factors, and the frequency is very little influenced either by the nature or numbers of the substituent groups. Wotiz and Mancuso [31] have summarized the literature values on fifty-eight allenes of various kinds, and supplementary data are given by Petrov [93] and Borisov [94]. Monosubstituted allenes absorb in the range 1980–1945 cm^{-1}, with the higher values corresponding to polar COOH or CH_2OH groups. In certain instances, particularly when the substituent is a carbonyl or nitrile group, the characteristic allene band appears as a well-defined doublet. The reasons for this are not known. Phenyl allenes have a slightly lower value (near 1925 cm^{-1}). Vinylallene absorbs at 1934 cm^{-1} [111] and divinylallene at 1935 cm^{-1} [112].

Further substitution has little effect. Asymmetric disubstituted allenes absorb in the range 1930–1955 cm^{-1}, and disubstituted non-terminal allenes between 1930 and 1915 cm^{-1}. A comparison between C_6H_5H—C=C=CH —C_6H_4—C_6H_5 and $(C_6H_5)_2C=C=CH_2$, which absorb at 1930 and 1925 cm^{-1} respectively, shows the small difference between these two types of substitution. A small number of tri- and tetra-substituted allenes have been studied, and these likewise absorb in the 1920–2000-cm^{-1} range.

3.8.2. The CH$_2$ deformation of allenes and its overtone band

Mono- or unsymmetrically disubstituted allenes have an additional character-istic frequency from the out-of-plane deformation of the terminal CH$_2$ group [31, 93]. This is parallel to the corresponding absorption near 900 cm^{-1} in vinyl or vinylidene compounds, but it now occurs at lower frequencies (875–840 cm^{-1}). As with the vinyl compounds, the band is quite strong and is not much influenced by the nature of the substituents. This is, of course, to be expected in the present case in view of the distance they are removed along the chain. Like the vinyl compounds also, this absorption has a very characteristic overtone absorption of remarkably high intensity for a band originating in this way. It occurs very close to, or slightly higher than twice the value of the fundamental. This negative anharmonicity is another very close parallel with the vinyl group bands which behave in the same way. Disubstituted allenes, RCH=C=CHR, also show a CH deformation in the same region. Petrov [93] quotes the narrow range 875–870 cm^{-1} in hydrocarbons.

3.9. Factors controlling the stretching frequencies of triple bonds

The vibrations of triple bonds have long been recognized as providing excellent group frequencies, and perhaps for this reason there has been a tendency among chemists to assume that mass and coupling effects can safely be ignored, and the whole of any observed frequency shifts interpreted in terms of changes in the electron distribution within the bonds. Thus, it is common to find a shift of, say, 20 cm^{-1} in a C≡N stretching frequency being discussed in terms of changes in the covalent/ionic ratios within the bond. As will be seen this has no validity if the element to which the nitrile carbon atom is attached is altered, although it may have some significance if this element remains the same.

With a simple linear system X—Y≡Z it is possible to write down the basic equations that connect the vibrational frequencies with the masses of X, Y and Z and with the force constants of the X—Y and Y≡Z bonds. If interaction terms are neglected it is then a simple matter to compute the changes which will occur in the XY and YZ stretching frequencies when the mass of X is varied from zero to infinity. For this calculation the force constants of both bonds are regarded as remaining unchanged during this operation. Alternatively, the impact of changes in the XY force constant on both stretching frequencies can be evaluated in a calculation in which the mass of the three atoms is held constant, along with the force constant of the Y≡Z bond.

Of course, neither approach can be realized experimentally, as changes in the mass of X or in the force constant of the XY bond are almost always accompanied by changes in the electron distribution over the whole system, so that the YZ force constant also varies. The approach also suffers from the deficiencies inherent in an over-simplification of this type. Thus, in studies on the mass effect it is usual to assign a force constant to the X—Y bond which corresponds either to the kCH or kCC value, and it is assumed that the work required to compress this bond is then independent of the nature of the atoms. In practice, for very light atoms, such as hydrogen, there is a well-marked tendency for the hydrogen atom to ride along with the movement of Y in the Y—Z stretching mode. The HY bond is not therefore compressed to the same extent as other bonds, and this has a direct impact on the frequency. Nevertheless, the results of calculations of this kind are very instructive, and it is very interesting to compare them with the experimental results. As will be seen, it seems probable that force constant and mass effects have a much greater effect upon the X—Y≡Z stretching frequencies than have any chemical factors arising from changes in the electron distribution within the bonds.

The calculations of the effects of changes in the mass of X with other factors remaining constant have been made by Lord and Miller [32] in the case of the acetylenes, and by Whiffen [33] for the nitriles. Both give essentially the same result, and this is illustrated in Fig. 3.1, which is reproduced from Whiffen's paper [33]. The calculations lead to two frequencies for the two stretching

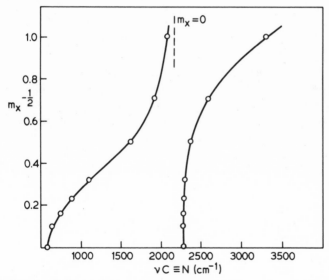

Figure 3.1. Variations of X—C and C≡N frequencies with the mass of X [33]

vibrations of the X—Y≡Z system, but do not, of course, indicate which is which. For masses of 12 up to infinity for X, the higher frequency is clearly the C≡N stretching mode, and this does not alter by more than 15 cm^{-1} over this whole range. For changes of X which do not involve hydrogen or deuterium the direct mass effect of X on $\nu C \equiv N$ can therefore be ignored. Between a mass of 12 and 1.5 the two stretching frequencies approach each other, but the lines do not cross. Instead they repel each other in the way shown in the figure. In this range both frequencies are strongly coupled, and it would be unrealistic to describe either in terms of an isolated vibration of one or other of the bonds. For masses below 1.5 the frequencies of the two links become sufficiently different for the coupling to vanish, and the separate bands now correspond once more to individual bond vibrations. However, it will be seen that they have now changed over, in that it is now the C—H stretching band that has the higher frequency.

Experimentally these predictions are well borne out. The strong coupling in DCN as opposed to HCN is well shown by the $\nu CH/\nu CD$ ratios, and also by solvent studies, in which the proton is engaged in hydrogen bonding. With HCN only the νCH band is affected, whereas with DCN both the two stretching bands are shifted [50]. Similar solvent effects have also been reported for the acetylenes [35]. So far as the observed frequencies are concerned, the agreement with the prediction is good. Acetonitrile absorbs at 2267 cm^{-1} (calculated 2295 cm^{-1}), and the values for halogenated nitriles are also good. However, the value for the CN radical (mass 0) at 2068 cm^{-1} is lower than the predicted value of 2170 cm^{-1}, and this probably reflects a substantial change of the $C \equiv N$ force constant. For the chemist, however, this result indicates that the effects of mass changes on $\nu C \equiv N$ may safely be ignored providing the masses are greater than twelve.

However, a more significant effect emerges when one considers the impact of changes in the X—C force constant on the νCN frequency. It will be seen from Fig. 3.1 that if the mass of X is maintained at 12 and the force constant of the X—C bond is reduced progressively from 4.6 md/A to zero the frequency corresponding to νCN must change from 2255 to 2170 cm^{-1}. This follows from the fact that the condition where kX—C is zero is the same as that when there is zero X mass (2170 cm^{-1}). The progression between these two values is likely to be reasonably linear, as the single-bond X—C frequency is already well removed from the triple-bond frequency, and a reduction in the force constant will only increase the separation further. This result suggests that a change in the strength of the bond adjacent to the nitrile link will have a substantial effect upon its frequency. This is due to the change in the work which has to be done in the compression of the X—C bond during the stretching of the $C \equiv N$ link. A change of 1.0 md/A in the X—C force constant will alter νCN by as much as 30 cm^{-1}. Very similar results are obtained in the case of acetylene.

Experimental confirmations of these results must necessarily be indirect, as it is not possible in practice to alter the X—C force constant without changing either the masses or the chemical environment. Nevertheless, there is ample evidence for the reality of these effects. If one considers the bond-length data (derived from microwave studies) on the halogenated nitriles, and on acetonitrile, one finds that rC≡N is longest in FCN, shortens progressively throughout the halogen series and shows a further contraction in CH_3CN. The data available on N^{14} quadrupole coupling are also consistent with these observations. This certainly indicates that chemical effects are operating which are altering the C≡N force constants, but from this data one would expect the force constants and the frequencies to follow the order $F < Cl < Br < I < CH_3$. In fact, as Table 3.1 shows, vCN is highest in FCN and that throughout the halogen series it falls as the C≡N bond length decreases. The position of carbon in the frequency series is also out of line with the electronegativity of this element, as it occurs between fluorine and chlorine.

The frequency order $F > CH_3 > Cl > Br > I$ is in fact the order of the force constants of X—C bonds, indicating that it is the compression of these links that is the dominant term in deciding vCN, and that these outweigh any changes resulting from inductive effects which are apparently working in the opposite direction.

A direct experimental check on these findings would involve a comparison between the changes of vCN with the changes in the force constants of the adjoining links. However, owing to the difficulties in evaluating interaction terms in the nitriles and acetylenes, it is not possible to obtain sufficient reliable values directly. Indeed, some workers quote ascending values for the halogen–carbon bond force constant in the halonitriles, and others the descending values, the result depending entirely on the arbitrary choice of interaction constants. The problem is well illustrated by the force field calculations of Whitten [114]. However, a good general measure of the trend of X—C force constants with changes of X can be obtained from the CH_3X series, for which a series of selected values have been tabulated by Cottrell [37]. If one assumes that chemical factors can either be ignored or are similar in the CH_3X and XC≡N series, so far as the X—C bonds are concerned, one can compare the vCN values of a range of XCN compounds with the kCX values for the corresponding CH_3X compounds. This comparison is shown in Fig. 3.2 for both the nitriles and the acetylenes. In both cases the agreement is remarkably good. This, of course, does not prove that interaction effects with the adjacent bonds are the sole factors which control vCN, and there is no doubt that chemical effects which change kCN are also operative. This is indeed obvious from the bond-length changes. Nevertheless, it does show that the impact of interaction effects can be very considerable in this series.

There is also evidence on this point from the behaviour of CN groups in bridged systems. When nitriles associate through hydrogen bonds rCN increases and vCN falls in the expected way. However, when the nitrile is coordinated through the nitrogen atom, as in nitrile oxides, vCN rises. In this situation the real strength of the CN bond must be reduced, and the fact that despite this the frequency rises must be attributed to the additional restraint on the movement of the nitrogen atom. Whereas in normal nitriles this atom can vibrate without doing any work on external bonds, it can only do so in the

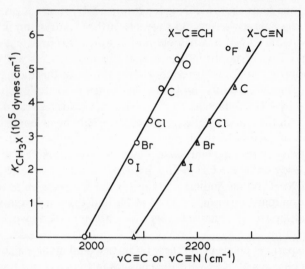

Figure 3.2. $\nu C{\equiv}C$ and $\nu C{\equiv}N$ frequencies vs. C—X force constants in CH_3X compounds

nitrile oxides if the N → O bond is compressed. The C≡N bond therefore becomes harder to stretch and νCN rises. A parallel effect is largely responsible for the rise of 100 cm^{-1} in the C≡C stretching frequencies of disubstituted compounds as compared with the mono derivatives.

It therefore seems certain that k_{CX} is a dominant term in deciding the precise frequencies of triple-bond stretching modes. This is an interesting contrast to the results with νCO (Chapter 5), where the experimental evidence suggests that k_{CX} is relatively unimportant as long as the bond angles remain normal. It is probable that in this and in the alkene series the carbon atom at the end of the multiple bond finds it easier to achieve its normal amplitude by bending the adjacent bonds rather than by stretching them, and substantially less energy is involved. This would be difficult in the triple bonds with 180° angles.

It must be concluded from these results that it would be very unwise to attach too much chemical significance to the frequency shifts of triple-bond stretching vibrations without first considering the impact of force-constant terms. However, when the element attached to the nitrile group is carbon, the changes in the C—C force constant with substitution are very small. Within this series therefore it is likely that the relatively small frequency shifts observed do reflect in some measure the polarity changes in the nitrile group. Besnainou *et al.* [113] have made a theoretical study of the factors producing frequency shifts in carbon substituted nitriles and have concluded that vibrational interactions are minimal and that the frequencies respond to the inductive and conjugative effects of the substituents. This is supported by the fact that good linear relationships have been demonstrated between the nitrile frequency (and also the intensity) and the Hammett σ values of the substituents in aromatic nitriles. The intensities are the more reliable measure as they show the larger changes. Good correlations have been found between the C≡N intensities in *meta* and *para* substituted benzonitriles and the σ_p^+ and σ_m substituent electronic constants [115, 116], and the fact that similar relationships can be observed for *ortho* substituted benzonitriles and for *ortho* tolunitriles has been used by Deady *et al.* [117] to show that there is no steric interaction in these series.

Ideally, of course, the variations in the triple-bond force constants should tell us all we want to know about chemical effects, as these are free from the disadvantages of frequency measurements. Unfortunately these are not available, even for relatively simply substituted systems, unless such assumptions are made on the nature of the force field and of the interaction terms as to render the results very questionable. Even in those cases in which reliable force-constant data are available, their comparison is sometimes disconcerting. Thus k_{CN} [34] for the CN radical is 16.38. This is one of the longest CN bonds known (1.17 Å), but k_{CN} for the CN— radical [34] is also close to this value at 16.4, and this is one of the shortest CN bonds known (1.13–1.15 Å). HCN for which a reliable value of the force constant can be obtained by isotopic substitution has [38] k_{CN} 18.68. It is therefore clear that the force constant does not uniquely characterize the bond, and that a given bond strength can be achieved by more than one arrangement of the electrons within the bond.

Perhaps the best hope for some assessment of these chemical factors lies in a combination of frequency (or where possible force-constant) measurements, combined with some independent measure of the polarity of the CN bond. Some preliminary studies of this kind have been reported by Mitra [39]. He determines the OH stretching frequency of an alcohol which is associated with the nitrile, and the variations in this frequency reflect the changes in the polarity of the CN bond. Thus he finds that vOH of an alcohol associated with BrCN is 3508 cm^{-1}, whereas with CH_3CN the value is 3451 cm^{-1}. This indicates that despite the lower frequency, bromonitrile is in fact less polar than acetonitrile. It is to the extension of methods of this kind, and perhaps also to intensity studies, that one must look for techniques for the evaluation of quantitative chemical effects upon triple bonds.

3.9.1. Nitriles

(a) Frequencies and intensities in organic nitriles

The basic principles that underlie the movements of the CN stretching frequency with changes of the substituents have been dealt with in the preceding section, and any chemist who has skipped this should go back and read it. Studies with substituents other than carbon are limited, but a detailed investigation of FCN has been reported by Dodds and Little [40], and $S(CN)_2$

by Long and George [47]. With carbon substituents the force constant of the adjacent C—C bond remains reasonably constant; this minimizes the physical effects discussed above. However, the frequency changes with different types of substitution are also very small [41–43]. The overall frequency range for alkyl nitriles is 2255 ± 10 cm^{-1}, although there is some small variation in the mean position in different solvents. There is also some small concentration dependence, due to the ability of the nitrile group to associate. This amounts to about 4 cm^{-1} in most cases, the frequency falling with concentration. In aromatic nitriles, as in $\alpha\beta$-unsaturated compounds, vCN is significantly lower. This must be a real result of the weakening of the CN bond, as the delocalization of electrons in conjugation would be expected to strengthen the adjacent bond and so raise vCN. However, the frequency range is again small. In benzonitriles the shifts on passing from good electron-donating substituents to good electron acceptors are small. Values for variously substituted benzonitriles are given by Deady *et al.* [117] and by Green and Harris [118]. With minor exceptions the overall frequency range is less than 10 cm^{-1}. These shifts have been correlated with Hammett σ and similar functions [43, 44, 115–117], and in the case of polycyclic aromatic nitriles with the atomic orbit coefficients of the non-bonding molecular orbitals of the parent odd alternate radicals [45]. With full olefinic conjugation there are small variations in both vC=C and vCN, which depend upon the degree of substitution at the double bond, and provided that due account is taken of both, it is possible to get some idea of the substitution in this way [46]. Conjugation with carbonyl groups in the cyanoformamides, appears to give low frequencies in the 2230 cm^{-1} range, comparable with aromatics [119]. *N*-dimethylcyanoformamide absorbs at 2230 cm^{-1}, but the frequency rises as the degree of substitution is reduced, and cyanoformamide itself absorbs at 2249 cm^{-1}. All these basic compounds were examined in the solid state and it may be that factors other than conjugation are partly responsible for the frequency shifts

Dinitriles, have been studied by Long and George [46] and by Bjorklund *et al.* [120]. Even the dihalomalonitriles absorb within the normal range and show no abnormalities.

The frequencies of CN stretching vibrations in alkyl nitriles are not very informative, except that they do enable us to differentiate between conjugated and saturated systems. A more sensitive indicator should be the intrinsic intensity, which should vary with the bond polarizability, and so should show greater sensitivity to the nature of the substituents or to the solvent system. Intensity measurements have been made by several groups, and some of the earlier work has been reviewed by Brown [49]. Alkyl nitriles have been studied very extensively by Thompson [41–43, 50, 51]. The intensities are significantly lower than in conjugated compounds, and show very wide variations, even in the same solvent. In simple alkyl nitriles the intensity rises steadily with chain length to a limiting value at C_5 or C_6 of 6.7×10^8 A (chloroform solution).

This compares with the value of 4.3×10^8 A for methyl cyanide in the same solvent. The impact of polar substituents is very large. Thus the value for $ClCH_2CN$ is only one-tenth that of the methyl derivative at 0.45×10^8 A, and even in $BrCH_2CH_2CN$ the value is reduced to 3.2×10^8 A. The attachment of a nitrogen atom has an even more marked effect, and in the compound $NCN(CH_3)_2$ the intensity rises to 110×10^8 A. There is a reasonable relationship throughout the series with the Taft σ^* values of the attached group, but some anomalies remain. In particular, the reduction in intensity which follows the introduction of an α-chlorine atom is not found when further α-chlorine atoms are introduced. In CCl_3CN the intensity actually rises somewhat to a value of 2.4×10^8 A. In studies on the cyanoacetamides, Haverbeke and Herman [124] have found that as the effective electronegativity of the substituents increases, (as measured by $\Sigma\sigma^*$) the intensity of $\nu C\equiv N$ first decreases, passes through zero and then increases again. In the compound $CCl_2(CN)CONH_2$ the infrared intensity of the $C\equiv N$ band is effectively zero.

The intensities of $\alpha\beta$ unsaturated nitriles have been discussed by Heilmann *et al.* [52], and shown to vary significantly with the degree of substitution at the double bond. There is, for example, an intensification by a factor of 2.3 on passing from $CH_2=CHCN$ to the corresponding fully substituted olefin. Such observations, coupled with the small frequency shifts of both bonds [46], can be valuable in identifying the substitution pattern. Benzonitriles have also been studied extensively, particularly by Thompson [43] and by Brown [44]. There is a reasonably good correlation between these intensity values and the Hammett σ values of the substituents. However, a better relationship is given if the σ_p^+ and σ_m values are employed [115–117]. The overall intensity in aromatics varies very widely, and there is a factor of about 25 between the intensity in *p*-nitrobenzonitrile and *p*-aminobenzonitrile. Polycyclic aromatic nitriles have been studied in relation to the νCN intensity by Figeys and Nasielski [101].

Intensity studies, therefore, offer a valuable additional parameter whereby the variations in the polarity of the CN bond can be studied with far more power than is possible from simple frequency measurements. However, some difficulties remain which need to be clarified before any final appraisal of their value can be made. In particular, observations such as those on the intensities of the α-halogenated nitriles, and the fact that the intensity in t-butyl cyanide is extremely low compared with the normal alkyl derivatives, are not easy to explain in simple chemical terms. The most likely explanation is probably the impact of interaction effects, which while too small to have much influence on the frequency, can nevertheless produce major changes in intensities. Chemists using these data should also bear in mind that they relate specifically to intrinsic intensities obtained from band-area measurements with high-resolution spectrometers.

A further complication arises from the very large changes in intensity which can result from a change of solvent. For example, the benzonitriles absorb two or three times as strongly in chloroform solution as they do in benzene. Several workers [41–44, 50, 51, 53, 121, 122] have studied these intensity changes, which were at first thought to be due to hydrogen bonding by the chloroform. However, more detailed studies with a wide range of solvents [121] have shown that the intensity declines as the basicity of the solvent increases and is not associated with the presence of a donor hydrogen atom. In pyridine for example the intensity is about one eighth of the value in chloroform. This is clearly a charge transfer rather than a hydrogen bonding interaction, and in contrast to the latter, the band intensity falls as the frequency is reduced. In IC≡N there is a linear relationship between the reduction in strength of the I—C bond and the PK_a values of the pyridine derivatives. HCN represents a special case, as it can act in a double capacity as a proton donor or acceptor, and this has been studied in detail by Caldow and Thompson [50, 51].

(b) Inorganic and coordinated nitriles

This topic is of specialized interest, and has recently been reviewed by Nakamoto [54], who gives not only extensive references but also much tabulated data on frequencies and force constants in individual ionic and coordination compounds. The data will therefore be summarized here but not discussed in detail. Inorganic cyanides in the solid state absorb over a wide frequency range (NaCN 2080 cm^{-1}, AuCN 2239 cm^{-1}), and so do the coordination compounds (2150–1985 cm^{-1}). These variations are usually discussed in terms of changes in the ionic/covalent character of the metal carbon bonds. Obviously, this is an important factor, but the interpretation of the directions of frequency shifts in these terms is not easy. An increase in the covalent character of the metal–carbon bond will certainly be accompanied by a change in the CN force constant and in the vibrational frequency. However, the fact that the C–metal bond now has a positive force constant and will resist the movement of the carbon atom will also have a large frequency effect. The cases of the nitrile oxides studied by Califano [55] are good examples of this difficulty. Here the CN force constant is almost certainly reduced on coordination, but νCN rises by about 100 cm^{-1}. Coordination to antimony pentachloride has also been studied [123]. Unlike the charge transfer situation this results in a frequency rise in νC≡N, due to the appearance of the N—Sb bond which now needs to be compressed during the vibration. These frequencies therefore rise by about 50 wavenumbers on coordination.

A number of more recent references [56–60] to nitriles in coordination complexes are listed in the bibliography. In addition, Brown [61] has reported some limited intensity studies in this field.

(c) X—C≡N deformation frequencies

In principle, the δX—C≡N absorption should be particularly useful in providing data on the ionic/covalent character of the C—X bond, and any double-bond character this may acquire through back donation into vacant d-orbitals. It occurs in the far infrared region, but has been extensively studied by coordination chemists. Nakamoto [54] tabulates the deformation frequency in some ten coordination compounds, and it is clear that it varies widely. In $Cr(CN)_6^{3-}$, for example, the band is at 694 cm^{-1}, whereas in $Hg(CN)_2$ it is at 341 cm^{-1}. Unfortunately, as Nakamoto points out, the C—X stretching frequencies of many metallic cyanides also occur in this region, leading to extensive frequency coupling effects. Observations on this band therefore give less chemical information than was hoped.

Hildago [62] has studied a number of organic nitriles and suggested that the deformation frequency falls in the narrow range $385–357 \text{ cm}^{-1}$. However, more recent studies have shown that the overall range is much wider and this mode is of no value as a group frequency. In benzonitrile for example the band at 399 cm^{-1} has been shown to originate in a different mode [118], and the bending frequency is at 167 cm^{-1}.

3.10. Isonitriles

Most of the available data on the intensities and group frequencies of isonitriles is contained in a single paper by Ugi and Meyer [63], although some is to be found in other papers by Ugi [64, 65]. In alkyl isonitriles in benzene solution the NC stretching frequency occurs at a lower value than in the corresponding nitrile, and is usually in the range $2146–2134 \text{ cm}^{-1}$. The band is reasonably intense, and like the nitriles, the intensity is very sensitive to substituent effects. Thus the intensity doubles on passing from isopropyl isocyanide to benzyl isocyanide. With aromatics, the frequency range is still narrow ($2125–2116 \text{ cm}^{-1}$) and is appreciably lower than in the saturated compounds. This, as with nitriles, is due to conjugation, but the parallelism stops at this point, because, owing to the inversion of the charge, substituent effects now operate in the opposite direction. In isonitriles, therefore, electron-donating substituents lower vNC and electron donors raise it. The relative intensities also invert so that the p-nitro derivative now gives the lowest intensity, while the intensity of the p-methoxy derivative is raised. This inversion of the frequency and intensity behaviour is good evidence that, provided one restricts the discussion to carbon substituents, for which force-constant effects will be reasonably constant, it is permissible to discuss the frequency and intensity changes of nitriles and isonitriles in chemical terms. Because isonitriles have a considerable degree of polarity in the NC bond, they exhibit donor/acceptor properties, and these have been studied by Cotton [66]. A particularly interesting example of the effects of this polarity is the fact that benzyl isocyanide is able to form a hydrogen bond with phenylacetylene [67], thus providing the only known example of a CH...C hydrogen bond.

3.11. Alkynes

The discussion on the nature of triple bond stretching vibrations in section 3.9 is, of course, just as relevant to the alkynes as to the nitriles, which were used as the main examples. Here again one must expect, in a linear system, significant mass effects on passing from mono- to disubstituted alkynes, and also significant force-constant effects, particularly as the restraints on the C≡C bonds are now being increased from both ends. The effects of changes in the nature of the substituents are well shown in Fig. 3.2. A representative selection of recent data on the absorption frequencies of alkynes is given in Table 3.2. Unless otherwise stated, the data refer to carbon tetrachloride solutions.

3.11.1. CH stretching frequencies in monosubstituted alkynes

The most comprehensive collection of data is that of Nyquist and Potts [68], but other useful papers are those of West and Kraihanzel [69], Brand, Eglinton and Morman [70] and Gastilovic *et al.* [71]. The frequency in non-polar solvents is not very sensitive to the nature of the substituents, as is to be expected from the fact that any polar effects would need to be relayed through the triple bond. Nyquist and Potts [68] give the narrow range 3320–3310 cm^{-1} for this absorption, but as will be seen from the table, somewhat higher values are given by alkoxy substituents [70], and lower values by COR and CN groups. The data given in the table for the halogen-substituted alkynes refer to the vapour state, and the corresponding solution values are probably 10–15 cm^{-1} lower. However, the overall variation of this frequency is not more than 40 cm^{-1}, and although polar effects do operate, their effect is small.

The same result is found with variously substituted phenyl acetylenes [72–74]. The frequency changes are extremely small, and there is little correlation with the electron-donating or accepting properties [72]. Brown [73] and Jouve [74] have also studied the intensity changes. Brown concluded that while the intensity of the C≡C stretching vibrations could be correlated with the Hammett σ functions of the substituents, those of the CH stretching bands could not. Jouve [74] has claimed a relation between the CH intensities and the corresponding CH chemical shifts in N.M.R. spectra, but there are some deviations from his plot, and the relation is not linear.

More important is the sensitivity to changes of phase or of solvent. Hydrogen attached to an *sp* carbon atom is markedly more polar than in saturated hydrocarbons, and is therefore able to associate freely with proton-accepting groups. This leads to frequency shifts of up to 120 cm^{-1} in extreme cases. Collections of data on the CH solvent shifts of variously substituted acetylenes are listed in the bibliography [69–71, 75–78, 102]. Self-association also occurs freely. If the substituent includes a polar oxygen or nitrogen atom the association naturally occurs there, if this is not so, the bond forms to the π cloud of the triple bond [69, 70]. This type of association is now well established, and it is this that is responsible for the substantial frequency shifts with change of phase. Phenylacetylene in the vapour absorbs at $3340 \, cm^{-1}$, but this falls to $3316 \, cm^{-1}$ in solution due to self-association [68]. Estimates of the hydrogen bond energy of alkynes have been made by Goel and Rao [125] and by Mesubi and Hammaker [126]. The agreement between the two is not good despite the fact that similar equilibrium coefficients were obtained in the two cases. However, it is clear that the energies involved are relatively small.

In many solution studies the CH stretching band has been found to exhibit a shoulder on the low-frequency side. Nyquist and Potts [68] attribute this to a Fermi resonance effect. This has been criticized [69] on the grounds that the bands persist in the deuterated compounds. However, as Pham Van Huong and Lascombe [77] show, this is not a valid criticism if the interaction involves the overtone of the CH (or CD) deformation mode, and they have shown that this is the case. However, the observation of a similar effect in *para* but not in mono or *ortho* substituted phenylacetylenes [77], remains unexplained.

3.11.2. vC≡C stretching frequencies

(a) *Monosubstituted acetylenes*

The data in Table 3.2 provide further confirmation for the assignment of this absorption to the 2140–2100-cm^{-1} range for carbon substituents, with conjugated systems at the lower-frequency end. The values for acetylenes with different elements attached to the triple bond are informative, as the order of frequencies is $F > OR > CH_3 > Cl > Br > I$. This is essentially the order of the force constants of the C—X bonds, and it does not relate to electronegativities or other measures of polarity. The frequencies are in fact determined largely by the strengths of the substituent bond, as is well shown by Fig. 3.2. The calculations of Hunt and Wilson [79] confirm this. They have computed the C≡C force constants for halogenated acetylenes and find that, despite the higher frequency, the force constant of F—C≡CH is in fact slightly lower than that of the chloro or bromo compounds.

However, it must not be supposed that polar effects are completely absent. The big frequency jump with fluorine substitution seems disproportionately large, and the frequency does not lie on the line of Fig. 3.2. Moreover, there are significant changes in both vCH and δCH which must point to some rearrangement of the electron density. The shifts arising from coupling effects are therefore probably modified to some extent by polarization effects acting on the π cloud. Potts and Nyquist [67] comment on the small upward shifts which result from the substitution of halogens at the α-carbon atom. These contrast with the downward shifts that occur with chain branching, and they ascribe them to polarization interactions. Similar findings are reported by Nyquist [127]. Complete vibrational assignments for the propargyl halides have been given by Evans and Nyquist [80].

Table 3.2. Acetylenes

| | RC≡CH | | | $R_1C≡CR_2$ | | | RC≡C—CH=CH₂ | |
R	vCH	vC≡C	δCH	R_1	R_2	vC≡C	R	vC≡C
F	3355v	2255v	578v	C₄H₉	CH₃	2240	C₅H₁₁	2228
Cl	3340v	2110v	604v	CH₃	Cl	2258	C₆H₁₃	2228
Br	3325v	2085v	618v	CH₃	Li	2225	C₈H₁₇	2229
I	3320v	2075v	629v	C₂H₅	Li	2227	(CH₃)₃C	2204
CH₃	3320	2130	630	(CH₃)₃C	Li	2200	(CH₃)₃Si	2147
C₂H₅	3320	2121	630	C₆H₅	Li	2213	(CH₃)₃Sn	2129
C₆H₅	3316	2115	648	Alkyl	COCH₃	2240	(C₂H₅)₃Sn	2127
			611	C₆H₁₃	CONH₂	2237		
CH₂I	3315	2128	637	RCH=CH	COCH₃	2195		
CH₂S	3317	2120	635	Cyclo-	COCH₃	2233		
CH₂Br	3315	2126	649	hexyl				
			637	CH₃	OC₆H₅	2252		
CH₂Cl	3315	2132	652	(CH₃)₃C	Cl	2243		
			637	(CH₃)₃C	Br	2216		
CH₂F	3322	2148	674	(CH₃)₃C	I	2191		
			636	(CH₃)₃Si	Cl	2137		
CH₂OH	3319	2132	663	(CH₃)₃Si	Br	2126		
			625	(CH₃)₃Si	I	2100		
CHO	3335v	2125v	691v					
COCH₃	3300	2114	746?	CHO	Cl	2211		
CH=CH₂	3320	2099						
CH=CHR	3300	2114		CHO	Br	2180		
C₆H₅CO	3306		646					
CN	3304		671	CHO	I	2159		
Li	3245s	1990						
Na	3216s							
K	3224s							

v, vapour state; s, solid.

(b) Disubstituted acetylenes

vC≡C is, of course, weak in these compounds and is forbidden when the substitution is symmetrical. There have been extensive studies on conjugated alkynes by Petrov and his school [81–85], and a good deal of new data is available on cyclic alkynes [86–89]. The behaviour is very similar to the monosubstituted alkynes, alkoxy groups giving high values and chain branching or conjugation, low values. As before, the larger halogens with low C—halogen force constants give low C≡C stretching frequencies. In the di-iodo compound it is as low as 2109 cm⁻¹ (Raman). For carbon substituents the frequency remains close to 2260–2210 cm⁻¹. The rise above the values for monosubstituted compounds is partly due to the mass effect of replacing hydrogen by another element, and partly to the additional work required to stretch the triple bond now that there is no longer the tendency for the heavier substituent to be carried along with the vibration.

When elements with vacant d-orbitals are directly attached there is some evidence that the triple bond is weakened by πd back-donation [71, 90–92, 103, 104, 128, 129]. The data included in the table for silicon and tin-substituted compounds show low stretching frequencies, whereas the lithium derivatives show normal values. However, the frequencies of the series $M(C≡CCH_3)_4$

where M is Si, Ge, Pb, and of the corresponding trivalent series where M is P, As or Sb give rather higher frequencies in the region 2192–2170 cm^{-1}, with only the antimony compound giving a lower frequency [128]. Interestingly the corresponding CF_3 derivatives show the frequency rise of about 30 cm^{-1} which is found in the alkyl series [129]. The fact that the CH frequencies in similarly substituted mono-derivatives show significant shifts supports the view that changes are due to back-donation.

3.11.3. The δCH≡ deformation frequency

The CH deformation frequency in monosubstituted alkynes is usually fairly strong and readily identified. It occurs in the 680–610 cm^{-1} range [68]. When the molecule is axially symmetric the two CH bending modes are degenerate, and only one band is found. However, the attachment of a planar group splits the degeneracy, and the band is then doubled. Phenylacetylene, for example, shows bands at 642 and 613 cm^{-1} which originate in bending modes at right angles to, and in the plane of the ring respectively.

However, doubling also occurs in other circumstances, as for example with compounds with polar substituents at the α-carbon atom. Potts and Nyquist [68] point out that substituents with some capacity to polarize the π cloud might well be expected to show two bands, whereas others would not. This is supported by Evans and Nyquist [80], who have assigned the doublets in propargyl halides to a' and a'' CH modes. These authors have also assigned all the other CH and CH_2 modes in this series and shown that they all change systematically in step with each other as one passes through the halogen series. Nyquist [127] reports similar results in propargyl alcohol. Moritz [105] has pointed out that the out-of-plane deformation of these compounds has many similarities with the CH_2 wagging mode of the vinyl and vinylidene series. In particular, he finds an excellent relation between the values for corresponding pairs of XCCH and XCH=CH_2 compounds. This can be useful in indicating the position of one of them if the other is known.

The behaviour of the deformation mode on hydrogen bonding has not been studied extensively. It can be expected from its nature to move towards higher frequencies as the strength of the hydrogen bonds is increased. Brand et al. [70] have shown that this is so. This deformation mode has a useful overtone band in the 1250 cm^{-1} region. It is often reasonably strong and is helpful in confirming the correct identification of the fundamental. This is especially so in the hydrogen-bonding studies, when the overtone, of course, shifts proportionately with the fundamental.

Bibliography

1. Ham and Willis, *Spectrochim. Acta,* 1960, **16**, 279.
2. Caldow and Thompson, *Spectrochim. Acta,* 1958, **13**, 212.

3. Svatek, Zahradnik and Kjaer, *Acta Chem. Scand.*, 1959, **13**, 442.
4. Foffani, Mazzucasa and Miotti, *R.c. Acad. Lincei*, 1960, **29**, 355.
5. Lieber, Rao and Ramachandran, *Spectrochim. Acta*, 1959, **13**, 296.
6. Lappert and Pyszora, *Proc. Chem. Soc.*, 1960, 350.
7. Sowerby, *J. Amer. Chem. Soc.*, 1962, **84**, 1831.
8. Tramer, *C. R. Acad. Sci. France*, 1961, **253**, 1679, 1780.
9. Barallat, Legge and Pullin, *Trans. Faraday Soc.*, 1963, **59**, 1764.
10. Stevenson, Coburn and Wilcox, *Spectrochim. Acta*, 1961, **17**, 933.
11. Lewis, Nyholm and Smith, *J. Chem. Soc.*, 1961, 4590.
12. Chatt and Duncanson, *Nature*, 1956, **178**, 997.
13. Kinell and Strandberg, *Acta Chem. Scand.*, 1959, **13**, 1607.
14. Kuhn and Mecke, *Chem. Ber.*, 1960, **93**, 618.
15. Tramer, *J. Chim. Phys.*, 1962, **59**, 232.
16. Pecile, Giacometti and Turco, *R. C. Acad. Lincei*, 1960, **28**, 189.
17. Turco and Pecile, *Nature*, 1961, **191**, 66.
18. Derkosch, Scholog and Woidich, *Monatsh. Chem.*, 1957, **88**, 35.
19. Miller and Carlson, *Spectrochim. Acta*, 1961, **17**, 977.
20. Miller and Baer, *Spectrochim. Acta*, 1962, **18**, 1311.
21. Lieber and Oftedahl, *J. Org. Chem.*, 1959, **24**, 1014.
22. Lieber, Rao, Chao and Hoffman, *Analyt. Chem.*, 1957, **29**, 916.
23. Lieber and Thomas, *Applied Spectroscopy*, 1961, **51**, 144.
24. Fujita, Makamoto and Kobayashi, *J. Amer. Chem. Soc.*, 1956, **78**, 3295.
25. Rao and Hahl, *Chem. and Ind.*, 1952, 987.
26. Meakins and Moss, *J. Chem. Soc.*, 1957, 993.
27. Kazicyna, Reutov and Buckovskij, *J. Phys. Chem. Moscow*, 1960, **34**, 850.
28. Yates, Shapiro, Yoda and Fugger, *J. Amer. Chem. Soc.*, 1957, **79**, 5756.
29. Fahr, *Liebigs Ann.*, 1958, **617**, 11.
30. Kazicyna, Kikot, Ashkinadze and Reutov, *Doklady Akad. Nauk. S.S.S.R.*, 1963, **151**, 573.
31. Wotiz and Mancuso, *J. Org. Chem.*, 1957, **22**, 207.
32. Lord and Miller, *Applied Spectroscopy*, 1956, **10**, 115.
33. Whiffen, *Chem. and Ind.*, 1957, 193.
34. Calculated from the data in ref. [36].
35. Josien, *Conference on Solvation Phenomena*, Calgary, 1963, p. 18.
36. Herzberg, *Molecular Spectra and Molecular Structure. 1. Diatomic Molecules*, Von Nostrand, New York, 1950.
37. Cottrell, *The Strengths of Chemical Bonds*, Butterworths, 2nd ed., 1958, pp. 273 *et seq.*
38. Allen, Tidwell and Plyler, *J. Chem. Phys.*, 1956, **25**, 302.
39. Mitra, *J. Chem. Phys.*, 1962, **36**, 3286.
40. Dodds and Little, *Spectrochim. Acta*, 1960, **16**, 1083.
41. Thompson and Steel, *Trans. Faraday Soc.*, 1956, **52**, 1451.
42. Jesson and Thompson, *Spectrochim. Acta*, 1958, **13**, 217.
43. Mander and Thompson, *Trans. Faraday Soc.*, 1957, **53**, 1402.
44. Brown, *J. Amer. Chem. Soc.*, 1958, **80**, 794.
45. Figeys-Fauconnis, Figeys, Geuskens and Nasielski, *Spectrochim. Acta*, 1962, **18**, 689.
46. Heilmann and Bonnier, *C.R. Acad. Sci. France*, 1959, **248**, 2595.
47. Long and George, *Spectrochim. Acta*, 1963, **19**, 1731.
48. Long and George, *Spectrochim. Acta*, 1963, **19**, 1717.
49. Brown, *Chem. Reviews*, 1958, **58**, 581.
50. Caldow and Thompson, *Proc. Roy. Soc.*, 1960, **A254**, 1.

51. Caldow, Cunliffe Jones and Thompson, *Proc. Roy. Soc.*, 1960, **A254**, 17.
52. Heilmann, Bonnier and Arnaud, *C.R. Acad. Sci. France*, 1959, **248**, 3578.
53. Bayliss, Cole and Little, *Spectrochim. Acta*, 1959, **15**, 12.
54. Nakamoto, *Infrared Spectra of Inorganic and Coordination Compounds*, Wiley, New York, 1963.
55. Califano, Moccia, Scarpatı and Speroni, *J. Chem. Phys.*, 1957, **26**, 1777.
56. Fackler, *J. Chem. Soc.*, 1962, 1957.
57. Gerrard, Lappert, Pyszora and Willis, *J. Chem. Soc.*, 1960, 2182.
58. Brune and Zeil, *Zeit. Naturf.*, 1961, **16a**, 1251.
59. Hildago and Mathieu, *An. Soc. Esp. Fis. Quim.*, 1960, **56A**, 9.
60. Caglioti, Sartori and Scrocco, *J. Inorganic and Nuclear Chem.*, 1958, **8**, 87.
61. Brown and Kubota, *J. Amer. Chem. Soc.*, 1961, **83**, 4175.
62. Hildago, *C.R. Acad. Sci. France*, 1959, **249**, 395.
63. Ugi and Meyer, *Chem. Ber.*, 1960, **93**, 239.
64. Ugi and Steinbruckner, *Chem. Ber.*, 1961, **94**, 2802.
65. Ugi and Bodesheim, *Chem. Ber.*, 1961, **94**, 2797.
66. Cotton and Zingales, *J. Amer. Chem. Soc.*, 1961, **83**, 351.
67. Ferstandig, *J. Amer. Chem. Soc.*, 1962, **84**, 1323.
68. Nyquist and Potts, *Spectrochim. Acta*, 1960, **16**, 419.
69. West and Kraihanzel, *J. Amer. Chem. Soc.*, 1961, **83**, 765.
70. Brand, Eglinton and Morman, *J. Chem. Soc.*, 1960, 2526.
71. Gastilovic, Shigorin, Graceva, Cekulaeva and Sastakarstij, *Optics and Spectroscopy*, 1961, **10**, 595.
72. Allen and Cook, *Can. J. Chem.*, 1963, **41**, 1084.
73. Brown, *J. Chem. Phys.*, 1962, **38**, 1049.
74. Jouve, *C.R. Acad. Sci. France*, 1963, **256**, 5120.
75. Murahashi, Ryutani and Hatada, *Bull. Chem. Soc. Japan*, 1959, 1001.
76. Wojrkowiak and Romanet, *C.R. Acad. Sci. France*, 1960, **250**, 3980.
77. Pham Van Huong and Lascombe, *C.R. Acad. Sci. France*, 1962, **254**, 2543.
78. Pham Van Huong and Lascombe, *J. Chim. Phys.*, 1962, 719.
79. Hunt and Wilson, *J. Chem. Phys.*, 1961, **34**, 1301.
80. Evans and Nyquist, *Spectrochim. Acta*, 1963, **19**, 1153.
81. Petrov, Kolesova and Porfir'eva, *J. Gen. Chem. Moscow*, 1957, **27**, 2081.
82. Petrov and Semenov, *J. Gen. Chem. Moscow*, 1957, **27**, 2941, 2947, 1958, **28**, 71.
83. Petrov, Porfir'eva and Semenov, *J. Gen. Chem. Moscow*, 1957, **27**, 1167.
84. Jakovlera, Petrov and Zavgordni, *Optics and Spectroscopy*, 1962, **12**, 200.
85. Petrov and Jakovlera, *Optics and Spectroscopy*, 1959, **7**, 817.
86. Sondheimer, Amiel and Gaoni, *J. Amer. Chem. Soc.*, 1962, **84**, 270.
87. Sondheimer and Wolovsky, *J. Amer. Chem. Soc.*, 1962, **84**, 260.
88. Domnin and Kolinskij, *J. Gen. Chem. Moscow*, 1961, **33**, 1799.
89. Eglinton and Galbraith, *J. Chem. Soc.*, 1959, 889.
90. Cumaevskij, *Optics and Spectroscopy*, 1961, **10**, 69.
91. West and Kraihanzel, *Inorganic Chem.*, 1962, **1**, 967.
92. Buckert and Zeil, *Spectrochim. Acta*, 1962, **18**, 1043.
93. Petrov, Jakovlera and Kormer, *Optics and Spectroscopy*, 1959, **7**, 237.
94. Borisov and Sverdlov, *Optics and Spectroscopy*, 1963, **15**, 14.
95. Kristian, Kovac and Antos, *Coll. Czech. Chem. Comm.*, 1964, **29**, 2507.
96. David, *Analyt. Chem.*, 1963, **35**, 37.
97. Cummins, *Austral. J. Chem.*, 1964, **17**, 838.
98. Hirschmann, Kniseley and Fassell, *Spectrochim. Acta*, 1964, **20**, 809.
99. Kniseley, Hirschmann and Fassel, *Spectrochim. Acta*, 1967, **23A**, 109.
100. Hirschmann, Kniseley and Fassel, *Spectrochim. Acta*, 1965, **21**, 2125.

101. Figeys and Nasielski, *Spectrochim. Acta,* 1966, **22**, 2055.
102. Boobyer, *Spectrochim. Acta,* 1967, **23A**, 325.
103. Mathis, Sergent, Mazerolles and Mathis, *Spectrochim. Acta,* 1964, **20**, 1407.
104. Shostakovskii, Shergina, Komarov and Maroshiv, *Izvest. Akad. Nauk. S.S.S.R. Ser. Khim.,* 1964, 1606.
105. Moritz, *Spectrochim. Acta,* 1967, **23A**, 167.
106. Sejnker, Senjavina and Zeltova, *Doklady Akad. Nauk. S.S.S.R.,* 1965, **160**, 1339.
107. Dobramsyl, Fritzer and Kettle, *Spectrochim. Acta,* 1975, **31A**, 905.
108. Mogul, *Nuclear Sci. Abstracts,* 1967, **21**, 47014.
109. Chi and Leroi, *Spectrochim. Acta,* 1975, **31A**, 1759.
110. Poletti, Paliavi, Giorgini and Cataliotti, *Spectrochim. Acta,* 1975, **31A**, 1869.
111. Klaboe, Torgrimsen, Christensen, Hopf, Eriksson, Hagen and Cyvin, *Spectrochim. Acta,* 1974, **30A**, 1527.
112. Phongsatha, Klaboe, Hopf, Cyvin and Cyvin, *Spectrochim. Acta,* 1978, **34A**, 537.
113. Besnainou, Thomas and Bratoz, *J. Mol. Spectroscopy,* 1966, **21**, 113.
114. Whiffen, *Spectrochim. Acta,* 1978, **34A**, 1165, 1173, 1183.
115. Deady, Katritzky, Shanks and Topsom, *Spectrochim. Acta,* 1973, **29A**, 115.
116. Exner and Svatek, *Coll. Czech. Chem. Commun.,* 1971, **36**, 534.
117. Deady, Harrison and Topsom, *Spectrochim. Acta,* 1975, **31A**, 1665.
118. Green and Harrison, *Spectrochim. Acta,* 1976, **32A**, 1279.
119. Desselyn and Le Poivre, *Spectrochim. Acta.* 1975, **31A**, 635, 647. Desselyn, Vansant and Van der Verken, *ibid,* 625. Desselyn and Van der Verken, *ibid,* 641.
120. Bjorklund, Augdahl, Christensen and Sroensen, *Spectrochim. Acta,* 1976, **32A**, 1021.
121. Leeuw and Zeegers-Huyskens, *Spectrochim. Acta,* 1976, **32A**, 617.
122. Matsuzaki, Furusawa and Toyoda, *Spectrochim. Acta,* 1977, **33A**, 907.
123. Masson, Payne and Leroy, *Spectrochim. Acta,* 1977, **33A**, 21.
124. Haverbeke and Herman, *Spectrochim. Acta,* 1975, **31A**, 959.
125. Goel and Rao, *Trans. Faraday Soc.,* 1971, **67**, 2828.
126. Mesuri and Hammaker, *Spectrochim. Acta,* 1975, **31A**, 1885.
127. Nyquist, *Spectrochim. Acta,* 1971, **27A**, 2313.
128. Sacher, Pant, Miller and Brown, *Spectrochim. Acta,* 1972, **28A**, 1361.
129. Lemmon and Jackson, *Spectrochim. Acta,* 1973, **29A**, 1899.

4

Unassociated XH Vibrations

4.1. Introduction

The vibrational frequencies of XH bonds provide one of the largest and most reliable blocks of group frequencies. The stretching vibrations in particular show little sensitivity to mass effects and are decoupled from the other fundamental modes of the molecules [1]. It follows that, with certain reservations, the observed frequencies are an accurate measure of the force constants of the bonds, and their changes with structure might therefore be expected to run parallel to many chemical and physical properties, such as changes in reactivity or in bond length. In cases in which the stretching vibration is split into symmetric and asymmetric modes it can also be shown that the mean frequency is a function of the force constant [1], and the separation of the two bands can be used to obtain useful information on structural changes. In the case of XNH_2 stretching frequencies, for example, the separation is a direct function of the HNH bond angle, and can therefore be used to follow changes in the hybridization of the nitrogen atom [44]. The reservations mentioned amount only to the requirements that comparisons between the frequencies of one molecule and another be made in the same phase, that there is no hydrogen bonding, that in the case of XH_2 and XH_3 groups the bonds are equivalent, and that interactions do not occur with overtone or combination bands of lower-frequency fundamentals.

This last is relatively uncommon with XH modes, although XD vibrations are very frequently split due to interaction of this kind. An obvious case is that of aldehydes, in which the CH stretch of the CHO group occurs as a doublet, due to Fermi resonance interaction with the overtone of the CH deformation mode. The deformation modes themselves are much more subject to coupling effects and are correspondingly, generally less useful. This is not true of certain specific modes of CH_2 and CH_3 groups, but the OH deformation frequency is strongly coupled with the C—O stretch, and the NH_2 deformation is, of course, coupled with other frequencies in amides. Nevertheless, because the stretching and deformation modes both depend upon the electronic environment of the bond, a good deal of useful information can be derived from the systematic study of both. For example, if a lowering of an XH stretching frequency is attributed to an increase in the p character of the X orbit towards the hydrogen atom there must be a rise in the frequency of the corresponding deformation mode. This follows from the directional character of p orbits as compared with s, so that a bond which becomes easier to stretch as a result of increased p character will necessarily be harder to bend. In a few special cases in which the frequency changes are due to local interactions within the intramolecular environment, this linking of the behaviour of the stretching and bending bands is not found. Thus when one of the methyl groups of ethane is replaced by the CCl_3 group, both the stretching and the bending frequencies of the remaining methyl group are raised.

This chapter will be concerned with the origins of changes in free XH frequencies and with the relationships which these changes bear to alterations in such properties as bond lengths, dissociation energies, reactivities, polarities, etc. The special cases of hydrogen-bonded vibrations are considered separately in Chapter 8. The major changes which follow alteration in the X atom itself are reasonably well understood and are discussed first. The minor but very significant alterations which occur with changes in the substituents on any one atom X are both interesting and more difficult. The changes which occur in vCH in the series CH_3, CH_2= and CH≡ can be readily rationalized in terms of the changing hybridization of the carbon atom. The bond would be expected to shorten as the s character of the bonding orbitals is increased, and indeed the frequencies are roughly in the ratio 25:33:50, which would be expected from the sp^3, sp^2 and sp series. This accounts satisfactorily for the main frequency ranges in which absorption from these groups is found. However, more subtle effects need to be considered if one is to account satisfactorily for the smaller changes found within any one group. In the case of the methyl group it has been shown (Chapter 1) that the stretching frequencies are not affected by electronegativity effects but by intramolecular interactions between hydrogen atoms which lie *gauche* to each other or to a methyl group. It has also been shown that substantial frequency changes arise from interactions between C—H bonds and lone pair electrons in the *trans* position. It will be shown later that all these effects operate also on other XH bonds of the first row elements. Some second row elements show these effects to some extent, although, unlike the first row they generally follow a pattern related to Taft σ^* values. Indeed, it now seems clear that for some elements neither the frequency nor the force constant is sufficient to adequately characterize the bond and that these measurements must be suplemented by others involving properties such as the intrinsic intensity or the acidity of the proton, if this is to be achieved. It is also important that the whole pattern of group frequency behaviour should be taken into account. For example, any suggested explanation of the frequency rise of NH_2 stretching modes in the series CH_3NH_2, $C_6H_5NH_2$ and CH_3CONH_2 must at the same time explain the frequency fall in the similar OH bond in the series CH_3OH, C_6H_5OH and

CH₃COOH. These aspects are therefore considered in Section 3 of this chapter before the individual group frequencies are discussed in detail in Section 4.

4.2. Changes in XH stretching frequencies following alterations in the X element

Simple calculations using Hooke's law show that the mass effects on XH frequencies will be extremely small. Such as they are, one would expect a small frequency fall to be associated with an increase in the mass of X. In fact, as one goes across the Periodic Table from an element such as carbon to another such as fluorine the frequencies rise sharply. There is a steady fall on going down any one column of the table, but this again is entirely disproportionate to the changes which would result from mass effects alone, so that it is clear that the alterations in vXH with the nature of X are to be sought primarily in the chemical differences in the nature of the bonds themselves and in their different bond lengths. Table 4.1 summarizes some data on both vXH and on rXH for some simple hydrides, and it will be seen that there is no smooth relationship between either and the atomic weight of X.

There have been many empirical approaches which have attempted to correlate the force constant of a bond between atoms, with two parameters, one of which is the bond length and the other some function which measures the polarity of the atoms in question. Thus Gordy's rule makes use of electronegativity values and Badger's of constants which vary with the position of the atoms in the Periodic Table, and so indirectly with the effective nuclear charge. Lippincott's [3] Delta function model has been applied with great success, and this incorporates functions which relate vXH to the radius,

Table 4.1. XH stretching vibrations cm⁻¹—vapour-phase values

	vHX, cm⁻¹		HX.A°	Bond angle HXH°
HF	3961		0.9175	,,
HCl	2886		1.2744	,,
HBr	2558		1.408	,,
HI	2230		1.608	,,
H₂O	3637	3756	0.958	104.45
H₂S	2615	2627	1.345	92.25
H₂Se	2360	2350	1.47	91
NH₃	3414	3337	1.008	106.6
PH₃	2327	2421	1.417	93.8
AsH₃	2122	2185	1.519	91.6
SbH₃	1891	1894	1.707	91.5
CH₄	2914	3020	1.094	Tetrahedral
SiH₄	2180	2183	1.479	,,
GeH₄	2106	2114	1.527	,,
SnH₄	1910	1860	1.70	,,

to an electronegativity term which is refined to take account of the particular valence state of X and to the dissociation energy. Unfortunately none of these factors can conveniently be studied in isolation from the others. It is not possible in an XH bond to change X without simultaneously altering r, K and D; and the electronegativity value nearly always changes also. Nevertheless, the success of these simple relationships supports the generalization that the frequency of a given XH bond will depend primarily upon the bond length and on the bond strength, the latter being measured either by some appropriate electronegativity function or, in the case of diatomics, by the dissociation energies. Because these parameters cannot be varied independently and because of the very real difficulties in putting the rather vague elec- tronegativity concept on an adequate quantitative footing which would make proper allowances for changes in valency states, no satisfactory proof of this generalization is possible. However, some further measure of support can be found from a consideration of the existing data.

Along any one row of the Periodic Table the covalent radii of the elements show only small changes as the nuclear charge increases, the major jumps occurring as one completes a valency shell and passes from one row to the next. This is not surprising, because such radii are measured from the homopolar bonds (C—C, F—F, etc.) in which changes in the effective nuclear charge on one side of the bonding electrons are counterbalanced by similar changes on the other. With XH links the situation is totally different, as Table 4.1 shows, and the radii decrease sharply as N, the effective nuclear charge, increases. This is the simple result of the difference in the effective nuclear charge on either side of the bonding electrons. As the electronegativity of X increases, the bonding electrons are attracted more and more towards the X atom and the light hydrogen atom moves with them to maintain maximum overlap. In the extreme cases of first-row elements the resulting molecular orbital leads to a bond length that is shorter than the sum of either the covalent or the ionic radii. This bond shortening is therefore a direct result of the changes in N, and one can therefore predict that within any one row of the Periodic Table the frequency of νXH (or the force constant) will be a simple function of N, despite the fact that the radii and nuclear charges both change. This prediction is realized in practice and is illustrated in Fig. 4.1, in which force-constant values taken from Cottrell's compilation [4] are plotted against N. A simple linear relation holds for each row of the table, the differences between the rows originating in the change in covalent radii. The screening effect of the filled valency shells is not significant in this, as within each row all the values of N are reduced in proportion. The pleasing feature of Fig. 4.1 is the fact that all lines pass, as they should, through the origin, in agreement with the fact that the force constants of the imaginary rare gas hydrides are zero.

The XH force constants can also be compared with the known bond lengths. This is done in Fig. 4.2 for the first-row elements passing across the

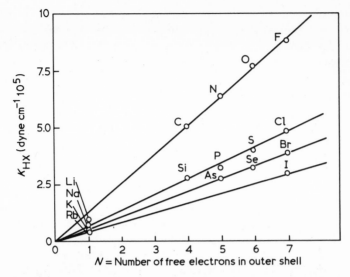

Figure 4.1. Variation of XH force constants with nuclear charge N

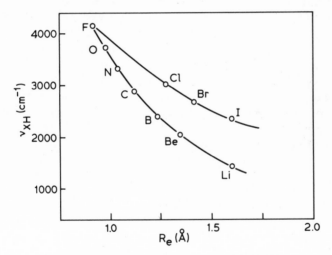

Figure 4.2. Variations of νXH with R_eXH

table, and for the halogen halides, passing down. The former well illustrates the bond-shortening effect as the nuclear charge rises, while the different slope of the latter shows the resultant of two effects, the increase in radius and the diminution in effective nuclear charge due to the screening effects of the inner filled shells. As one passes across the Periodic Table νXH rises, primarily as a result of a polarity effect, so that within any one row relationships will exist with electronegativities and other properties primarily dependent upon this. As one passes down only one row, the dominant factor is probably the radius change, although the screening effect will also play some part. Properties which depend primarily on radius and to a lesser extent on nuclear charge will therefore be related to frequencies within any single vertical row. Thus there is an excellent linear relationship between KHX and the dissociation energy for the hydrogen halides [5].

4.3. Changes in XH stretching frequencies with alterations in the substituents at X

XH stretching frequencies of different elements vary widely in their response to substituent and to conjugation effects. Some elements, such as oxygen, are very sensitive to substitution, and vOH ranges from 3698 cm^{-1} in $Mg(OH)_2$ to values as low as 3530 cm^{-1} in isopropyl benzene hydroperoxide or 3504 cm^{-1} in CF_3COOH. Sulphur hydrogen frequencies, in contrast, seem to be relatively insensitive to change, so that dithiobenzoic acid has the same SH frequency as ethyl mercaptan. However, the differences are not limited to the scale of the shift, and the alterations in the directions of response of XH frequencies to similar substituents are even more striking. Attachment of an aromatic ring or a carbonyl group lowers vOH and raises vNH$_2$ or vNH despite the fact that intensity studies on the two series show that there is an increase in the XH polarity in both cases. The rise with vNH$_2$ has been explained in terms of the hybridization change from sp^3 to sp^2 nitrogen leading to a shorter NH link, but a similar if smaller effect should operate also in the case of OH, where the frequency falls. The introduction of p substituents, such as nitrogroups, which would be expected to increase the sp^2 character of the X element raise vNH$_2$ further but produce only a further fall in vOH.

Perhaps the most serious difficulties arise when one attempts to compare the changes in one of these frequencies with other properties of the bond, such as its acidity, which might be expected to change proportionately. If vOH or K_{OH}, for example, is a true measure of some unique electronic arrangement and is influenced by the polarity of the bond one might expect to find simple relationships between the frequencies and properties such as ΔvOH when the group is hydrogen bonded to some standard base such as ether. These regularities occur within closely similar groups, but there is no overall regularity. One has only to consider some of the vOH frequencies listed in the tables to see that this is so. *tert*-Butanol and triphenyl lead hydroxide absorb within 2 cm^{-1} of each other, but the latter is a very much weaker acid (Δv in ether only 20 cm^{-1}), and is so much stronger a base that it actually reacts with phenol. Similarly, it is obvious that KOH (3600 cm^{-1}) and phenol (3609 cm^{-1}) are totally different as regards the polarity of their hydroxyl groups, and although the former frequency is admittedly measured in the solid state, the known O...O distances are well over 3.0 Å, so that any hydrogen bonding effects must be very small. This topic will be discussed in more detail under the individual group frequencies, but it is already clear that in these first-row elements neither the frequency nor the force constant provides a useful characterization of the bond and that it is possible to have two or more bonds of the same strengths which are totally different in their polarities and in their chemical properties. This is not to suggest that the frequency values are unimportant. On the contrary, if they are supplemented by other spec-troscopic measurements, particularly of the proton-donating power to a standard base and also of the proton-accepting power from a standard acid, they should provide in the result a very clear picture of the true state of the bond. These possibilities are at present only just beginning to be explored, but seem to hold great promise.

The explanation of the failure of the stretching force constants of first-row elements uniquely to characterize the XH bonds probably lies in the fact mentioned earlier that the bond lengths in this series are significantly shorter than the sum of either the covalent or the 'ionic radii'. This is a well-established fact that has been known for many years, and Schomaker and Stephenson [6] have produced an empirical equation which relates the observed contraction to the electronegativity of the X atom. The contraction in HF is as large as 0.172 Å as compared with the covalent radii, and in CH_4 this has fallen to 0.049 Å. This can only mean that a plot of bond length r vs percentage ionic character must take some general form such as Fig. 4.3, in which a minimum occurs. In so far as K or v follows r, this must then take the form of the dotted curve with a central maximum. The force constant might itself change with ionic character, without there necessarily being a change in

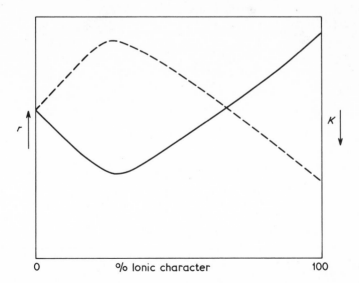

Figure 4.3. Diagrammatic representation of variations of radius (r) and force constant (K) of an XH link with ionic character

r, but there is no reason why this second effect should eliminate the maximum in Fig. 4.3. For any single value of r or of K there are accordingly at least two corresponding electronic arrangements within the bond corresponding to totally different polarities. This is an idealized situation which refers to a single X atom in a single state of hybridization. A change from sp^3 to sp^2 could well produce an alteration in the shape of the curve and even of the position of the point of changeover. Then K or v would correspond to an infinity of possible polarities. It is for this reason that overall relationships between vXH and chemical properties cannot be expected to have any validity, although we shall still expect to find such relationships within closely related series with similar states of hybridization of the central atom. Thus vOH for phenols is linearly related to the Hammett σ values of the substituents, to the pK_a values and to the frequency shifts which occur on association with ether. vOH of acids is similarly related to pK_a values and probably also to those other functions, but the slopes of the separate lines are not the same, and there is no single correlation which embraces the whole range of both phenols and acids.

One other implication of Fig. 4.3 is that for a largely covalent bond, vXH will rise initially with an increase in ionic character but that this will slowly fall off and be succeeded by a frequency fall as the polarity rises higher. This

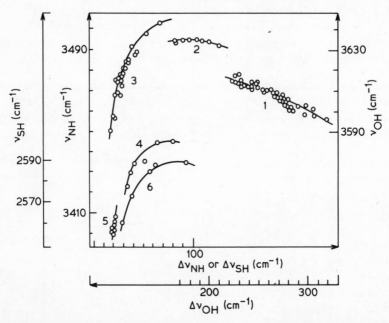

Figure 4.4. Variation of unperturbed frequencies v(XH) against frequency shifts Δv (XH) of various types of XH bonds on passing from an inert solvent to a solution in dioxane. (1) Phenols; (2) benzyl alcohols; (3) anilines; (4) N-methylanilines; (5) benzylamines; and (6) thiophenols. (Reproduced from Figure 2 of Laurence and Berthelot [123].)

suggests one possible explanation for the differences in the two series νNH in $CH_3NH_2 < C_6H_5NH_2 < CH_3CONH_2$ whereas νOH in $CH_3OH > C_6H_5OH > CH_3COOH$. These possibilities have been investigated by Laurence and Berthelot [123]. They measured the frequency shifts of various types of XH bonds on passing from an inert solvent to a solution in dioxane. These shifts are a measure of the polarity of the bonds, and so of their ionic character. When these values are plotted against the original unperturbed frequencies the lines shown in Figure 4.4, are obtained. It will be seen that these represent various segments of the theoretical curve of Figure 4.3. Each type of XH bond will have its own particular shape of curve so that separate segments are given by the individual groups.

These same authors have also explored the relationship between the XH frequencies of various aromatic compounds and the Hammett σ values of the substituents. They point out that even within a single limited series the relationship is not always linear. The phenols and the benzoic acids give straight line relationships, with the frequencies falling as σ rises. The anilines give an almost linear plot with the slope in the other direction. However, some others show a curvature similar to parts of the line in Figure 4.3. In the thiophenols for example, the frequencies rise initially with the σ value, then show little change and finally start to fall. Insofar as the Hammett values can be regarded as reflecting the polarity changes of the XH bonds, these findings therefore support the view that Figure 4.3 is a true picture of the ways in which XH frequencies can be expected to vary with the ionic character.

Finally these same authors have measured the NH frequencies of a series of anilines in a range of solvents of very different basicities. In this way the ionic character of the NH bond of each single compound can be varied. They have again taken the Hammett σ values of the substituents as a measure of the relative ionic characters in any single solvent, and have plotted these against the frequencies. Their results are reproduced in Figure 4.5. It will be seen that in carbon disulphide the frequencies rise as the Hammett σ value increases, but that when the same compounds are examined in trimethyl phosphate in which solvent all the NH bonds are much more polar, the opposite is true, and that after a small initial rise the curve levels off and begins to fall. The NH frequency of *para* nitroaniline is therefore the lowest of the series in trimethyl phosphate, and the highest in the same series in carbon disulphide. This appears to demonstrate very effectively the validity of the concept that the frequency will vary with ionic character in a manner indicated by Figure 4.3.

In addition to any frequency changes produced by the inductive and resonance properties of the substituents, one must also consider the results interactions with lone pair electrons *trans* to the XH bond, and of proximity effects from *gauche* hydrogen atoms or methyl groups. We do not yet have a sufficiently full understanding of these effects to be able to predict the polarity changes which may result. However, in the cases of the simple alcohols, the frequencies (and the intensities) rise on passing from *t*-butanol to methanol.

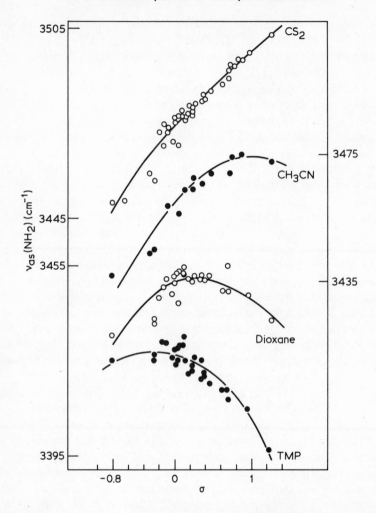

Figure 4.5. Frequencies, $\nu_{as}(NH_2)$, against σ for anilines in CS_2, CH_3CN, dioxane and trimethylphosphate. (Reproduced from Figure 4 of Laurence and Berthelot [123].)

These frequency changes are due to localised interactions rather than to normal inductive effects, and the intensity changes show that these do result in polarity changes. This is also apparent from the changes in pK_a values. The fact that the frequencies rise with the polarity whereas those of the phenols fall is another piece of evidence in support of the conclusions of Laurence and Berthelot.

Frequency changes will also result from any substantial donation of electrons on the X atom into a vacant orbital of another element, such as occurs in coordination compounds. Thus there are substantial falls in the unassociated NH_3 and NH_2 frequencies when coordination of this kind takes place.

4.4. vOH stretching frequencies

The OH stretching frequencies of alcohols, phenols and acids are presented in Tables 4.2 and 4.3, and those of compounds in which the OH group is attached to an element other than carbon in Table 4.4. It will be seen that the frequency

Table 4.2. vXH alkyl

	OH	COOH	CHO	SH	NH$_2$		CONH$_2$	
CH$_3$	3643	3539	2830	2597v	3398	3344	3528^a	3413
C$_2$H$_5$	3635		2816	2584	3411v	3365v	3530^a	3413
C$_3$H$_7$	3638		2584		3390	3322	3526^a	3410
iso-C$_3$H$_7$	3620				3383	3319	3528^a	3412
C$_4$H$_9$	3631		2818	2580	3387	3324		
iso-C$_4$H$_9$	3636							
sec-C$_4$H$_9$	3623		2810				3528^a	3412
tert-C$_4$H$_9$	3616	3536		2580				
Cyclohexyl	3620	3531	2571l.		3381	3316		
Benzyl	3616	3533			3390	3324	3519^a	3407
(C$_6$H$_5$)$_3$C	3612	3519						
Allyl	3612							
(Et)$_3$C	3617							
(iso-Pr)$_3$C	3625							
(Cyclopropyl)$_3$C	3620							
CF$_3$CH$_2$	3617				3438v	3371v		
ClCH$_2$CH$_2$	3623							
CCl$_3$	3636	3508	2863v				3517^a	3403
CF$_3$	3617	3504	2870v	2618v				
CBr$_3$			2848					
NH$_2$	3656v		2852		3350 3325v	3280v		
OCH$_3$			2840		3414v	3269v		
p-Nitrobenzyl		3522						
CHCl$_2$		3518						
CH$_2$CN		3516						
CH$_2$Cl		3527						
CH$_2$Br		3521						
CH$_2$I		3523						
(C$_6$H$_5$)$_2$CH		3523						
C$_6$H$_5$≡C		3517						
CH$_3$CH=CH		3541						
H	3614 3705	3518	2875 2780v	2597	3414v	3337v	3553	3439
SCH$_3$			2835					
OH					3350v	3297v		
C$_6$H$_5$	3609	3536	2807	2591	3480	3395	3540	3420

v Vapour. ^{a} Chloroform.   l. Liquid.

range overall is very considerable. It has been usual to attribute the whole of these changes within the range to inductive and resonance effects, but recent work has made it plain that other factors can make a considerable contribution. The response of the OH stretching frequency to the various structural effects is discussed below.

Table 4.3. νXH aryl

	OH	COOH	CHO	SH	NH₂		NHCOCH₃	NHCOCH₂Br
C_6H_5	3609	3536	2807	2591	3480	3395	3441	3403
para-OCH₃	3618	3542	2835	2572	3460	3382	3445	
OH	3617	3540						
$C_6H_5CH_2O-$	3613							
CH₃	3612	3541		2580	3470	3390	3443	3402
C_6H_5	3612			2570	3483	3398		
Cl	3608	3536	2830	2589	3482	3398	3441	3401
NH₂	3614	3543		2559	3453	3377	3447	
COOCH₃	3603	3538						
COOC₂H₃	3600				3500	3408		
CN	3594	3530			3505	3412	3437	3393
NO₂	3593	3528		2587	3509	3416	3438	3391
CHO	3592						3439	3399
N(CH₃)₂		3542			3453	3377	3443	3405
COOH			2830	2558			3441	3402
Br	3607	3536		2570	3485	3399	3444	
F	3614	3538			3474	3394	3447	
COCH₃	3601				3502	3410	3436	3393
meta-OCH₃	3612	3539			3485	3398		
CHO	3603							
Cl	3607	3532		2589	3490	3402	3448	
NO₂	3600	3528					3442	
OH	3608	3535			3497	3407		
Br	3604	3535		2575				
COCH₃	3607	3534			3486	3400		
F	3609	3536			3492	3405		
CN	3602	3530			3495	3406		
NH₂	3612							
N(CH₃)₂	3614	3541						
α-naphthyl	3609	3536			3472	3390		
β-naphthyl	3609	3533			3475	3390		

(a) Inductive and resonance effects

An initial appraisal of the data would suggest that inductive effects do affect the OH frequencies. The highest values are found with electron donors, such as silicon or magnesium, and much lower values for electron withdrawers such as fluorine. Indeed West and Baney [7] have proposed a linear relationship between frequency and electronegativity, although some of their data have been questioned by later workers.

However, a more detailed study of the data suggests that any electronegativity effects may well be small, or even, as with the CH system, absent. The high frequencies with silicon and magnesium could well originate in the donation of electrons into a vacant d orbital, whilst the low value in HOF could well be due to the influence of the lone pair electrons of the fluorine which lie *trans* to the OH bond. In other compounds such as H_2O_2 (3610 cm⁻¹), HOCl (3626 cm⁻¹) and HNO_3 (3650 cm⁻¹) the values remain reasonably close to those of the alcohols. Furthermore in the series *t*-butanol–methanol, the frequency rises as the chain branching is reduced. Chain branching would normally be expected to reduce the electronegativity, so that the direction of shift is opposite to that which would be expected. It is certainly true that in the phenols, relationships exist between the OH

Table 4.4. νOH frequencies involving elements other than carbon cm^{-1} (carbon tetra-chloride solution except where stated)

Salts			Silicon Derivatives		
LiOH	3678 solid		$(CH_3)_3SiOH$	3688	
NaOH	3637 solid		$(C_6H_5)_2Si(OH)_2$	3682	
KOH	3600 solid		$(C_6H_5)_3SiOH$	3677	
$Ca(OH)_2$	3644 solid		$(C_6H_5)_2SiHOH$	3675	
$Mg(OH)_2$	3698 solid		$(C_2H_5)_3SiOH$	3685	
Nitrogen Derivatives			*Other Elements*		
HONO		*trans* 3590	HOCl vap.		3626
		cis 3426 vap.	$(C_6H_5)_3GeOH$		3651
NH_2OH		3656 vap.	$(C_6H_5)_3SnOH$		3647
CH_3NHOH		3646 vap.	$(C_6H_5)_3PbOH$		3618
$(CH_3)_2NOH$		3636 vap.	Isopropylbenzene OOH		3530
C_6H_5NHOH		3585	$(CH_3)_3COOH$		3558
Acetoxime		3605	H_2O_2		3610 vap.
Acetaldoxime		3600	$(C_6H_5)B(OH)_2$		3666
α-Benzaldoxime		3590			
n-Heptaldoxime		3603			
Pyridine-2-aldoxime		3580			
Pyridine-4-aldoxime		3583			
α-Benzil oxime		3571			
p-Nitrobenzaldoxime		3580			

frequency and the Hammet σ value of the substituents, and the inclusion of a σ_1 term in the latter could imply some dependence on inductive effects. However, it is equally possible that even these effects operate primarily through their influence on the shape of the π cloud, and that there is no direct inductive effect along the σ bonds. This is supported by the fact that variations of the substituents of benzyl alcohols produce little or no change in νOH [123]. It is therefore not possible to conclude at this stage whether electronegativity effects play any part in determining νOH but it does seem clear that any part they do play is relatively small in comparison with the results of resonance.

The importance of resonance is clearly shown by the low OH frequencies of the carboxylic acids, and by the dependence of these frequencies and those of the phenols, on Hammett σ values, in which resonance contributions are a major term. Resonance will increase the sp^2 character of the oxygen orbitals and might therefore be expected to raise the frequency by shortening the OH bond. However, resonance also results in a considerable increase in the OH polarity, as evidenced by the increased acidity of the OH groups, and the overall effect must be considered in the light of the curve shown in Figure 4.3.

(b) Interactions with lone pair electrons in the trans configuration

It has been shown by partial deuteration studies that a CH or NH bond which lies *trans* to a lone pair of electrons on the adjacent atom shows a substantial fall in the stretching frequency [126]. This has been attributed to donation into an anti-bonding orbital in the XH bond. Interactions affecting the OH bond cannot be directly proven by this method, but there is every reason to suppose that they will occur. In hydrogen peroxide the molecule takes a skew configuration and there are no lone pairs *trans* to the OH bond. This absorbs at 3610 cm^{-1}. However, in the OOH^- ion in which such a lone pair is available the frequency falls to 3414 cm^{-1}. It could well be that the low frequencies of organic hydroperoxides are due to this effect.

Other evidence that lone pair effects operate on OH groups is provided by the widely different frequencies of the *cis* and *trans* forms of nitrous acid. The *trans* form absorbs at 3590 cm^{-1} which is not very different from the value of a phenol. However, the *cis* form absorbs at 3426 cm^{-1}, and it is only this form which has the OH bond *trans* to the nitrogen lone pair. Finally there is clear evidence of rotational isomerism in compounds of the type $(CF_3)_2 POH$ and $(CF_3)_2PSH$. Each gives two separate XH stretching bands, and that at the lower frequency is believed to originate in the isomer in which the XH bond lies *trans* to the phosphorus lone pair [127].

Lone pair effects of this kind will not arise very frequently as the attachment of oxygen to atoms with free lone pairs is limited to a relatively small number of systems. Even then the requirement that the lone pair must be *trans* to the OH must also be met if the frequency is to be affected. In oximes for example it would theoretically occur if the OH were *cis* to the $N\text{=}C$ bond. However, the normal form of cyclic dimer requires these bonds to be *trans* and oximes absorb normally near 3640 cm^{-1}.

(c) *Rotational isomerism*

Ingold [8] first drew attention to the importance of conformation effects in alcohols when he showed that the dipole moments of alcohols did not change with chain branching as did those of the alkyl halides. The band shape of the monohydric alcohols varies considerably. In just a few cases, such as methanol and tertiary butanol, it is sharp and symmetric, in most cases it is broad and asymmetric, sometimes with a shoulder on the low frequency side, and in a small number of instances it is a well defined doublet. The concept that the band breadth originates in the presence of rotational isomers has been investigated by many workers [15, 33, 128–135], and the fact that those alcohols such as methanol which can have only one conformation about the C—O bond show sharp symmetrical bands is good evidence in support of this. The difficulty in attempting to evaluate the effects of conformational change upon the OH frequency lies in the fact that the frequencies of the individual components of the asymmetric band must first be defined by graphical resolution methods. These involve a number of assumptions on band shapes and intensities which are not always justified. Nevertheless Dalton *et al.* [33] concluded that the presence of a methyl group close in space to the OH bond (i.e. in the *gauche* position) lowered the frequency by about 14 cm^{-1}, whilst one on the *skew* position lowered the frequency by about 7 cm^{-1}. This did not win any widespread acceptance at the time as it was difficult to see any mechanism which could be responsible for these effects. More recently Kreuger *et al.* [137], proposed that the broad band of ethanol was made up of two components, one of these would arise from the conformation in which the OH was *gauche* to two hydrogen atoms and would absorb at the same frequency as methanol, whilst the other would have the OH *gauche* to one hydrogen atom and to one methyl group, and absorb half way between the frequencies of methanol and *tert.*-butanol. Similarly the band of isopropanol was regarded as arising from components with the OH *gauche* to either two methyl groups or to one methyl group and a hydrogen atom. These various possibilities are illustrated below.

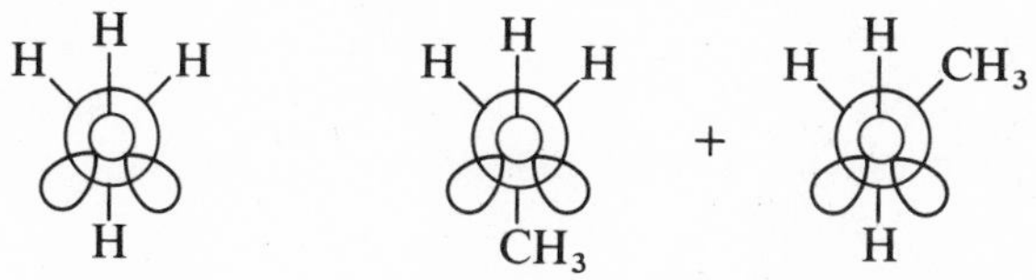

methanol
3643 cm^{-1}

ethanol
3643 cm^{-1}

+

ethanol
3630 cm^{-1}

3635 cm^{-1}

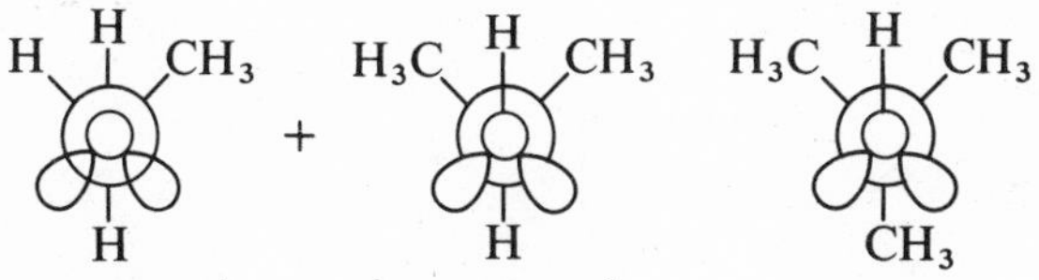

isopropanol
3630 cm^{-1}

+

isopropanol
3617 cm^{-1}

t-butanol
3617 cm^{-1}

3626 cm^{-1}

Kreuger accounted for the differences between the two conformations of primary and secondary alcohols in terms of the lone pair donation to a *trans* CH bond. He proposed that such a donation would raise *v*OH and that this would not occur with a *trans* methyl group. However, the evidence that lone pair donation by the oxygen atom raises *v*OH is very limited and there are now good grounds for supposing that lone pair donation can occur equally well into a C—C bond as into a C—H bond.

In the light of the recent work on alkyl compound using partial deuteration studies (Chapter 1), it would seem very probable that Kreuger's identification of the isomers and their frequencies is the correct one but that the shifts arise from direct interactions between the orbitals of the OH and those of a *gauche* C—H bond or methyl group. This mechanism is well established in the alkanes in which, as with OH the effect of a *gauche* methyl group is greater than that of a corresponding hydrogen atom.

The close analogy with the behaviour of the CH compounds would seem to make this the most likely explanation of the frequency behaviour of the alcohols and of their band shapes. However, final confirmation must await improved techniques of computerised resolution of the asymmetric band shapes. The concept of a lowering of the frequency by a *gauche* methyl group receives strong support from the work of Lutz and Van der Maas [135], and to a lesser extent from studies on hydroxy steroids of known conformation [33, 34]. Nevertheless it must be said that some residual difficulties remain. Thus, the replacement of a *gauche* methyl group by a *gauche* CF_3 group would be expected to result in a frequency rise as the interaction between the CH and OH bonds is eliminated. The compound $CF_3CHOHCH_3$ does indeed absorb at a high frequency ($3653 \, cm^{-1}$ vapour), especially as it has a single conformation in which the OH is *gauche* to a CF_3 group, and to a hydrogen atom [138]. However, $CF_3CHOHCF_3$ which exists in the two forms shown below, absorbs at $3666 \, cm^{-1}$ and $3626 \, cm^{-1}$ in the vapour [139]. The first value is comparable with methanol but is not higher as would be expected, whilst the second is a good deal lower than in $CF_3CHOHCH_3$ despite the fact that the conformations about the OH bond are the same. Furthermore these frequencies fall to 3615 and $3578 \, cm^{-1}$ in carbon tetrachloride, corresponding to lower frequencies than *t*-butanol. This illustrates the importance of comparisons being made in the same medium. Finally $CF_3C(OH)_2CF_3$ absorbs at $3635 \, cm^{-1}$ in the vapour which is lower than *t*-butanol in the same phase [140].

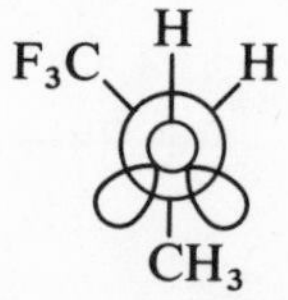

$3653 \, cm^{-1}$ vapour

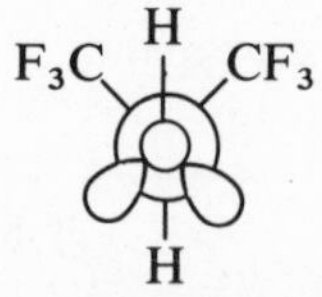

$3666 \, cm^{-1}$ vapour

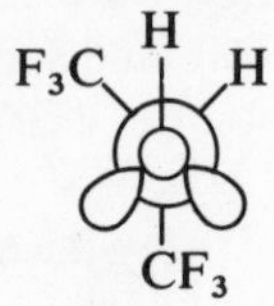

$3626 \, cm^{-1}$ vapour

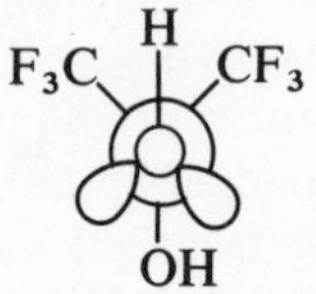

$3630 \, cm^{-1}$ vapour

There are also some difficulties in accounting adequately for some of the higher OH frequencies in heavily branched chain alcohols which show doublet OH bands, wholly in terms of interactions with hydrogen atoms and of methyl groups [134]. This has led Van der Maas and Lutz [135] to suggest that the shielding effect of the OH bond by the surrounding alkyl groups raises the frequency by keeping the bond in a non-polar environment. However, if this were so one would expect to find even greater shielding effects with the CF_3 group, and these do not seem to occur.

Studies on the rotational isomerism of alcohols substituted at the 2-position are complicated by the possibility of hydrogen bonding. Kreuger et al. [124, 125] have studied a number of 2-substituted ethanols and have shown that two or three OH bands are present. In the cases of the amino ethanols at least, it seems certain that the lowest frequency band is due to hydrogen bonding. Not only is it at too low a frequency for a free OH, but the frequency falls as the basicity of the amino group is increased. With the $N(C_2H_5)_2$ group for example the bands are at 3628 and 3472 cm^{-1}. With 2-cyano-ethanol however the occurrence of hydrogen bonding seems less likely as the bands appear at 3633 and 3619 cm^{-1}. 2-chloro-ethanol has been assigned OH bands at 3643 and 3624 cm^{-1} respectively due to the *trans* and *gauche* conformers [136]. However, these values relate to a nitrogen matrix rather than to a solution. In solution the bands are at 3623 cm^{-1} and 3594 cm^{-1} [10]. CF_3CH_2OH absorbs at 3620 cm^{-1} [99] and this is unlikely to be hydrogen bonded.

It is clear from the above discussion that the precise position of an OH stretching band is influenced by a number of factors and that the frequency alone is insufficient to fully characterise the bond. Some further characteris-ation is possible through intensity measurements but these are complicated by the presence of rotational isomers. The best hope for a full characterisation of the bond is probably a combination of frequency measurements with acidity and basicity studies. These would simply make use of the shift of νOH in a standard basic solvent, and of the shifts of νNH of say pyrrole when it is allowed to associate with the lone pairs of the oxygen atom. These three separate parameters should be sufficient to give a unique characterisation of the bond in a way that would relate to its chemical properties.

A number of authors have studied the acidities of OH groups in both alcohols and acids by measurements of the frequency shifts in a standard solvent [11, 13, 43, 123]. However, only a few measurements have been made on the corresponding basicities. Usually within a single related series the acidities and basicities are inversely related so that as the acidity increases the basicity falls. However, this is not always so. Thus on passing from $(C_6H_5)_3SiOH$ (3677 cm^{-1}) to $(CH_3)_3SiOH$ (3688 cm^{-1}) there is a marked increase in both the acidity and the basicity of the OH bond [11]. This must be an indication of the effects of the back donation of electrons into the vacant silicon d orbitals.

4.4.1. OH attached to carbon

(a) *Alcohols*

The data in Table 4.2 fully justify the tentative earlier findings that, provided measurements were made with sufficient precision, it is possible to differentiate primary, secondary and tertiary alcohols. The data are derived from a number of sources all showing good agreement with one another, and there is little doubt that this is so. Useful tables of data of this kind will be found in references [2, 10–16], and [21], [33] and [134]. There are, of course, exceptions to these generalizations. The case of benzyl alcohol, which absorbs at the position appropriate to a tertiary rather than a primary alcohol, is well known, and other instances occur when multiple bonds are situated on the α carbon atom [15]. Nevertheless, with these minor reservations the correlations work well, and can if necessary be supplemented by intensity studies [2, 13, 14, 16, 17, 18, 134], which similarly show a clear-cut distribution between the three separate classes of alcohols.

The most detailed studies of alcohols are those of Van der Mass and Lutz [134]. They have listed the peak frequencies and intensities of a large number of primary, secondary and tertiary alcohols. Of some fifteen primary alcohols other than methanol, nine with no branching before the γ carbon atom absorbed in the narrow range 3635–3639 cm^{-1}, (CCl$_4$) solution, whilst the remaining six with branching or rings at the β carbon absorbed at slightly higher frequencies (3639–3642 cm^{-1}). They deduce from this, and from the parallel behaviour of secondary and tertiary alcohols that branching at the β carbon causes a frequency rise of a few cm^{-1}.

The observed frequency range for sixteen secondary alcohols without other chain branching was 3626–3630 cm^{-1}, so that the effect of the branching at the α carbon is to reduce the frequencies by about 9 cm^{-1}. Chain branching at the β carbon again gave a small frequency rise. With more extensive chain branching at this point double OH bands begin to appear: 2:4-dimethylpentanol-3 for example, shows two bands at 3641 and 3614 cm^{-1}. This same doubling effect has been observed previously in such compounds as tricyclohexylcarbinol [35].

The cyclic secondary alcohols absorbed between 3621–3627 cm^{-1}, but branching at the β carbon again led to a small frequency rise. 2-methylcyclohexanol absorbs at 3631 cm^{-1} and 2:6-dimethylcyclohexanol at 3636 cm^{-1}.

Unbranched tertiary alcohols absorbed between 3615–3621 cm^{-1}, with slightly higher values for those branched at the β carbon. The frequency fall as compared with the secondary alcohols is again about 9 cm^{-1} which these authors assign as the result of the branching at the α carbon.

The use of the free OH frequency as a diagnostic of the steric arrangement in cyclohexanols has also been studied and earlier indications that axial isomers absorb at slightly higher frequencies than equatorial have been confirmed [20].

However, the differences are very small, often no more than 4–5 cm^{-1}, and there are no significant intensity differences between the separate conformers.

(b) Phenols

It has been known for many years that the frequencies of the monomeric OH group of phenols can be related to the Hammett σ and pK_a values of the substituents, provided substitution is not at the *ortho* position when either steric effects or hydrogen bonding may alter the position. More recent studies on phenols, using higher precision, have fully confirmed this finding [21–25]. Baker [23], Ingold [26], and Laurence and Berthelot [123] have shown that the frequencies are a function of Hammett σ values, and both Stone and Thompson [24] and Brown [25] have found that this is equally true of the absolute intensities. In this series, therefore, an increase in σ value corresponding to an increase in the sp^2 oxygen contribution leads to a more polar OH group and to a frequency fall. Thus the strongest acid of the series is *p*-nitrophenol which has the lowest frequency and the highest intensity. The inclusion of further fused rings also lowers the frequency as compared with phenol [21]. Canady [27, 28] has followed up the relationship with pK_a values and studied the possibility of similar relationships with thermodynamic functions. As is to be expected, νOH is a linear function of ΔF, the free energy of ionization, but is not directly tied to ΔH or ΔS, the heat content and entropy of ionization. This is attributed to solvent/solute interaction effects. Hydroquinone, resorcinol and pyrogallol have been studied in the vapour phase by Wilson [141].

Ortho-alkyl phenols have also been extensively studied [22, 29–31, 109–110, 142], and Ingold and Taylor [29] have given some particularly detailed tables of frequencies and intensities. Green *et al.* [142] have given details for a wide range of dimethyl phenols. The range is surprisingly wide (3624–3602 cm^{-1}) but they do not show much evidence of any rise due to a methyl group at the *ortho* position. This might have been expected in view of the effects of substitution in alcohols. These workers have also studied 2-chlorophenols which of course show two bands due to hydrogen bonding. When one *ortho* substituent is a tertiary butyl group the OH band doubles. This has been observed by several workers [22, 29, 30–32, 109–110], the two bands in 2-*tert*-butylphenol occurring at 3647 and 3607 cm^{-1}. There is general agreement that these arise from two conformers, the lower frequency band, with the normal phenolic OH frequency having the *trans* arrangement. This has been substantiated by solvent and temperature-dependence studies.

(c) Acids

The data for νOH given in Tables 4.2 and 4.3 are based in part on Goulden's values obtained some years ago. These have been supplemented by more recent values for some alkyl acids from Bellamy [36] and of benzoic acids by Brookes [37], Josien [38], Laurence *et al.* [123] and Guilleme *et al.* [143].

It will be seen that acid OH frequencies in carbon tetrachloride solution are markedly lower than the phenols and are often comparable with the frequencies of hydroperoxides. The *meta* and *para* substituted benzoic acids, which have been extensively studied by Laurence *et al.* [123] have OH frequencies which show a good linear relationship with Hammett σ values. Clearly the resonance effect rather than an inductive effect is the dominant factor in determining the frequencies of carboxylic acids, as the inductive effect of the carbonyl group is relatively small. It has been established by both Josien [38] and by Brookes [37] that for benzoic acids with *meta* or *para* substitution there is a reasonably good relationship between νCO and νOH whereby νOH falls as νCO rises. A similar but not identical relationship probably exists in the alkyl series—certainly CF_3COOH, which has the highest carbonyl frequency, also has the lowest νOH. This can be interpreted in terms of the differing contributions of the canonical forms (I) and (II). A substituent which raises νCO increases the contribution of (I) at the expense of (II). The charge on the oxygen atom in (II) is greater than that of (I), and from the earlier discussion on the relation of νXH to the charge on X it is to be expected that the OH bond will be shorter than in (I). This follows also from the hybridization (sp^2) of the oxygen atom of (II). Any increase in the contribution of (I) which raises νCO will therefore be accompanied by a fall in the frequency of νOH. This leads to the expectation that there will be some relationship between the frequencies of acids and their acidities, and comparison of, say, an acid with an alcohol. Within any one class of acid or alcohol there is a good linear relationship between νOH and the pK_a value.

$$R-C\overset{\displaystyle O}{\underset{\displaystyle O-H}{\Big\langle}} \qquad\qquad -R-\overset{+}{C}\overset{\displaystyle O^-}{\underset{\displaystyle O\cdot\cdot H}{\Big\langle}}$$

(I)   (II)

Goulden originally showed that alkyl acids gave a linear plot of this kind which was different from that of aryl acids. The relationship in the first case has been fully confirmed by Guilleme *et al.* [143], and in the latter by Josien [38] and shown to extend to pK_a values measured in non-aqueous solvents by Brookes [37] Guilleme has also shown that for non-aromatic (but including some conjugated acids) there is a relationship between the OH frequency and the equilibrium constants for dimerisation.

In plots of νOH against either pK_a or Hammett σ values, linearity is only obtained within a related series of acids so that the slopes for alkyl and halogenated acids are different from those of benzoic acids, and from those of phenyl acetic acids. This is a direct result of the effects discussed above which give rise to the curves shown in Figure 4.4. A further reflection of these effects is shown by the frequencies of the chlorinated acetic acids in different states.

The OH bands of acetic, mono, di, and trichloracetic acids all absorb within 1 cm^{-1} of each other in the vapour state [36]. This does not mean however that they have the same polarity as on solution in carbon tetrachloride, the frequencies become very different with the stronger acids showing the lower frequencies. This is another example of the situation found by Laurence and Berthelot [123] illustrated in Figure 4.5. The acids in the vapour phase must represent a situation at the turnover point of the curve of Figure 4.3 where the frequencies are insensitive to polarity changes, whilst the solution data represent a more polar situation where the frequencies fall off as the polarity increases.

In the benzoic acid series the data in the tables relate only to *meta* and *para* substituted compounds. However, *ortho* substituents also often behave normally, and their peaks fall on the pK_a line curve except in special cases in which large-group or hydrogen-bonding effects occur. Data for such compounds are given in references [37] and [38]. These include some interesting studies on *o*-halogenated benzoic acids. These show two carbonyl frequencies corresponding to forms (I) and (II), the difference arising from the field effect

(I)   (II)   (III)

of the halogen on the carbonyl oxygen in form (I). However, they show only a single vOH frequency which is essentially the same as that of the *meta* halogen-substituted acids. Thus there is no hydrogen bonding of the type suggested in (III), the energy barrier for rotation from the *cis* to the *trans* acid form being presumably too great to allow rotation into this form.

4.4.2. OH attached to nitrogen

Compounds of this type include HONO and $HONO_2$, the oximes and hydroxylamines. Only in the case of the oximes is any quantity of data available, and there is insufficient information to enable any firm conclusions to be drawn. Values for typical examples of these types are given in Table 4.4, but intercomparisons are not easy, most of the hydroxylamines, for example, having been studied in the vapour phase and most oximes in solution. However, it seems that the vOH frequencies are generally slightly lower than the corresponding C—OH compounds when studied in a comparable phase. The case of the *cis* and *trans* forms of nitrous acid is interesting, as the change of shape involves a shift of vOH of 164 cm^{-1}. The very low frequency of the *cis* form is almost certainly due to an interaction between the OH bond and the lone pair of the nitrogen atom, which in this form lies *trans* to the OH.

The data for N-methylhydroxylamines is due to Davies and Spiers [39] and for N-phenyl to West [7], the apparent disparity between the two being primarily due to differences in phase. There is a fall in vOH as the N-hydrogen atoms of hydroxylamine are replaced. This probably corresponds to changes in the contributions from canonical forms involving $^-N{=}\overset{+}{O}{-}H$ structures, the contributions of which would be expected to increase with the degree of substitution, and hence with the basicity of the nitrogen atom. vOH then falls as it does on passing from methanol to phenol.

Recent values for vOH in oximes have been given by Flett [21] and by Mason [40]. The frequency range is relatively narrow (3600–3580 cm^{-1}), as is to be expected, and only in the cases of α-benzil monoxime (3571 cm^{-1}) does the solution frequency fall below 3580 cm^{-1}. It is interesting to note that the low frequency in α-benzil monoxime cannot be attributed to hydrogen bonding with the carbonyl oxygen atom, as in this form the OH group is in the configuration in which it is twisted away from this atom. The vapour frequencies of oximes are higher by some 40–50 cm^{-1}. Further values for the free OH stretching band of aldoximes have been given by Hadzi and Premru [111]. They find that the frequencies of substituted benzaldoximes can be plotted against the Hammett σ values of the substituents to give a straight line of negative slope. Although there are clear-cut differences between the associated OH frequencies of corresponding *syn* and *anti* forms, the free OH values are always the same for both.

4.4.3. vOH with oxygen attached to other elements

There seems to be general agreement that hydroperoxides absorb in the 3560–3530 cm^{-1} range, although the number of such compounds studied in a reasonably pure state is still small. West and Baney [7] quote 3558 cm^{-1} for *tert*-butyl hydroperoxide, and Zarkov and Rudnevskij [41], 3530 cm^{-1} for isopropylbenzene hydroperoxide, and other data for this group are given by Kovner *et al.* [42]. Silicon hydroxy compounds, have been studied by West [7, 11]. Here the frequencies are all high. Substitution of phenyl for methyl groups on the silicon atom lowers vOH so that $(C_6H_5)_3SiOH$ absorbs at 3677 cm^{-1} and $(CH_3)_3SiOH$ at 3688 cm^{-1}. This is accompanied by a very substantial rise in the acidity and a fall in the basicity. The relatively small frequency change therefore corresponds to a substantial alteration in the polarity of the OH bond, due to the alteration in the state of hybridization of the oxygen atom.

Studies with other elements are usually limited to a single compound. West [43] has studied the phenyl-substituted derivative $(C_6H_5)_NXOH$ of germanium, boron, tin and lead and has also measured their acidities and basicities. The very wide range of polarities which can be found within a small range of vOH is well illustrated by this series. On passing from $(C_6H_5)_3GeOH$ to $(C_6H_5)_3SnOH$, for example, vOH alters by only 4 cm^{-1}. However, the frequency shifts on association with ether are 198 cm^{-1} for the germanium compound and less than 10 cm^{-1} for the tin. Conversely, the tin compound is the much stronger base. Measurements of the shift of νOH of phenol when this associates with the oxygen atom give $\Delta\nu$ values of 470 cm^{-1} for the tin derivative and 288 cm^{-1} for the germanium. The polarity differences between these two materials therefore appear to be very substantial.

4.5. νNH stretching frequencies

Neither ν_{as} nor ν_s of primary amines or amides is coupled with any other fundamental. ν_{as} is therefore a realistic function of the NH stretching force constant [1], and indeed falls close to the value of νNH in related secondary amines or amides. Thus ν_{av} for aniline is within a few cm^{-1} of νNH of methylaniline, while νNH and νND of mono-deuteroaniline each correspond closely to ν_{av} for the NH$_2$ and ND$_2$ compounds. It is therefore possible to consider all νNH stretching frequencies on a unified basis. Because of the relationship with the force constant, it is to be expected from generalized rules, such as Badger's rule, that there will be a smooth relationship between νNH (ν average for NH$_2$) and the bond length r for all amines. Bernstein [1] has plotted such a relationship, and a reasonable measure of agreement is found. However, while this generalization will be broadly true, it is perhaps unlikely to be true in detail. It is to be expected that as the state of the hybridization of the nitrogen atom changes from sp^3 to sp^2 the NH bonds will shorten and the frequencies will rise. However, if one considers the factors discussed in relation to νOH above, and in connexion with Fig. 4.3, it seems likely that more than one electronic arrangement will be possible within the NH link for any given value of the force constant or the frequency. Furthermore, the nature of the nitrogen-bonding orbital itself will not be the sole criterion of the frequency. This will depend also upon the charge of the nitrogen atom and on the geometry of the other nitrogen orbitals. If one were to take an sp^3 nitrogen atom, and by altering the other substituents were able to increase the s character of the NH bonding orbital to a fully sp^2 state, the overall force field would still differ from that of an NH group in an initial sp^2 state. This is because in the first case the nitrogen atom would be surrounded by three other orbitals, roughly tetrahedrally arranged, while in the second there would be the normal trigonal arrangement. The incidence of the charge effects on the nitrogen atom is well shown by the series HN$_3$, HNCS and HNCO. The angles the hydrogen atom makes with the main chain are well known and presumably reflect the hybridization at the terminal nitrogen atom. These are 112.39°, 130.32° and 128.5°. However, the shortest NH bond and highest frequency is that in HNCO, which has the intermediate value for this angle. The bond length is not therefore uniquely determined by the hybridization, even in the closely related series. Mason [44] has also shown that the hybridization and the nitrogen nuclear charge are not always directly linked, although, of course, this is often the case within a similar series. The fact that the separation of the two NH stretching bands of benzylamines remains essentially constant with a wide range of different *para* substituents whereas the frequencies differ is also good evidence that the frequencies may not be wholly determined by the bond angles.

The values of νNH in a variety of different situations are given in Tables 4.2, 4.3, 4.5 and 4.6. The factors responsible for the variations of frequencies are as follows.

Table 4.5. νNH frequencies—cm^{-1} variation with X substituent vapour value

NH_2NH_2	3350	3325	3280	HNCO	3531
$OHNH_2$	3350	3292		HNCS	3536
CH_3NH_2	3398	3344		NH_3	3497
CH_3ONH_2	3414	3269		CH_3CONH_2	3555
$CHO\ NH_2$	3545	3450			3435
$NH_2CH{=}NOH$	3530	3424			

Table 4.6. νNH in X CONHY

Y	CH_3	CH_2Cl	$CHCl_2$	CCl_3	CH_2Br	X $CHBr_2$	CBr_3	CF_3	CH_2OCH_3	CH_2O	H
Methyl	3478			3462		3450		3470			3466
Ethyl	3462		3441	3449	3435	3439	3441	3454	3438	3446	
Propyl	3461		3439	3448	3432	3438		3456	3439	3447	
iso-Propyl		3429	3430	3439	3422	3427	3430	3447	3427	3430	
Butyl	3460	3433	3439	3445	3432	3437		3454		3446	
sec-Butyl	3450	3422		3438	3420	3422		3443	3422	3430	
iso-Butyl	3471			3451	3433	3440		3456	3440	3449	
tert-Butyl	3453	3421	3427	3435	3419	3425	3429	3446	3421	3429	
C_6H_5	3441	3409	3419	3422							3434
p-Nitro C_6H_5	3430			3415	3391						

After Nyquist, Reference 67.

(a) Inductive and resonance effects

As with the CH and OH bonds it is difficult to see any major frequency changes which can be associated with inductive effects. It is true that $HONH_2$ absorbs at rather lower frequencies than CH_3NH_2 but the frequencies of CH_3ONH_2 are higher than either. Substitution of a CF_3 group for a CH_3 on the nitrogen atom of secondary amides produces little change in the NH frequency. The direct substitution of chlorine on to the nitrogen atom of amides does result in a frequency fall of about 40 cm^{-1} [144], but the fact that the same values are found on substitution with bromine or iodine would suggest that this is not due to inductive effects. As with the phenols good correlations are found between the NH frequencies of anilines and methyl anilines and the Hammett σ values of the substituents, and these include a σ_i factor. However, it may well be that this operates primarily by alterations in the shape of the cloud.

In contrast, there can be little doubt of the importance of the resonance factor in determining vNH. Methyl amine in the vapour state absorbs at 3398 and 3344 cm^{-1}, whereas acetamide absorbs at 3555 and 3435 cm^{-1} in the same state. The bond shortening due to the increased sp^2 contribution is clearly shown by the frequencies whilst the opening out of the HNH bond angle is shown by the increase in the separation of the antisymmetric and symmetric bands from 54 cm^{-1} to 120 cm^{-1}. Unlike the phenols and acids, the increase of the sp^2 character leads to a frequency rise. As explained earlier this is a consequence of the lower polarity of the NH bond so that it lies on the left-hand side of the curve in Figure 4.3. However, as Laurence and Berthelot [123] have shown this situation can be reversed if the studies are made in very polar solvents in which the polarity of the NH bond is considerably increased. The NH frequencies of *para*nitroaniline are therefore the lowest of the series in trimethyl phosphate solution but the highest of the series in carbon disulphide.

(*b*) *Interactions with a* trans *lone pair on the adjacent element*

Interactions of this kind are well established with CH bonds and are to be expected with NH bonds when suitably substituted. In practice this situation is only feasible with oxygen and nitrogen atoms on the NH and only then if they have a suitable conformation. In the hydroxylamines the preferred conformations are such that the oxygen lone pairs are not *trans* to the NH and the frequencies are normal. In the hydrazines however this effect results in considerable frequency shifts. Hadzi *et al.* [145] have examined a large number of hydrazines using partial deuteration techniques. The NHD derivative of *cis*-dimethylhydrazine has two NH bands although there is only one NH bond. This clearly arises from rotational isomerism. The bands are at 3362 and 3190 cm^{-1}, indicating that the NH bond which lies *trans* to the lone pair has been so weakened that its frequency has fallen by 165 cm^{-1}. Indeed in the original undeuterated compound the two NH frequencies are separated by only a further 16 cm^{-1} as a result of the coupling. It would therefore be more appropriate to identify the two NH stretching bands of the unsymmetrically substituted hydrazines, as arising from the individual stretching frequencies of the separate NH bonds, which are only loosely coupled, rather than as antisymmetric and symmetric modes. These authors have obtained similar results from a substantial number of differently substituted hydrazines, and have shown that the effect can be seen on the NH as well as on the NH$_2$ group. They have also found two NH bands in the compound C_6H_5 CH=NNHD, indicating that the lone pair of an sp^2 nitrogen is equally available for interaction.

One other example is probably that of *cis*diimide (NH=NH). This unstable species absorbs at 3070 cm^{-1} [146] and the geometry is such that each NH bond is *trans* to the lone pair of the other nitrogen atom. Unfortunately the *trans* form absorbs so weakly that the NH band cannot be identified, but the *cis* frequency is clearly very low when compared for example with that of methylene imine which absorbs at $3280\ cm^{-1}$.

(c) Intramolecular interactions and rotational isomerism

In Chapter 1 evidence is given that the presence of a *gauche* CH bond will lower a CH stretching frequency by about $25\ cm^{-1}$, and that a *gauche* CH_3 group will lower it by about $32\ cm^{-1}$. A parallel effect is to be expected with the NH bond, and evidence that this is so is available from steric isomers and from rotational isomerism.

The most convincing evidence of intramolecular effects with a methyl group on the α carbon, comes from the studies of Mathis *et al.* [147, 148], on substituted aziridines. A selection of their data is given below.

(1) $3325\ cm^{-1}$ (2) $3323 + 3306\ cm^{-1}$ (3) $3306\ cm^{-1}$ (4) $3305\ cm^{-1}$

(5) $3325\ cm^{-1}$ (6) $3307\ cm^{-1}$ (7) $3209\ cm^{-1}$

It will be seen that the substitution of a methyl group at the carbon results in two bands, one at the original frequency and the other some $17\ cm^{-1}$ lower. With two methyl groups on the same carbon only the lower frequency band is shown. The fact that the frequency is only lowered when a methyl group is on the same side of the ring as the NH hydrogen atom is well shown by compounds such as 5 above which absorbs at the same frequency as the unsubstituted aziridine. Two methyl groups on the same side of the ring as the NH produce twice the shift (compound 7). The fact that these changes arise from intramolecular interactions rather than from substituent inductive effects is evident from the fact that compound 6 with three methyl groups absorbs at the same frequency as compounds 3 and 4 which have only two, and as compound 2 which has only one.

The average lowering of frequency from an α methyl, ethyl or phenyl group on the same side of the ring was found to be $19.5\ cm^{-1}$, whilst two such groups gave a fall of $37\ cm^{-1}$.

These results are in line with earlier studies of Katritzky *et al.* [149] on the overtones of NH stretching bands. He found a frequency fall of about $40\ cm^{-1}$ in the first overtone on substitution with a methyl group at the α

carbon. At that time he attributed it to an inductive effect, but in the light of the results of Mathis, it is almost certainly an intramolecular effect.

Other examples of this effect in ring systems are given by Mathis *et al.* [150, 151] in cyclic phosphoramides. Here again the substitution of a methyl group on the α carbon to an NH results in a frequency fall of about 20 cm^{-1} provided the methyl group is on the same side of the ring.

In open chain systems effects of this kind can only be detected by the presence of rotational isomers. This has been studied in diethylamine by Verma [152]. In the vapour phase this exists in two forms identified as *trans/trans* and *trans/gauche*. These absorb at 3405 and 3345 cm^{-1} respectively. The existence of such a large difference between the rotamers shows that a sizeable intramolecular interaction is taking place. In fact the projections of Verma show that in the low frequency *trans/gauche* form the NH bond is very close in space, and directed towards one of the hydrogen atoms of a —CH$_2$ group. However, this cannot yet be taken as decisive evidence, as another study of this molecule [154], assigns the higher frequency band as a combination tone and suggests that the frequency difference between the two rotamers is only 24 cm^{-1}. The fact that there is a gradual fall in the NH$_2$ stretching frequencies of primary amines with increased branching at the carbon, just as there is with the alcohols is further evidence for these effects.

Unfortunately there are not sufficient data available on compounds in which halogens replace hydrogen atoms at the α carbon atom, to enable us to establish whether this results in a frequency rise. This does happen with CH bonds and is attributed to the removal of the interaction with a *gauche* hydrogen atom. However the stretching frequencies of trifluroethylamine, in which the NH bonds lie nearly parallel to the C—F bonds and have no *gauche* hydrogen atoms, are at 3428 and 3371 cm^{-1} in the vapour [153], and this is significantly higher than the values for ethylamine itself.

4.5.1. Primary amines and amides

A substantial amount of new precise data has accumulated on the NH stretching frequencies and intensities of aromatic primary amines [44–46, 123, 155, 156] and on a smaller number of alkylamines [47, 153, 157] and diamines [57]. The bulk of this frequency data is included in Tables 4.2 and 4.3. In addition, Mason [44, 48, 78] has tabulated lists of frequencies of amino groups attached to aromatic and heterocyclic rings, and Bryson [49] has dealt with some forty-four naphthylamines. It will be seen from the tables that both v_{as} and v_s rise steadily with an increase in the Hammett σ values of the substituents. The relationship is not truly linear, and is better (as is perhaps to be expected) if v^2 is used instead [45]. The relationship has been discussed in detail by Brownlee *et al.* [155] and by Laurence and Berthelot [123]. Both find a better linearity if Hammett $\sigma_R{}^0$ values are used rather than the $\sigma_R{}^-$ values which give better linearity with the phenols. The same conclusion was reached by Butt and Topsom on the methyl anilines [158], although the intensities gave a better relation with $\sigma_R{}^-$. They concluded that non-planarity of the amino group was the primary cause of this difference. However, as Laurence *et al.* have pointed out the linearity or otherwise of this plot is very much dependent on the solvents used. The intensities of both bands give a more satisfactory linear plot with σ values, but the intensity of the symmetric vibration is greater than the other, and it is more sensitive to substituent effects.

The intensity changes, like the frequency shifts, have been interpreted in terms of an increasing sp^2 character of the nitrogen atom as σ rises [44, 48]. These relationships do not, of course, always hold with *ortho* substituents where steric interactions or hydrogen bonding may occur. A parallel relationship between νNH and the σ values of substituents in 1- and 2-naphthylamines has been described by Bryson [49]. Direct relationships between kinetic data and ν_{as} and ν_s are also reported by Titov *et al.*[50]. Linear plots for both frquencies were realized against the -log K values for the reaction of thirty-four differently substituted anilines with reagents such as *p*-nitrobenzoyl chloride. The rise in intensity on passing from alkylamines to arylamines is very large, and must indicate an increased polarity in the NH link. This polarity increases further as the σ values of the aryl substituents increase. This is to be expected in view of the known increased acidity of sp^2 NH groups as against sp^3. There have been some interesting attempts to rationalize the frequency and intensity behaviour of primary amines (and amides) in these terms, an increased frequency being associated with a shorter NH bond with more sp^2 character, and accordingly with an enlarged NH_2 angle. This question is closely linked to a second topic: the validity and origin of the empirical relationship between ν_{as} and ν_s, which was described by Bellamy and Williams, and this has also been the subject of a number of publications. The most thoughtful contribution on the hybridization aspect is that of Mason [44]. He points out that if the ν_{as} and ν_s vibrations are assumed to be wholly uncoupled (as is reasonable) the valency force-field equations of Linnett can be applied to derive K_{NH} and also the HNH bond angle. These equations state that

$$4\pi^2\nu_s{}^2 = K\,[1/M_H + (1+\cos\theta)/M_N]$$

and

$$4\pi^2\nu_{as}{}^2 = K\,[1/M_H + (1-\cos\theta)/M_N]$$

and thus K and θ can be derived. Using θ, it is then possible to derive coefficients expressing the s character of the nitrogen orbitals bonding to hydrogen. The fractional s character so obtained was shown to give linear plots against either the NH force constants K or the NH bond absolute intensity expressed as the bond dipole gradient. The compounds used for this study were almost wholly amino derivatives of heterocyclic compounds, and it is possible in these to evaluate by standard methods the π-electron density on the amino-group nitrogen atom. This was also done, and these values also gave reasonably good linear relationships. However, it is less certain that the relationships are universally valid. Only two non-aromatic amines were included in this study—cyclohexylamine and lithium amide, and in the latter case the impact of hydrogen bonding in the solid cannot be ignored. It is clear that the bond length of the sp^3 NH groups will be longer than that of the sp^2 compounds, so that the general trend of the aromatic series will be followed, but it seems somewhat unlikely that the same linear functions will apply to the two types of series. One must not therefore assume that there is an overall relationship between vNH (or KNH) and the s character of the nitrogen orbitals, although such a relation clearly exists within related series and forms the basis of the relationships with reactivities and with σ values described above. This conclusion is supported by the work of Titov [171] who has evaluated the s character of the NH bonds of various amines of different types, from the stretching frequencies. He has compared these with the Pk_{BH}^+ values and shown that good linear relationships hold for each separate class (i.e. alkylamines, anilines, etc.), but that there is no overall relationship between all classes.

Somewhat similar considerations apply to the Bellamy and Williams relationship $v_s = 0.876\ v_{as} + 345.5$ (cm^{-1}). This has been rationalized by Stewart [51] on the grounds that to a reasonable approximation it can be shown that $v_s = 0.98\ v_{as}$, and as the constant 345.5 is approximately $0.1\ v_{as}$, this gives the original relationship. More detailed criticisms have been given by Varshavskii [52] and by Finkel'stejn [53], who show that deviations of up to 6 cm^{-1} on either side of the predicted values can be obtained if one considers a wider range of compounds than those used originally. This still leaves the equation in a generally useful form for its original purposes, such as the detection of non-symmetric hydrogen bonding, but does imply that there is no universal relationship between v_{NH} and θ, the bond angle, and that the charge on the nitrogen atom must also be taken into account. Conversely, it is to be expected that even better approximations than the Bellamy-Williams equation can be obtained if the compounds studied are limited to a closely related series. Kreuger [46] finds $v_s = 1023.3 + 0.682\ v_{as}$ is valid with an error of only ± 1 cm^{-1} for *meta*- and *para*-substituted anilines, and Whetsel *et al.* [54] also find a high precision in similar compounds in the overtone region ($v_s = 1304.6 + 0.790\ v_{as}$). A different relationship has been described for the amides by Puranik *et al.* [55]. Here v_s is equated to $1.1214\ v_{as} - 542.5$. The number of compounds studied is relatively few, but there has been a good deal of discussion on the origins of this difference [46, 56]. Kreuger associated this primarily with angle effects, and Moritz [60] prefers an interpretation involving interactions between the NH and CO groups in the *cis* configuration.

In all of this work the emphasis has been concentrated on the NH frequencies. However, as the equations of Linnett show, the separation of the antisymmetric and symmetric bands is also related to the HNH bond angle, provided the NH bonds are equivalent. In general the mean frequencies parallel the changes in separation but there are cases such as the benzylamines in which the frequencies change whilst the separation remains the same. It could well be that the separation is a more realistic measure of the bond angles than the frequencies which may be affected by changes in the charge at the nitrogen atom. Mathis *et al.* have suggested that this is so [159], and this has been largely substantiated by the results of Gotze and Garbe [172]. These workers have demonstrated an excellent linear relationship between the HNH bond angles and the separation of the NH stretching bands over a wide range of different amine types, including some organometallic amines with very low bond angles and correspondingly small frequency separations. They give the equation $\theta_{HNH} = 0.241\Delta v + 91.5$ which could be valuable for the direct determination of the amine bond angles.

The separation of the two stretching bands of primary amines or amides is also useful in indicating situations in which the bonds are non-equivalent, as the separation is then substantially increased. It is also possible to assess the frequency difference of the original uncoupled bonds in some cases. This of course is readily done by partial deuteration to NHD when the two NH stretching bands correspond to the two separate NH bonds [156, 160]. However, a good approximation can be made without this. This is derived as follows.

In the diagram below the two lines in the first row represent the *as.* and *s.* frequencies of an NH_2 group in which the bonds are identical. These are split apart from the mean frequency v_m by the coupling which shifts each band by an equal amount (*a*).

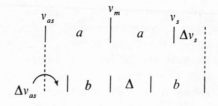

In the second row the two central bands separated by Δ represent the theoretical positions of the uncoupled NH bands of the same amine when one band is moved to lower frequency by the formation of a 1 : 1 complex. The free NH band appears at the mean frequency of the original amine. These are the bands which would be seen experimentally in a partial deuteration experiment. However, in the NH_2 compound the coupling splits them apart by equal amounts (*b*). This is always less than (*a*) as the coupling is reduced by the non-equivalence. It will be seen by dropping verticals that the result of the non-equivalence is to produce a much greater shift in the symmetric band than in the antisymmetric. This is indeed the result of forming 1 : 1 complexes in inert solvents, and some workers have found this puzzling. Moreover, it will be seen that the overall length of the first row $(2a + \Delta v_s)$ is the same as that of the second $(2b + \Delta + \Delta v_{as})$. However, a is also equal to $b + \Delta v_{as}$. By substituting the second equation into the first one arrives at the simple solution $\Delta = \Delta v_{as} + \Delta v_s$. The sum of the shifts of both bands is therefore equivalent to the frequency difference of the uncoupled bonds. If this treatment is extended further it will be found that on formation of the 2 : 1 complex in which the equivalence of the NH bonds is restored, the shift of the antisymmetric band is considerably greater than that of the symmetric, and the symmetry is restored.

Non-equivalence of the NH bonds is not limited to hydrogen bonding situations and occurs also when one NH bond is affected by lone pair effects and the other is not. It has been shown in the hydrazines for example that the coupling is very low and that the two observed bands are better described as the stretching frequencies of the two individual NH bonds with only weak coupling. Bellamy and Pace have studied the fall off of coupling as the individual bond strengths are altered. They conclude that the coupling will vanish altogether if the individual bond frequencies differ by more than 200–250 cm^{-1} [156]. This is supported by the results of Vinkler [173] who has shown by partial deuteration that the coupling contributes only 16 cm^{-1} to the band separation in the complex thioacetamide/pyridine.

Little new data have been given on the free NH stretching frequencies of primary amides, although benzamide has been studied in detail by Kniseley *et al.* [58] and formamide and its variously deuterated derivatives by Suzuki [59]. Monomeric acetamide and urea have been studied by matrix isolation techniques [161] as have the thioamides [162, 173]. In both cases the band separation is considerably greater than in the amines, corresponding to the wider HNH angles. However it is interesting to find that the separation in the thioamides is the same as in the amides indicating that the sp^2 contributions are similar.

4.5.2. Secondary amines and amides

There is little apparent difference between the factors controlling vNH in secondary amines and those in the primary series. The replacement of one hydrogen atom of the NH_2 of aniline by a methyl group gives an NH frequency of 3433 cm^{-1}, very close to the mean v_{NH} value of aniline. Similarly, the correlations between frequencies or intensities and Hammett σ values, developed by Kreuger and Thompson [45] for the aniline series, were found to be equally valid for the methylanilines. Data for a series of compounds of this type will be found in their paper and also in papers by Moritz [60], Dyall and Kemp [112], Butt and Topsom [158], Laurence and Berthelot [123] and Kreuger and Jan [163]. The latter authors associated the failure of the frequencies to give full linearity with the normal Hammett σ values with an overlying effect whereby the NH frequency is reduced when the lone pair electrons are donated into a *trans* CH link. However, in the light of the findings of Butt and Topsom, and of Berthelot, the real causes may lie elsewhere. Kreuger and Jan [164] have also studied NH stretching bands in cyclic imines, and have shown that axial bonds absorb at lower frequencies than equatorial bonds. In the piperazines for example the difference is about 35 cm^{-1}. This may arise from a difference in the local environment of the NH bond. A substantial amount of data on νNH frequencies in the *N*-heteroaromatic hydroxy compounds has been given by Mason [61]. In such compounds νNH is, of course, higher in frequency than in the alkyl amines, just as it is in pyrrole and in methylaniline. The intensity is also enhanced, so that some large part of this shift at least must be associated with the increased sp^2 character of the nitrogen/hydrogen bonding orbital.

Considerably more data have been published on νNH in secondary amides. Katritzky [62, 63] has listed values for variously substituted ethyl urethanes and for compounds of the series XNHCOMe or XNHCOC$_6$H$_5$, where X is either an aromatic or a heteroaromatic ring. Some data on alkyl secondary amides have been given by Jones [113] and also by Beer *et al.* [64], although the latter concentrated primarily on assignments of the lower-frequency modes. However, the most substantial volume of data is in papers by Russell and Thompson [65], Nyquist [66–68] and by Hallam [165–167]. Cyclic amides such as δ valerolactam in which the amide group has the *cis* conformation absorb in the monomeric state at slightly lower frequencies (3440–3420 cm^{-1}) than open chain amides in the *trans* form (3460–3440 cm^{-1}). In many cases, the latter show a weak shoulder on the low frequency side and this has led to extensive studies on the possibility of rotational isomerism [66, 67, 113, 165–167]. In a few instances such as the formamides, and some sterically hindered amides there is a real contribution from the *cis* form, but this is usually small, and most alkyl amides exist wholly in the *trans* form. When these amides show a low frequency shoulder on the NH band it can usually be attributed to the overtone of the carbonyl absorption [67]. In N-Halogen-substituted secondary amides, two NH stretching bands are shown at lower frequencies (near 3420 and 3385 cm^{-1}), and Klein has studied the possibility that these originate in *cis* and *trans* forms [168–169]. He concludes that the *cis* forms do make a contribution but only when the substituents are large enough to produce a steric effect. In the case of phosphoramidates there is also a difference between νNH in the *cis* and *trans* forms, and these compounds exist predominantly in the *cis* configuration [68]. Nyquist [66] has studied the effects of *meta* and *para* substituents on νNH in acetanilides, in α-trichloroacetanilide and in α-bromo-acetanilide. Each shows a general trend of νNH (and νCO) with Hammett σ values, although the shifts themselves are significantly smaller than those of substituted anilines (cf. Table 4.3). However, they also observed some very interesting shifts in νNH, following α halogen substitution, and corresponding effects are also found in the α-halogenated alkylamides. The introduction of a halogen atom in the α position lowers νNH and raises its intensity. The introduction of further halogen atoms at the same point raises νNH again, although not sufficiently to restore the original value. This time the intensity remains unaltered from that of the mono halogen derivative. These results, many of which are included in Tables 4.3 and 4.6, are ascribed to a hydrogen bonding effect between the halogen and the NH group which initially lowers νNH, followed by inductive effects arising from further substitution, which operates in the opposite direction. However, the situation here is a very complicated one, as νNH also falls with the size of the *N*-alkyl substituent. *N-tert*-butyl-2-chloracetamide has νNH 3421 cm^{-1} as against 3433 cm^{-1} for the *N-n*-butyl derivative. The configuration of both the CO and the NH groups with respect to the halogen atoms is clearly very important here, and the fact that νCO does not double as it does in the α-halogenated ketones and esters is also significant. The general results do seem to suggest that the configuration of the mono α-halogenated amides is not (I) as suggested by dipole moment studies, but is closer to (II). The rise in νCO on the substitution of a second and of a third halogen atom (III) would then be ascribable to the field effect which would also operate to change νNH because of the alteration in the resonance of the system. The

(I) (II) (III)

interpretation based on hydrogen bonding is also supported by the observation that there is only a very small shift of νNH in α,α,α-trifluoromethyl derivatives, which would be consistent with the inability of this group to form H-bonds of any strength. Fluorine atoms in mono- and disubstituted compounds have more H-bonding ability, and it would be interesting to see whether νNH went down significantly in these. The further studies on the *ortho*-halogenated acetanilides of Dyall and Kemp [112] are also interesting in this context. In this connexion, Lichtenberger and Geyer [69] have already suggested on other grounds that there is a hydrogen bond between the NH link and the oxygen atom of an *ortho* ether substituent in substituted benzanilides. Herman and Bièvre [77] have given details on ν_{CO} and ν_{NH} in chloro and fluoro acetamides with various degrees of substitution, but the low values for νNH found probably imply that these spectra relate to associated states, and are therefore not relevant to this discussion. Data on νNH in acyl hydrazones and in semicarbazones have been given by Hadzi [115, 116].

4.6. Silicon and germanium hydrides

4.6.1. Silicon hydrogen stretching frequencies

There has been a substantial volume of new work in this area, both in the measurement of the frequencies themselves in a wide variety of molecular environments and on the interpretation of the frequency changes with substitution. Kniseley *et al.* [70] have studied eighty silanes and have produced a valuable correlation chart, although detailed frequencies are cited for only a few molecules. More data are given by Smith and Angelotti [71], Ebsworth *et al.* [72], Ponomarenko [73] and Cumaevskij [74], and details from some of these sources are given in Table 4.7. It will be seen that there is little distinction between symmetrical and antisymmetrical modes, these usually falling within 1 cm^{-1} of each other; also that there is a general tendency for the frequency to rise with increasing inductive power of the substituents.

Table 4.7.

X	$HSiX_3$ νSiH	H_2SiX_2 νSiH	δSiH$_2$	CH_3XSiH_2 νSiH	δSiH$_2$	CH_3X_2SiH νSiH	$C_6H_5X_2SiH$ νSiH	ClX_2SiH νSiH	Cl_2XSiH νSiH
F	2315	2248	982	2185	975	2227			
Cl	2258	2229	953	2200	960	2214	2212	2258	2258
Br	2236	2219	942	2198	955		2193		
I		925		2190	947				
CH$_3$	2118	2145	961	2145	961	2118	2121	2168	2214
C$_2$H$_5$	2097							2153	2205
n-Propyl	2108	2127							2206
C$_6$H$_5$	2126	2143	933	2141		2124		2168	2212
p-ClC$_6$H$_5$		2145		2145					
OCH$_3$	2203								
OC$_6$H$_5$	2196					2165			
CH$_3$SiO	2173								

Both Smith and Angelotti [71] and Ponomarenko *et al.* [73] have sought for some direct relationship between ν_{SiH} and the electronegativity of the substituents. While, however, plots of the sum of the Gordy electronegativity values of the substituents against ν_{SiH} give reasonably linear plots over a small series of related compounds, there are serious divergences when a wider range of compounds are employed. Instead, Smith and Angelotti [71] propose a system of E values whereby each substituent group is allocated an E value in cm^{-1}, the sum of which for all the substituents of SiHX$_3$ is the observed frequency. The fact that E values are commonly obtained from a single compound, such as E(C$_6$H$_5$) from SiH(C$_6$H$_5$)$_3$, but that they can then be used with remarkable success to predict ν_{SiH} in other compounds with mixed substituents is remarkable evidence for the additivity of the shift effects of the substituent groups. The E values so obtained follow a smooth-curve relationship with Gordy electronegativities.

However, as Thompson [75] has pointed out, E values have only a limited application and bear no direct relationship to recognized measures of the inductive effect. Instead he has been able to show that the same data can be equally effectively applied to a relationship with the sum of the Taft σ^* values of the substituents, so that $\nu Si—H = 2106 + 17.5\Sigma\sigma^*$. This is a valuable relation and can successfully predict most frequencies within reasonable limits. Kriegsman *et al.* [79] have demonstrated a similar relationship for trisubstituted silanes and have shown that the intensities of the bands likewise follow a linear relationship with Taft σ^* values. However, as Webster [76] points out, there are some residual anomalies. In the trialkyl silanes the νSiH frequencies diminish in the order $Me > iso\text{-}But > n\text{-}Pr = n\text{-}Bu = Et > iso\text{-}Pr$. This is the same order as that given by NMR chemical shifts on the same protons. It is, however, a little different from that of the Taft σ^* values, so that other factors than polarity itself appear to play some minor role in determining the frequency. In this connexion a comparison of the frequency and chemical shift changes in aryl silanes is particularly interesting. In the infrared the replacement of methyl groups by benzene rings raises ν_{Si-H} only very little, in agreement with the fact that the σ^* values of the latter are only slightly greater. In contrast, there is a major change in the chemical shift values. This is interpreted by Webster as indicating that there is a progressive increase in the $d\pi\text{-}dp$ bonding between the silicon and carbon atoms of the phenyl rings as the proportion of the latter is increased. The NMR studies certainly indicate that this is so, but it then implies that substantial changes in degree of utilization of the d orbitals of silicon can occur without any corresponding changes in ν_{SiH}. This again underlines the suggestion made earlier that neither ν_{XH} nor K_{XH} will always uniquely characterize the electron distribution within a given bond.

4.6.2. Germanium hydrogen stretching frequencies

The GeH stretching absorption appears, as expected, at rather lower frequencies than that of silicon. In all other respects the behaviour is closely parallel to the silanes. Ponomarenko *et al.* [80] have given some frequency data showing that ν_{GeH} is primarily a function of the inductive effect of the substituents and that like ν_{SiH} it can be expressed in terms related to an electronegativity function. Trichlorogermane absorbs at $2155\,cm^{-1}$, and both vinyl and phenylgermane absorb at slightly higher frequencies than the alkylgermanes. This is in accord with the general concept of the control of the frequencies by inductive effects. Mathis *et al.* [81, 82] have carried this further and shown that the σ^* relationship is also valid both for the frequencies themselves [81] and for their absolute intensities. They find $\nu_{GeH} = 2008 + 16.5\Sigma\sigma^*$ and in carbon tetrachloride $A_{GeH} = -0.26\Sigma\sigma^* + 2.24$, that is ν increases with increases in the inductive power of the substituents but A decreases.

The infrared spectra of some hydrides of germanium, such as $n.Ge_4H_{10}$, $n.Ge_5H_{12}$ and $iso\text{-}Ge_4H_{10}$, have been reported by Drake and Jolly [83]. These absorb in the expected 2045–2080-cm^{-1} range and have no unusual features.

4.7. Hydrides of other elements

4.7.1. PH stretching frequencies

The PH stretching vibration is reported by Thomas and Chittenden [84] as falling within the range 2440–2288 cm^{-1} in nineteen different compounds. This is substained by their detailed findings [117] and those of other workers [85–89, 118, 119] on phosphonates, phosphine oxides and phosphonic acid monoesters. This is a surprisingly large overall range for a heavy element hydride, but it seems certain that it does reflect a genuine change in the PH force constant of the PH bond rather than extraneous effects due to hydrogen bonding involving the PH group.

Phosphonates [85, 86, 117] show the highest frequencies of the series, generally absorbing in the range 2455–2420 cm^{-1}. Similar values are given by the monoesters [87]. Phosphine oxides [88, 117] absorb at the other end of the scale, usually in the 2340–2280-cm^{-1} range, while esters of phosphinic acid [89], which represent an intermediate situation, usually show two bands, one near 2380 cm^{-1} and the other near 2340 cm^{-1}. In general, the directions of shift of vPH with changes in substitution run parallel to those of vPO, and it is therefore tempting to attribute the whole of these shifts to alterations in the inductive effects of the substituents. However, while this is no doubt a major factor, the presence of double PH bands in the phosphinic acid esters shows that other factors must also be important. Wolf $et\ al.$ [89] have attributed the presence of these two bands to rotational isomerism, and this is supported by the changes in the relative intensities which occur with changes of state, and more particularly by the changes in intensities when $ortho$ substituents are introduced into the ring in compounds of the type $C_6H_5P(OC_2H_5)OH$. The difference of 40 cm^{-1} between the two PH bands cannot then be attributed to inductive effects working along the bond, and it may well arise from a lone pair donation from one of the oxygen atoms into a $trans$ P—H bond. The intensities of PH bonds have been measured and shown to be reasonably constant, and relatively weak [85]; the half bandwidths are considerably greater than those of CH vibrations, but despite this there is little evidence for hydrogen bonding. Shifts of as much as 50 cm^{-1} can occur with changes of phase [88], but these are most probably connected again with changes in the polarity of the phosphorus atom due to interactions of the P=O link. The shifts with basic solvents are very small [120]. The overtone of the PH stretching band has been identified [90] as a weak absorption near 5285 cm^{-1}, but is of little practical use.

$$(RO)_2P \cdot NH \cdot C_6H_5 \qquad\qquad (RO)_2-P\begin{smallmatrix}H\\ \diagup \\ \diagdown \\ N-C_6H_5\end{smallmatrix}$$

(I)   (II)

Kabatchnik *et al.* [119] have studied the spectra of some fifteen esters thought to have the structure (I). In fact, they find that in all instances these compounds exist in the form (II). This is an interesting parallel to the case of the hydrogen phosphonates, where the pentavalent (PH) structure is usually preferred to the trivalent P(OH) possibility.

4.7.2. SH and SeH stretching frequencies

vSH falls within the narrow range of 2600–2550 cm^{-1} in dilute solution in carbon tetrachloride. In the liquid state or in more concentrated solutions association effects lower these values, usually by about 20 cm^{-1}. The general trends within this range are somewhat parallel to vOH, in that alkyl mercaptans show the highest frequencies and dithioacids the lowest. However, there is one important distinction, in that electron-attracting substituents in an aromatic ring such as the *p*-nitro group lower vOH and raise vSH, conversely electron donors such as *p*-NH$_2$ lower vSH and show higher vOH values. This is evident from Table 4.3, from which it will be seen that the vSH parallels the behaviour of vNH$_2$ in this respect. The reasons for this are similar to those for the NH group discussed in Section 4.3. Indeed Laurence and Berthelot [123] have shown that the SH stretching frequency is a particularly interesting one in that when it is plotted against the SH polarity a curve, rather than a straight line is obtained with a turnover point near 2590 cm^{-1} (see Figure 4.4). Similarly a plot of thiophenol frequencies against Hammett σ values is non-linear, showing a turnover point in the same region.

The data in Table 4.3 are taken from a number of sources, of which the papers of Miller and Krishnamurphy [97], of David and Hallam [98, 121], of Dollish *et al.* [170] and of Laurence *et al.* [123] are the most useful. Earlier data on thiophenol and its substituted derivatives have been given by Spurr and Byers [91], Josien *et al.* [92] and Jur'ev *et al.* [94]. Bulanin *et al.* [93] has given some data on alkyl mercaptans and Dininny [95] on CF$_3$SH in the vapour phase (2618 cm^{-1}).

Little is available on the intensities in this series, although it should be remarked that in alkyl mercaptans, in contrast to the thiophenols, this is so low that the band is frequently not detectable in the infrared. The free SH band of trithiocarbonic acids occurs in the 2560–2550-cm^{-1} region, and of the COSH group in the 2595–2560-cm^{-1} range [122].

A small number of alkyl and aromatic compounds containing the SeH group have been studied by Sharghi and Lalezari [96]. In the liquid state all absorb in the narrow range 2280–2300 cm^{-1}. No shifts occurred on dilution with benzene, from which it was deduced that self-association does not occur.

4.7.3. BH stretching frequencies

No systematic regularities have been described in these frequencies other than the differentiation between the broad classes of BH_2 and BH groups and the bridged systems in which a hydrogen atom is shared between two boron atoms. There is not, for example, any observable difference between the stretching frequency of an apical BH link in a compound such as decaborane and that of BH links elsewhere, although there is NMR evidence that the nature of the bonding is different [99].

BH_2 stretching vibrations appear as symmetric and anti-symmetric bands in the overall range 2640–2350 cm^{-1} [99], although in the simpler substituted diboranes the ranges are much narrower (v_{as} 2640–2570 cm^{-1}, v_s 2535–2485 cm^{-1}) [100]. The BH group appears, of course, as a single band only in the range 2565–2480 cm^{-1}, the lower frequencies occurring in the dialkoxy boranes [101, 102].

The bridging BH frequencies are much lower, and usually appear as a complex series of bands in the range 2100–1600 cm^{-1} [99, 100]. In the special cases of substituted diboranes the band ranges again narrow, and the various peaks have been assigned in detail by Lehmann *et al.* [101].

4.7.4. Metal–hydrogen stretching frequencies

(*a*) *Tin hydrides*

A small number of hydrides of tin have been studied by Mathis-Noel *et al.* [103] and also by Cummings [104]. The overall range is apparently small, $(C_6H_5)_3SnH$ absorbing at 1800 cm^{-1} and tributyl SnH at 1855 cm^{-1}. There is not apparently any splitting into anti-symmetric and symmetric modes in SnH_2 compounds, of which the small numbers studied absorb near 1830 cm^{-1}.

(*b*) *Transition metal hydrides*

X—H stretching frequencies in coordination compounds involving Pt, Ir, Ru, Os and Re have been described by Chatt and by Adams [105–107]. As expected, the frequencies fall in the 2200–1900-cm^{-1} range, the highest frequencies being given by platinum and the lowest by ruthenium. However, as in such materials, one is never concerned with the use of this band to identify the metal, the primary interest lies in the frequency shifts which occur in any one metal series, with changes in the various ligands and in their relative positions. In compounds in which the hydrogen atom is *trans* to a halogen the frequency is significantly higher than in compounds in which it is *trans* to a normal ligand such as $P(C_2H_5)_3$. Thus in (I), νXH occurs at 2095 cm^{-1}, in (II) it is a 2197 cm^{-1}, while in (III) both bands appear at 2177 cm^{-1}, at 2028 cm^{-1} (CCl_4 solution). This is of some importance in enabling the configuration of such materials to be determined. Changes in the nature of the halogen atom do not make large differences in νXH. Thus in $[C_2H_4(PMe_2)_2]_2Ru.H.$—Halogen (*trans*), RuH changes from 1891 cm^{-1} with chlorine substitution to only 1898 cm^{-1} with iodine. However, a change in ligand even to $C_2H_4(PEt_2)_2$ raises this frequency to 1938 cm^{-1} (chloride).

These metallic hydride coordination compounds also show an interesting behaviour in proton-accepting solvents, whereby νXH is raised in polar solvents when it is in the *trans* configuration to a halogen, but is virtually unaffected when it is in the corresponding *cis* position. The reasons for this have been discussed by Adams [108].

Bibliography

1. Bernstein, *Spectrochim. Acta*, 1962, **18**, 161.
2. Motoyama and Jarboe, *J. Phys. Chem.*, 1966, **70**, 3226.
3. Lippincott and Schroeder, *J. Amer. Chem. Soc.*, 1956, **78**, 5171.
4. Cottrell, *The Strengths of Chemical Bonds*, Butterworths, London, 1958. Second Edition.
5. Nakamoto, *Infrared Spectra of Inorganic and Coordination Compounds*, Wiley, New York, 1963, p. 10.
6. Schomaker and Stephenson, *J. Amer. Chem. Soc.*, 1941, **63**, 37.
7. West and Baney, *J. Phys. Chem.*, 1960, **64**, 822.
8. Ingold, *Structure and Mechanism in Organic Chemistry*, Bell, 1953.
9. Cannon and Stace, *Spectrochim. Acta*, 1958, **13**, 253.
10. Josien and Pineau, *C.R. Acad. Sci.*, Paris, 1960, **250**, 2559.

11. West and Baney, *J. Amer. Chem. Soc.,* 1959, **81**, 6145.
12. Ford and Marshall, *J. Polymer Sci.,* 1956, **22**, 360.
13. Barrow, *J. Phys. Chem.,* 1955, **59**, 1129.
14. Brown, Saudri and Hart, *J. Phys. Chem.,* 1957, **61**, 698.
15. Arnaud and Armand, *C.R. Acad. Sci., Paris,* 1962, **255**, 1718; 1961, **253**, 1426.
16. Moccia and Thompson, *Proc. Roy. Soc.,* 1959, **A.254**, 22.
17. Brown, *J. Amer. Chem. Soc.,* 1958, **80**, 6489.
18. Brown and Rogers, *J. Amer. Chem. Soc.,* 1957, **79**, 577.
19. Mukherjee and Grunwald, *J. Phys. Chem.,* 1958, **62**, 1311.
20. Chiurdoglu and Masschelein, *Bull. Soc. Chim., Belg.,* 1959, **68**, 484.
21. Flett, *Spectrochim. Acta,* 1957, **10**, 21.
22. Puttnam, *J. Chem. Soc.,* 1960, 5100.
23. Baker, *J. Phys. Chem.,* 1958, **62**, 744.
24. Stone and Thompson, *Spectrochim. Acta,* 1957, **10**, 17.
25. Brown, *J. Phys. Chem.,* 1957, **61**, 820.
26. Ingold, *Can. J. Chem.,* 1960, **38**, 1092.
27. Bavin and Canady, *Can. J. Chem.,* 1957, **35**, 1555.
28. Canady, *Can. J. Chem.,* 1960, **38**, 1018.
29. Ingold and Taylor, *Can. J. Chem.,* 1961, **39**, 471, 481.
30. Goddu, *J. Amer. Chem. Soc.,* 1960, **82**, 4533.
31. Bellamy, Eglinton and Morman, *J. Chem. Soc.,* 1961, 4762.
32. Bellamy and Williams, *Proc. Roy. Soc.,* 1960, **254A**, 119.
33. Dalton, Meakins, Robinson and Zaharia, *J. Chem. Soc.,* 1962, 1566.
34. Dalton, McDougall and Meakins, *J. Chem. Soc.,* 1963, 4068.
35. Cook and Reece, *Aust. J. Chem.,* 1961, **14**, 211.
36. Bellamy, Osborn and Pace, *J. Chem. Soc.,* 1963, 3749.
37. Brookes, Eglinton and Morman, *J. Chem. Soc.,* 1961, 106.
38. Josien, Peltier and Pichevin, *C.R. Acad. Sci., Paris,* 1960, **250**, 1643.
39. Davies and Spiers, *J. Chem. Soc.,* 1959, 3971.
40. Mason, *J. Chem. Soc.,* 1960, 22.
41. Zarkov and Rudnevskij, *Optics and Spectroscopy,* 1959, **7**, 848.
42. Kovner, Karjakin and Efimov, *Optics and Spectroscopy,* 1960, **8**, 128.
43. West, Baney and Powell, *J. Amer. Chem. Soc.,* 1959, **81**, 6145.
44. Mason, *J. Chem. Soc.,* 1958, 3619.
45. Kreuger and Thompson, *Proc. Roy. Soc.,* 1957, **A.243**, 143.
46. Kreuger, *Nature,* 1962, **194**, 1077.
47. Orville-Thomas, Parsons and Ogden, *J. Chem. Soc.,* 1958, 1047.
48. Mason, *J. Chem. Soc.,* 1959, 1281.
49. Bryson, *J. Amer. Chem. Soc.,* 1960, **82**, 4862.
50. Titov, Litvinenko, Levcenko and Izmajlov, *J. Chem. Ukr.,* 1961, **27**, 481.
51. Stewart, *J. Chem. Phys.,* 1959, **30**, 1259.
52. Varshavskii, *Optics and Spectroscopy,* 1961, **11**, 369.
53. Finkel'stejn, *Optics and Spectroscopy,* 1962, **12**, 454.
54. Whetsel, Robertson and Krell, *Analyt. Chem.,* 1958, **30**, 1598.
55. Puranik and Ramiah, *Nature,* 1961, **191**, 796.
56. Moritz, *Nature,* 1962, **195**, 800.
57. Baldwin, *Spectrochim. Acta,* 1962, **18**, 1455.
58. Kniseley, Fassel, Farquhar and Gray, *Spectrochim. Acta,* 1962, **18**, 1217.
59. Suzuki, *Bull. Chem. Soc., Japan,* 1960, **33**, 1359.
60. Moritz, *Spectrochim. Acta,* 1960, **16**, 1176.
61. Mason, *J. Chem. Soc.,* 1957, 4874.
62. Katritzky and Jones, *J. Chem. Soc.,* 1960, 676.
63. Katritzky and Jones, *J. Chem. Soc.,* 1959, 2067.

64. Beer, Kessler and Sutherland, *J. Chem. Phys.*, 1958, **29**, 1097.
65. Russell and Thompson, *Spectrochim. Acta*, 1956, **8**, 138.
66. Nyquist, *Spectrochim. Acta*, 1963, **19**, 1595.
67. Nyquist, *Spectrochim. Acta*, 1963, **19**, 509.
68. Nyquist, *Spectrochim. Acta*, 1963, **19**, 713.
69. Lichtenberger and Geyer, *Bull. Chem. Soc. Fr.*, 1957, 824.
70. Kniseley, Fassell and Conrad, *Spectrochim. Acta*, 1958, **15**, 651.
71. Smith and Angelotti, *Spectrochim. Acta*, 1959, **15**, 412.
72. Ebsworth, Onyszchuk and Sheppard, *J. Chem. Soc.*, 1958, 1453.
73. Ponomarenko and Egorov, *Bull. Acad. Sci., U.R.S.S.*, 1960, 1133.
74. Poljakova and Cumaevskij, *C.R. Acad. Sci., U.R.S.S.*, 1960, **130**, 1037.
75. Thompson, *Spectrochim. Acta*, 1960, **16**, 238.
76. Webster, *J. Chem. Soc.*, 1960, 5132.
77. Herman and Bièvre, *Bull. Chem. Soc. Belg.*, 1959, **68**, 558.
78. Elliot and Mason, *J. Chem. Soc.*, 1959, 1275.
79. Kriegsman, Kessler and Reich, *Z. Chem.*, 1961, **1**, 346.
80. Ponomarenko, Egorov and Vzenkora, *C.R. Acad. Sci., U.S.S.R.*, 1958, **122**, 405.
81. Mathis, Satge and Mathis, *Spectrochim. Acta*, 1962, **18**, 1463.
82. Mathis, Constant, Satge and Mathis, *Spectrochim. Acta*, 1964, **20**, 515.
83. Drake and Jolly, *J. Chem. Soc.*, 1962, 2807.
84. Thomas and Chittenden, *Chem. and Ind.*, 1961, 1913.
85. Honalla and Wolf, *Bull. Soc. Chim. Fr.*, 1960, 129.
86. Wolf, Mathis-Noel and Mathis, *Bull. Soc. Chim. Fr.*, 1960, 124.
87. Thomas and Clark, *Nature*, 1963, **198**, 855.
88. Miller, Miller and Rogers, *J. Amer. Chem. Soc.*, 1958, **80**, 1562.
89. Wolf, Miquel and Mathis, *Bull. Soc. Chim. Fr.*, 1963, 825.
90. McIvor, Hubley, Grant and Grey, *Can. J. Chem.*, 1958, **36**, 820.
91. Spurr and Byers, *J. Phys. Chem.*, 1958, **62**, 425.
92. Josien, Castinell and Saumagne, *Bull. Soc. Chim. Fr.*, 1952, 648.
93. Bulanin, Denisov and Puskina, *Optics and Spectroscopy*, 1959, **6**, 754.
94. Jur'ev, Rozancev and Egorov, *Bull. Moscow University*, 1958, **13**, 215.
95. Dininny and Pace, *J. Chem. Phys.*, 1959, **31**, 1630.
96. Sharghi and Lalezari, *Spectrochim. Acta*, 1964, **20**, 237.
97. Miller and Krishnamurphy, *J. Org. Chem.*, 1962, **27**, 645.
98. David and Hallam, *Trans. Faraday Soc.*, 1964, **60**, 2013.
99. Bellamy, Gerrard, Lappert and Williams, *J. Chem. Soc.*, 1958, 2412.
100. Lehmann, Wilson and Shapiro, *J. Chem. Phys.*, 1960, **32**, 1088, 1786; **33**, 590.
101. Lehmann, Onak and Shapiro, *J. Chem. Phys.*, 1959, **30**, 1215.
102. Lehmann, Weiss and Shapiro, *J. Chem. Phys.*, 1959, **30**, 1222, 1226.
103. Mathis-noel, Lestre and De Roch, *C.R. Acad. Sci., Paris*, 1956, 243, 257.
104. Cummings, Private Communication.
105. Chatt, Duncanson and Shaw, *Proc. Chem. Soc.*, 1957, 343.
106. Chatt and Hayter, *Proc. Chem. Soc.*, 1959, 153.
107. Adams, *Proc. Chem. Soc.*, 1961, 431.
108. Adams, in *Spectroscopy*, Ed. Wells, Institute of Petroleum, London, 1962, p. 265.
109. Baker, Karlinger and Shulgin, *Spectrochim. Acta*, 1964, **20**, 1467.
110. Baker, Karlinger and Shulgin, *Spectrochim. Acta*, 1964, **20**, 1477.
111. Hadzi and Premru, *Spectrochim. Acta*, 1967, **23A**, 35.
112. Dyall and Kemp, *Spectrochim. Acta*, 1966, **22**, 467.
113. Jones, *Spectrochim. Acta*, 1966, **22**, 1555.
114. Dyall and Kemp, *Spectrochim. Acta*, 1966, **22**, 483.
115. Hadzi and Jan, *Spectrochim. Acta*, 1967, **23A**, 571.
116. Hadzi and Jan, *Rev. Roumaine. Chim.*, 1965, **10**, 1183.

117. Chittenden and Thomas, *Spectrochim. Acta,* 1965, **21**, 861.
118. Schindlebauer and Steininger, *Monats. Chem.,* 1961, **92**, 868.
119. Kabatchnik, Gilyarov and Popov, *J. Gen. Chem. Moscow,* 1962, **32**, 1581.
120. David and Hallam, *J. Chem. Soc.,* 1966A, 1103.
121. David and Hallam, *Spectrochim. Acta,* 1965, **21**, 841.
122. Tice and Powell, *Spectrochim. Acta,* 1965, **21**, 835.
123. Laurence and Berthelot, *Spectrochim. Acta,* 1978, **34A**, 1127.
124. Kreuger and Mettee, *Can. J. Chem.,* 1965, **43**, 2970.
125. Kreuger and Mettee, *Can. J. Chem.,* 1965, **43**, 2888.
126. Bellamy and Mayo, *J. Phys. Chem.,* 1976, **80**, 1217.
127. Dobbie and Straughan, *Spectrochim. Acta,* 1971, **27A**, 255.
128. Oki and Iwamura *Bull. Chem. Soc. Japan,* 1959, **32**, 950.
129. Eddy, Showell and Zell, *J. Amer. Oil Chem. Soc.,* 1963, **40**, 92.
130. Aaron and Rader, *J. Amer. Chem. Soc.,* 1963, **85**, 3046.
131. Aaron, Ferguson and Rader, *J. Amer. Chem. Soc.,* 1967, **89**, 1413.
132. Ditter and Luck, *Bunsenges Phys. Chem.,* 1969, **73**, 526.
133. Piccolini and Winstein, *Tetrahedron Letters,* 1959, **4**.
134. Van der Maas and Lutz, *Spectrochim. Acta,* 1974, **30A**, 2005.
135. Lutz and Van der Maas, *Spectrochim. Acta,* 1978, **34A**, 915.
136. Perttilia, Murto and Halonen, *Spectrochim. Acta,* 1978, **34A**, 469.
137. Kreuger, Jan and Weiser, *J. Mol. Structure,* 1970, **5**, 375.
138. Murto, Kivinen, Edelmann and Hassinen, *Spectrochim. Acta,* 1975, **31A**, 479.
139. Murto, Kivinen, Vitala and Hyomaki, *Spectrochim. Acta,* 1973, **29A**, 1121.
140. Murto, Kivinen, Manninen and Perttilia, *Spectrochim. Acta,* 1975, **31A**, 217.
141. Wilson, *Spectrochim. Acta,* 1974, **30A**, 2141.
142. Green, Harrison and Kynaston, *Spectrochim. Acta,* 1972, **28A**, 33.
143. Guilleme, Chabanel and Wojtkowiak, *Spectrochim. Acta,* 1971, **27A**, 2355.
144. de Klein and Plesman, *Spectrochim. Acta,* 1972, **28A**, 673.
145. Hadzi, Jan and Ocvirk, *Spectrochim. Acta,* 1969, **25A**, 97.
146. Rosengren and Pimentel, *J. Chem. Phys.,* 1965, **43**, 507.
147. Mathis, Martino and Lattes, *Spectrochim. Acta,* 1974, **30A**, 713.
148. Martino, Mathis, Imberlin and Lattes, *Spectrochim. Acta,* 1974, **30A**, 741.
149. Baldock and Karritzky, *J. Chem. Soc. B.,* 1968, 1470.
150. Mathis, Barthelat, Kraemer, Navech and Mathis, *Spectrochim. Acta,* 1973, **29A**, 63.
151. Barthelat, Mathis, Bousquet, Navech and Mathis, *Spectrochim. Acta,* 1973, **29A**, 79.
152. Verma, *Spectrochim. Acta,* 1971, **27A**, 2433.
153. Wolff, Horn and Rollar, *Spectrochim. Acta,* 1973, **29A**, 1835.
154. Gamer and Wolff, *Spectrochim. Acta,* 1973, **29A**, 129.
155. Brownlee, DiStephano and Topsom, *Spectrochim. Acta,* 1975, **31A**, 1685.
156. Bellamy and Pace, *Spectrochim. Acta,* 1971, **28A**, 1869.
157. Wolf and Ludwig, *J. Chem. Phys,* 1972, **56**, 5278.
158. Butt and Topsom, *Spectrochim. Acta,* 1978, **34A**, 975.
159. Mathis, in *Structure et proprietes moleculaires,* Vol. VII, p. 434, Ed. Masson, Paris, 1970.
160. Brink and Bayles, *Spectrochim. Acta,* 1974, **30A**, 835.
161. King, *Spectrochim. Acta,* 1972, **28A**, 165.
162. Walter and Winkler, *Spectrochim. Acta,* 1977, **33A**, 205.
163. Kreuger and Jan, *Can. J. Chem.,* 1970, **48**, 3227.
164. Kreuger and Jan, *Can. J. Chem.,* 1970, **48**, 3236.
165. Hallam and Jones, *J. Mol. Structure,* 1970, **5**, 1.
166. Cutmore and Hallam, *Spectrochim. Acta,* 1969, **25A**, 1767.

167. Hallam and Jones, *J. Mol. Structure,* 1968, **1**, 425.
168. Klein and Plesman, *Spectrochim. Acta,* 1972, **28A**, 673.
169. Klein, *Spectrochim. Acta,* 1972, **28A**, 687.
170. Dollish, Fateley and Bentley, *Characteristic Raman Frequencies of Organic Compounds,* Wiley, New York, 1974, p. 47.
171. Titov, *J. Mol. Structure,* 1973, **19**, 301.
172. Gotze, and Garbe, *Spectrochim. Acta,* 1979, **35A**, 461.
173. Vinkler and Walter, *Spectrochim. Acta,* 1979, **35A**, 367.

5

Carbonyl Frequencies

5.1. Introduction

This is the most intensively studied of all group frequencies. Carbonyl absorptions are sensitive to both chemical and physical effects, and due allowance must be made for both in assessing the likely position of vCO in a given structure. It seems that under standardized solvent conditions, and in the absence of hydrogen bonding, the chemical effects predominate, provided that the carbonyl bond angle remains close to 120°. This has led to many useful generalizations relating changes in vCO to changes in other properties such as Hammett σ values, half-wave potentials, ionization potentials and the like. While they are often very useful, such relationships are best applied within the limited range of compounds on which they are based, and should not be used indiscriminately with compounds of widely different structure.

Many factors are involved in determining the precise frequency of a given carbonyl group X_2CO. These include not only those, such as inductive, resonance and field effects, which alter the force constant of the CO bond but also physical factors, such as mass and angle effects, vibrational coupling and changes in the force constants of the adjacent bonds. Phase changes, solvent effects and hydrogen bonding also play a significant part in determining the final frequency. In the following discussion these various factors are considered separately, but it must be realized that in practice the ultimate frequency is determined by the resultant of all of them. It is only in rare cases that one can assign the whole of a frequency shift to any single cause. Indeed, many of these effects cannot be studied in isolation, and changes in the X substituent which lead to alterations in kCO will inevitably be accompanied by changes in mass, in the C—X force constants and possibly also by changes in the bond angles. While our present understanding of the situation is usually sufficient to enable an intelligent guess to be made of the likely frequency range of a specific carbonyl group, it is still desirable to compare the molecule in question with some others of closely similar structure. For this reason extensive tables have been included which give measured vCO values for various X and Y substituents. In the sections which follow the discussion of the factors which influence group frequencies, and the recent literature on the various carbonyl types is reviewed and discussed.

5.2. Mass effects

Both the carbon and oxygen atoms of the carbonyl group move during the vibration, and they have nearly equal amplitudes. Alterations in the mass of either by isotopic substitution must therefore lead to a frequency change. This is well substantiated in practice. Karabatsos [1] has listed the CO frequencies of di-isopropyl ketone and its analogues in which the carbonyl carbon atom is ^{13}C or the oxygen atom ^{18}O. The first changes νCO from 1712 to 1675 cm^{-1}. This is almost exactly the calculated shift for the simple case in which no account is taken of the mass of the remainder of the molecule. However, this does not imply that νCO is essentially a diatomic vibration, as this result is equally consistent with Halford's [2] calculation that νCO is composed of 74 per cent of the diatomic mode and 26 per cent of νC—C. This latter view is supported by the shifts which result from ^{18}O substitution. In the *iso*-propyl ketone this is 31 cm^{-1}, and Halman and Pinchas [3] report similar shifts in ^{18}O substituted benzophenone (29 cm^{-1}). However, instances of this kind of isotopic substitution are uncommon, and much greater interest attaches to the problem of the changes of mass of the substituent groups. This situation has been explored theoretically by many workers [2, 4–6], notably by Halford [2], Overend and Scherer [4] and Bratoz [5]. Initially one considers the hypothetical situation, parallel to that of isotopic substitution, in which the masses of the X substituents of the X$_2$CO molecule are varied systematically from one to infinity without any alterations in the strengths of the X—C or CO bonds. In this simplified situation, which is not, of course, realizable in practice, one finds that the mass effect operates primarily to change the frequency of the νC—X stretching mode. Initially with a mass of unity this frequency is very much higher than νCO, but by the time the mass has risen to 12 it is very much lower. At some intermediate values these frequencies approach each other, and interaction occurs following the no-crossing rule. The frequencies are then mixed, and in this range neither can profitably be associated with νC—X or νCO, as neither of the upper roots of the secular equation can justifiably be identified with separate modes. This situation has already been discussed in the case of the X—C≡N system, and the only additional feature is that some dependence of the frequencies on the XCX angle must now be expected. The results are illustrated diagrammatically in Fig. 5.1, which is based on some simplified calculations by Whiffen. This shows very clearly the effects of both mass and angle changes.

It will be seen that changes of mass above a value of about 12 have so small an effect upon νCO that they may well be ignored. However, a small but real mass effect is to be expected on passing from aldehydes to ketones, while in

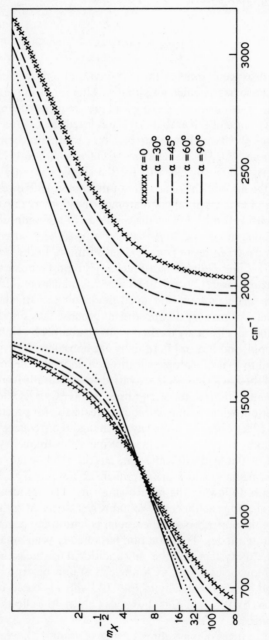

Figure 5.1. Variations in X—C and C=O stretching frequencies with mass and with angle α in

deuterated aldehydes, where the coupling is extensive, more substantial shifts are to be expected. In practice, one does not find that aldehydes absorb at lower frequencies than the corresponding ketones, as these calculations would suggest, but this is simply because it is not in reality possible to change the mass of X from 1 to 12 without at the same time altering the force constant of the C—X link. Other effects then come into play which will be discussed later. It would seem that these are sufficiently large to offset the fall in frequency that would otherwise occur.

In general, these theoretical predictions are borne out in practice, so that, for example, there is little change in νCO when the ^{14}N atom of benzamide is replaced by ^{15}N [7, 238]. The suggestion has been made that the low carbonyl frequency of di-*tert*-butyl ketone is due to some mass effect [8], but this seems unlikely, and the change probably originates largely in steric effects, which lead to a change in the CCC angle. Some interesting small shifts occur when a methyl group in the vicinity of the carbonyl is deuterated, and this has similarly been ascribed by some workers to a mass effect. Thus, deuteration of the carbomethoxy group in esters leads to a small shift of νCO to lower frequencies [9, 10, 12], and this also occurs when an α-methyl group is deuterated, as in acetic acid monomers [11] or in CD_3COOCH_3 [10]. However, no changes occur when an α-methylene group is deuterated [12] or on the replacement of OH by OD in acid monomers [11]. It seems almost certain that these are not true mass effects but that they arise from some small coupling between νCD in the deuterated methyl compounds and νCO, which is probably sufficiently close to νCD for this to occur. No similar effect is found on the complete deuteration of acetic acid dimer, but in this case the lowering of νCO due to coupling is offset by the weaker hydrogen bonds of the deuterated system. Deuteration of the methyl group alone does lead to the expected fall [11].

5.3. Frequency interaction effects

Closely allied to the mass effects which arise when the mass of the substituent lies between 2 and 12 are those interactions which result from the presence close to the carbonyl of a bond of similar absorption frequency and of a symmetry which allows it to interact. The result is then exactly similar to the repulsion effects illustrated in Fig. 5.1. The extreme case is that of two identical carbonyl groups such as occur in symmetrical anhydrides, each of which would be expected to absorb at the same frequency. In fact, as is well known, two bands appear on either side of the expected mean position. These can be assigned as symmetric and anti-symmetric modes. As will be seen later, the impact of such effects is very dependent upon the geometry of the system. However, it must be admitted that a number of problems still remain. It is very surprising that the coupling between the *trans* carbonyl groups of biacetyl is apparently so small (7 cm^{-1} as evidenced by the difference between the infrared and Raman frequencies [276], whereas the coupling of even β diketones gives a separation of 20 cm^{-1} and acetic anhydride gives a difference of 69 cm^{-1}. Colthup and Orloff [276] have calculated that on the basis of a simple valency force field the separations should be 89 cm^{-1}, 7 cm^{-1}, and 7 cm^{-1} respectively. They show that figures much closer to the observed values can be obtained using interaction constants calculated from molecular orbital theory, but this does not in itself explain why these interaction constants should be so large in some cases. Interactions resulting in frequency splitting can also occur due to the presence of overtones of lower-frequency fundamentals near to the carbonyl frequency. These can become enhanced in intensity due to Fermi resonance, and the positions of both bands can then be affected. This is a relatively uncommon occurrence with the carbonyl absorption, but a number of well-documented instances are known.

5.3.1. Interactions through Fermi resonance

A number of instances are known in which compounds containing only a single carbonyl group show what appear to be multiple carbonyl absorptions. Typical examples are ethylene carbonate (1810 and 1780 cm^{-1}), benzoyl chloride, cyclopentanone and some unsaturated cyclic lactams. The incidence of Fermi resonance in the first of these has been well shown by solvent-dependence studies [13]. In polar solvents with active hydrogen atoms vCO is lowered by association effects, but it is found that as the 1810-cm^{-1} band moves down towards that at 1780 cm^{-1} the interaction is increased and the intensity of the latter grows. At the same time, because of the increased interaction the lowering of vCO is significantly less than would be expected from the simple linear-type solvent relations established for other carbonyl groups. The shifts in the 1780-cm^{-1} band are, of course, much smaller and reflect only the changing incidence of Fermi resonance.

With benzoyl chloride a number of possible explanations for the double carbonyl band have been canvassed, including rotational isomerism, hot bands, intermolecular association, etc. Studies by Josien et al. [14], by Rao [15] and by Jones [18] on the effects of changes of temperature and of solvent now seem to have established clearly that the doubling is due to a Fermi resonance effect. It is noteworthy in this connexion that benzoyl bromide, iodide and fluoride show only single carbonyl bands. With para substituted benzoyl-chlorides there is a considerable variation in the relative intensities and positions of the two bands in the carbonyl region [277, 278]. However, the true carbonyl frequencies after correction for Fermi resonance show only a small sensitivity to the nature of the substituent. Benzaldehyde derivatives are also subject to Fermi resonance effects. Whilst the parent compound has only a single carbonyl band, two or even three bands are shown by many meta and para substituted derivatives [279]. These have been shown to originate in Fermi resonance interactions by the solvent shift method. Cyclopentanone has been similarly studied [16, 17]. In this case the resonance arises from an overtone or combination band involving some vibration of the α-methylene group, as the double band does not appear in 2,2,5,5-tetra-deuterocyclopentanone.

The origins of the multiple bands in some unsaturated lactones are less well established, but it is likely that these also originate in Fermi resonance. $\alpha\beta$-Six-membered ring lactones [18] give bands at 1775–1740 and 1740–1715 cm^{-1}, while $\alpha\beta$-unsaturated five-membered ring lactones [19] show bands at 1790–1777 and 1765–1740 cm^{-1}. Other examples of resonance are the double bands in the carbonyl region of $\alpha\beta$ unsaturated acid chlorides and bromides which have been shown by solvent shifts to originate in Fermi resonance rather than in the presence of two conformers [280], and in some deutero-formates when the C=O band resonates with the C—D out of plane bending mode [281].

5.3.2. Frequency interactions between two carbonyl groups

The extent to which frequency coupling effects between two carbonyl groups occur depends upon a number of factors. These include: (*a*) the proximity of the two groups; (*b*) the angle between the carbonyl groups; and (*c*) the degree to which the individual frequencies approach each other. The first of these is of less importance than the angle between the carbonyl bonds, so that the separation of the bands in cyclic *cis*-1,2-diketones is smaller than in many planar 1,3-dicarbonyl systems. Interaction even persists in 1,4-systems such as the aryl peroxides, in which there is a considerable degree of coplanarity.

The likely incidence of angle effects is self-evident from the fact that carbonyl bonds at right angles to each other are unable to interact, whereas those that are coplanar can do so to a maximum extent. One therefore finds that the extent of the splitting falls off sharply as soon as one begins to depart from a planar system. In many ways this is analogous to the extensive splitting between the symmetric and antisymmetric modes of linear carbon dioxide as compared with the much smaller splitting in the bent sulphur dioxide. The values of the original individual carbonyl frequencies are also important. The further these are apart, the less interaction there will be. In the great majority of organic compounds containing two different carbonyl functions the groups are separated by one or more carbon atoms, and so do not lie in the same plane. This, coupled with the fact that the frequencies are initially different, reduces the interaction so much that each of the two bands can quite properly be assigned to one of the characteristic groups alone. Thus the keto form of acetoacetic ester has two carbonyl bands which can safely be assigned to the individual keto and ester groups. Similarly, a compound such as the diketo form of a 2-aroylcyclohexanone [20] shows two carbonyl bands at the normal positions for saturated and $\alpha\beta$-unsaturated ketones. In contrast, the planar unsymmetric anhydride acetotrifluoroacetic anhydride has two carbonyl bands which can be clearly identified by solvent studies as symmetrical and unsymmetrical modes [21]. Finally, one must consider the relative orientations of the carbonyl dipoles. If the two groups lie in the same plane but have their carbonyl groups aligned in opposite directions there will be no change of dipole moment during the symmetric vibration. In consequence, only a single carbonyl band will appear (the asymmetric mode), despite the fact that extensive vibrational coupling is taking place. The impact of these various factors is best illustrated by the various specific situations discussed below.

(a) 1,3-Dicarbonyl systems, COXCO

Anhydrides. In all anhydrides there is some resonance between the canonical forms (I) and (II), and this is sufficient to hold the COXCO system in a planar configuration. Extensive vibrational interaction then occurs, leading to two carbonyl bands which are normally separated by about 65 cm^{-1}. There is good reason to suppose that the higher of these two frequencies is due to the symmetrical vibration. This is an unusual situation in the infrared, as the antisymmetrical mode usually takes the higher frequency, but a parallel exists in the case of butadiene in which the symmetric C=C stretching mode has a higher frequency than the anti-symmetric vibration.

$$RCO-O-COR \qquad\qquad R-\overset{\overset{\displaystyle O^-}{|}}{\underset{}{C}}=\overset{+}{O}-\overset{\overset{\displaystyle O}{\|}}{C}-R$$

$$\text{(I)} \qquad\qquad\qquad\qquad \text{(II)}$$

In open-chain systems the symmetric band is usually slightly stronger than the other, but an interesting change occurs as one passes to cyclic compounds [21, 23, 62, 209]. As the COOCO group is bent round in a ring the dipole moment change during the symmetric mode is reduced. (In the ultimate case in which the dipoles are oppositely oriented the bands are forbidden in the infrared.) In consequence, cyclic anhydrides can be distinguished from open-chain systems by the intensity reversal which occurs in the carbonyl bands. It is even possible to differentiate between five- and six-membered rings, as the intensity of the higher-frequency band is further reduced in the former and now appears as a relatively weak absorption compared with the strong peak due to the anti-symmetric mode. In agreement with these assignments one finds that the reverse situation holds in the Raman spectra, in which the higher-frequency band of the cyclic anhydrides is much the more intense.

The band separation of about 65 cm^{-1} is remarkably consistent but exceptions do occur. For example in the maleic anhydrides, the band separation ranges from 59 cm^{-1} in the mono-bromo compound to 81 cm^{-1} in the mono-methyl derivative [282, 283]. However, in these there is extensive coupling with the C=C frequency so that variations are to be expected.

The size of the splitting, as compared with the 1 : 2-diketones remains something of a puzzle, as do the high frequencies and intensities. Konarski [284] has suggested that there is a pulsed vibration between the carbonyl groups and the lone pair electrons of the central oxygen atom, which leads to a considerable electron flow during the antisymmetric mode. The fact that the splitting is much reduced in thiophthallic anhydride which absorbs at 1742 and 1707 cm^{-1} is consistent with this [285]. Ernstbrunner [367] has offered an alternative explanation involving a combination of mechanical coupling and Fermi resonance to explain the size of the splitting, but in view of the fact that the splitting is much greater than in *cis* alpha diketones, it does seem probable that the major contribution comes from electronic rather than mechanical coupling, and is in some way connected with the electron flow which must take place during the antisymmetric vibration.

Imides, CONHCO. These systems have not been as fully studied as the anhydrides, but they would also be expected to have a planar structure and therefore to show twin carbonyl absorptions. In cyclic systems this is certainly so, and their behaviour is exactly parallel to that of the anhydrides. Phthalimides [24] show two carbonyl bands, of which the higher-frequency band is of weaker intensity. Isocyanate dimers [25] and cyanuric acid behave similarly. In aromatic isocyanate dimers [25] the extreme case is realized in which the direction of the carbonyl dipoles is directly opposed, as in (III). The higher-frequency band then vanishes as expected. The band splitting is generally less than in the anhydrides, being only 20–25 cm^{-1} in the glutarimides [286], but in conjugated compounds such as 3 : 5-dioxypyrrolizidine the coupling is increased to give a separation of 82 cm^{-1} [287]. This is generally in accord with expectations. However, and interesting anomaly

$$C_6H_5-N-C=O$$
$$O=C-N-C_6H_5$$
(III)

occurs in open-chain compounds. These have a *trans/trans* structure with parallel carbonyl groups as the most stable structure in the crystal, and as the CONHCO system is essentially planar one would expect extensive coupling as with the anhydrides. Early studies suggested that there might be two carbonyl bands [26] but more recent work has shown that only one can be clearly identified [288 289]. In dipropionamide for example the carbonyl band is at 1730 cm^{-1}, and a second band at 1670 cm^{-1} has been clearly shown to exhibit parallel dichroism and cannot therefore be a second carbonyl band. Two carbonyl bands are shown by the *cis/trans* conformations which can exist in solution. However, even in these it is not clear that coupling makes any substantial contribution to the frequency difference. The *cis* carbonyl is known to be hydrogen bonded whilst the *trans* is not and so should absorb at a lower frequency in any case. A potential energy distribution obtained from a normal coordinate study of *cis/trans* diacetamide shows that most of the energy lies in the separate vibrations of the individual bonds and that the coupling terms are relatively small [290].

`   In line with these findings is the report that the N-formylacetamides show two bands which correspond closely to the expected values for the two different types of carbonyl present and do not appear to show coupling [287]. The absence of coupling in such systems raises a difficult problem for which we have as yet no explanation. However, it must cast doubts on the pulsed vibration theory used by Konarski [284] to explain the behaviour of the anhydrides, as the same mechanism should operate in the other cyclic imides.

(b) *1,3-Diketo systems*, COCH$_2$CO, *etc.*

In acetylacetone in the diketo form the two carbonyl groups do not lie in the same plane. Coupling is therefore very small, and although the structure of the band has been resolved by Mecke and Funck [27], the splitting is small. The difference between the symmetric and antisymmetric frequencies is only 20 cm^{-1}. This is always the situation with symmetrical 1,3-diketones, and when two bands occur in unsymmetrical compounds they can safely be assigned to the individual carbonyl groups. However, the situation is different in cyclic systems, in which there is a much greater tendency for the carbonyl groups to lie in one plane. The effect is particularly noticeable in compounds such as (IV), (V) and (VI), in which the presence of the double bond induces coplanarity. In all of these compounds two carbonyl bands appear separated by 30–40 cm^{-1}.

Coupled vibrations are also observed in cyclic malonates [30] and in cyclohexane-1,3-diones [31]. Abramovitch [32] and Klein [291] reported multiple bands in some open chain malonates which they ascribed to the presence of rotational isomers.

5.3.3. 1,4-Dicarbonyl compounds

With two intervening atoms the degree of coupling between the carbonyl groups is very limited. Only in the peroxides, which are planar and in many ways parallel to the anhydrides, is this effect found. The degree of separation of the two bands is reduced (about 25 cm^{-1}), and as would be expected from the relative angles of the carbonyl dipoles, the higher-frequency band is less intense than the other. The occurrence of vibrational coupling in these compounds has been clearly demonstrated by solvent studies [22]. Some instances of 1,4-carbonyl interactions in esters have been reported by Mazur and Sondheimer [33], but these are of a wholly different kind. There is no vibrational coupling, and the splitting originates in field effects (see later) which arise when the two carbonyl oxygen atoms are sufficiently close together. The perturbation is well shown in compounds such as 16,22-dicarbonyl steroids.

5.3.4. 1,2-Dicarbonyl compounds

Most 1 : 2-dicarbonyl compounds occur in the *trans* conformation so that the C=O bond would be expected to couple strongly giving single bands in the infrared and Raman spectra at widely different frequencies. Surprisingly, this does not always happen and in the diketones and diacid halides the coupling is virtually negligible. Thus biacetyl which is known to exist only in the *trans* form shows C=O bands at 1715 cm^{-1} (infrared) and 1720 cm^{-1} (Raman), whilst the *cis-ortho*quinones also show only a single band in the infrared. Other 1 : 2-dialkylketones absorb in the 1720–1700 cm^{-1} range when in the *trans* form, and only show evidence of multiple carbonyl absorptions when heated to high temperatures [292]. Benzil is a special case in which the carbonyl groups take an azimuthal angle of 90° to each other, and this does show a double band in the infrared.

The oxalyl halides also exist mainly in the *trans* form, and the carbonyl coupling is again very small [293, 294]. Oxalyldifluoride for example absorbs at 1853 cm^{-1} in the infrared (solid) and at 1867 cm^{-1} in the Raman (liquid). Not only is the coupling minimal in these two series, but there appears to be very little evidence of any conjugation between the carbonyl groups. In biacetyl the frequency is that of a saturated ketone, and the alkyl and aryl ketone frequencies show little evidence of any lowering as a result of the carbonyl/carbonyl conjugation. Similarly the frequency of oxalyl difluoride is essentially normal.

Alkyl and aryl oxamides also take the *trans* form except in a few special cases, but now there is evidence of coupling and the carbonyl frequencies are different in the infrared and Raman. With oxamide itself the symmetric and antisymmetric bands are at 1706 and 1655 cm^{-1} [295] but the differences in the N-dialkyloxamides are smaller, varying from 26–47 cm^{-1}. In N-diaryloxamides the differences are still smaller, in the range 20–30 cm^{-1} [296]. There is no obvious reason why there should be variations of this kind, or indeed why the oxamides should show coupling while the diketones do not.

In contrast to this the oxalate esters in solution show two bands due to the presence of rotational isomers. *cis*dimethyloxalate has two bands [34] as has diethyloxalate which absorbs at 1770 and 1745 cm^{-1}. Diphenyloxalate has a single C=O band at 1776 cm^{-1} in the solid corresponding to the antisymmetric mode of the *trans* form, but in solution two bands appear at 1792 and 1763 cm^{-1} when both *cis* and *trans* forms are present [296]. Here again the frequencies show no evidence of any conjugation effects between the two carbonyl bonds.

In methylene oxalate, in which the molecule is locked in the *cis* form the coupling is more evident and this absorbs at 1862 and 1797 cm^{-1} [297, 298].

5.4. The effects of changes in bond angles and in the strengths of the adjacent bonds

(*a*) *Cyclic systems*

During the vibration of the carbonyl group both atoms move with almost equal amplitudes. In order to accommodate the movement of the carbon atom some compression or deformation of the adjacent C—X bonds must take place. A coupling effect then comes into play which can lead to a change in vCO without any corresponding change in the carbonyl force constant. The coupling is, however, of a different kind from that discussed in Section 5.3, and does not originate in the fact that the CO and CX frequencies approach one another.

The incidence of this effect is best seen in cyclic systems in which the XCOX bond angle can be varied systematically. These also have the advantage that the whole of the movement of the carbon atom must be accommodated by the compression of the CX bonds which cannot now deform. Calculations of the effects of bond-angle changes in C—CO—C systems have been made by Bratoz [5], Halford [2], Overend and Scherer [4] and others. These indicate that vCO will rise by 1.5–2 cm^{-1} for each degree by which the CCC bond angle falls below 120°, and will fall by a corresponding amount for each degree by which the bond angle is opened out. This is sufficient to account for the whole of the carbonyl frequency rise which occurs on passing from six-membered rings to rings of smaller sizes. It should be noted that this interpretation is supported by the fact that there is no corresponding change in vSO or vPO on passing from six- to five-membered ring systems. This is to be expected because the sulphur and phosphorus atoms have a much smaller amplitude than has the corresponding carbon atom, and coupling effects are therefore minimized. If the changes in the carbonyl frequencies originated primarily in hybridization changes one would expect to find similar effects in the SO and PO compounds.

However, it is not possible to alter the CCC bond angle without at the same time altering the hybridization of the carbon orbits directed towards the oxygen atom. A reduction of the bond angle below 120° would be expected to increase the *s* content of this orbital and thereby shorten the CO bond length.

Many chemists have preferred to interpret the changes of vCO with ring size in these terms. Hall and Zbinden [36] have tabulated extensive data on cyclic systems, from which they conclude that the observed frequencies show a fair correlation with reaction rates and that hybridization changes are a major factor in the frequency changes. Deschamps [37] reaches a similar conclusion through a comparison of vCO values in fulvenic ketones with bond indices computed by a linear combination of atomic orbitals, although he also points to some discrepancies which cannot be accounted for in this way.

The issue is very similar to that posed by the frequency rises of the C=C vibration as the ring size diminishes. However, in this last case there are also data available on the endocyclic systems, and these show very clearly that the angle effects rather than the changes in hybridization dominate the frequency changes. The frequency rise on passing from *cyclo*butene to *cyclo*propene, is to be expected from the increased coupling whereas hybridization changes should lead to a frequency fall.

Some further support for this is obtainable from basicity measurements on the carbonyl groups. Basicity is measured by the frequency shifts of polar XH groups on forming hydrogen bonds to the carbonyl, and it is found that the changes which follow alterations with ring size are extremely small [38]. This suggests that the electronic make up of the C=O bond does not change with ring size. However, it must be admitted that this is not a decisive argument as it is found that the carbonyl basicity does not change very much in the series acetone/acetophenone/benzophenone in which there is undoubtedly a change in the carbonyl force constant. Nevertheless it would seem that coupling rather than hybridization changes is the controlling factor in ring systems and in open chain ketones in which the CCC angle is increased by steric effects [39].

This is not to suggest that hybridization effects can be wholly ignored. Table 5.1 is derived from that of Hall and Zbinden [36] and lists δvCO values for various systems in different sizes of ring. It will be seen that the shifts on

Table 5.1. Frequency shifts of vCO in various cyclic systems as compared with an acyclic analogue (δv values in cm^{-1})

Compound type	Monocyclic				Bicyclic		
	4	5	6	7	5	6	7
Lactams		+31	−13	−15	+37	−1	−29
N-Methyl lactams		+46		0			
Lactones	+83	+40	+5	−8	+29	+4	
Carbonates		+72	+31			+16	+7
Ketones	+69	+30	0	−10	+35		
Ureas		+23	+23	−6		+17	
Imides		+36	+32			+18	
N-Methyl imides		+5	−1			−4	
N-Acetyl lactams		+37	−7	−7	+38	+11	
Urethanes		+52	+12			−6	−14
Anhydrides		+37	−14			−19	

passing from one size of ring to another are not uniform. This is to be expected, because the C—O bond of carbonates, for example, is stronger than the C—C bonds of ketones. The reduction of bond angle therefore has more impact on vCO in the former case. However, it could equally well be argued that the C—N bond of amides is a strong one due to resonance, and it is probably no less strong than C—O. Nevertheless, the frequency difference between five- and six-membered ring lactams is much the same as in ketones and very different from the carbonates. There are other differences, such as the high frequencies of six-ring ureas and their failure to show a further shift in five-membered rings, which cannot be accounted for simply on the basis of physical coupling effects. In these cases some significant contribution from hybridization effects must also be present.

(b) Open-chain systems

In acyclic carbonyl compounds the bond angles will normally be sufficiently close to 120° to render angle effects effectively constant. However, the recognition that coupling with C—C bonds does occur must imply that a change to some stronger bond such as C—F or to a weaker one such as C—Cl will again alter vCO independently of any force constant change. However, the probable impact of such effects is very difficult to calculate, particularly as the movement of the carbon atom could now be equally well accommodated by a deformation mode. The parallel problem in the case of C=C frequencies has already been discussed.

Some calculations suggest that changes in vCO arising from changes in the strengths of the adjoining bonds could be very substantial. For example, it has been suggested that the whole of the 100-cm^{-1} frequency difference between F_2CO and Cl_2CO is due to the replacement of the strong CF link by the relatively weak C—Cl link [4]. However, it seems unlikely that this is so. Basicity measurements with pyrrole or phenol as donors show that the basicities of saturated carbonyl compounds vary in a regular way with vCO. This contrasts with the corresponding results for cyclic systems and indicates that the frequency shifts are accompanied by systematic changes in the carbonyl force constants, and therefore have their origins largely in chemical forces. The residual effects due to coupling appear to be small.

This conclusion is supported by the observed order of carbonyl frequencies in the CH_3COX series. If the frequencies were determined purely by the strengths of the CX bonds the expected order would be $F > CH_3 > Cl > Br$. On the other hand, chemical considerations based on the relative inductive effects would predict the observed order $F > Cl > Br > CH_3$. There would need to be entirely disproportionate inductive effects in acetyl chloride (vCO 1820 cm^{-1}) if coupling effects were also extensive, as the latter would be expected to result in a considerably lower frequency than that of acetone. It would be foolish to suppose that coupling effects can be entirely ignored in all open-chain compounds, and it is probable that some part of the exceptionally high νCO value of F_2CO is due to the very strong CF bonds. Nevertheless, it would seem that these effects are generally very much smaller than the chemical effects which arise from changes in the force constant of the carbonyl link.

5.5. Chemical effects

Under this heading we will consider those factors which lead to a change in the electronic distribution within the carbonyl link. We are therefore concerned with changes in νCO which arise from real changes in the force constant. Conjugation effects which do change the C=O force constants due to delocalisation can also lead to additional frequency changes due to coupling effects with the C=C mode. The contributions from the two different factors are not easy to separate and conjugation will therefore be discussed under chemical effects. Changes due to hydrogen bonding, which also involve some change in kCO, will be treated separately.

Chemical effects are usually classified as inductive, resonance (or mesomeric) and field effects, and in general the behaviour of a given carbonyl frequency with alterations in the X substituent can be satisfactorily accounted for in qualitative terms through the impact of these effects. If the X substituent is replaced by one having a greater electron-attracting power the formal positive charge on the oxygen atom is increased. This reduces the disparity between the electron-attracting powers of the carbon and oxygen atoms, and the polarity of the bond is reduced. As ionic radii are greater than covalent radii, this results in a contraction of the bond and in a rise in νCO. This is in line with the observation that as carbonyl frequencies rise the oxygen atoms become less basic (i.e. less ionic) [38, 214]. One also finds that compounds with high values of νCO show little sensitivity to solvent effects or to phase changes (so far as νCO is concerned), whereas compounds with low carbonyl frequencies show considerable sensitivity.

The inductive effect operates primarily on the σ bonds. The resonance effect, in contrast, is primarily concerned with the degree of delocalization of the π electrons of the CO bond. It is obvious that in conjugated systems the delocalization of these electrons will weaken the CO bond and lengthen it so that the frequency will fall. A parallel effect occurs when the X substituent carries a suitably oriented lone pair of electrons. Thus in amides the low frequencies found for νCO are attributed to a substantial contribution from the canonical form $\overset{+}{\diagdown N}=C-\overset{-}{O}$, which offsets the otherwise strong inductive effect of the nitrogen atom. In most cases both of these effects are operating simultaneously as, for example, in acids, esters and amides, and it is therefore convenient to consider them together. Field effects can be treated separately; they do not operate along the bonds but directly across intramolecular space. There is little doubt that these also produce real changes in the electronic environment and in the carbonyl force constant. Dewar [41, 42] prefers to regard all those changes previously ascribed to inductive effects as arising instead through direct polar interactions across space.

5.5.1. Inductive and resonance effects

The combination of these two effects provides a very satisfactory basis for the qualitative understanding of the behaviour of most carbonyl frequencies following alterations in their substituents. The exceptions are those cases in which coupling or angle effects occur and the special cases of field effects which will be discussed later. Frequencies which are higher than those of acetone in the same medium can be regarded as examples of compounds in which the inductive effect outweighs any resonance, whereas the reverse is true of lower frequencies. This interpretation is applicable not only to simple cases, such as the high frequency of acetyl chloride or the low frequency of acetamide, but also to complex situations. Thus the remarkable carbonyl frequency of N-acetyltetrazole ($1790 \, cm^{-1}$) can be seen to be the logical result of the almost complete suppression of resonance by the competition of the tetrazole ring for the lone-pair electrons of the nitrogen atom [251, 252]. Similarly, the high CO frequencies of vinyl esters as compared with alkyl esters are probably due to the competition between the carbonyl group and the olefinic double bond for the lone-pair electrons of the oxygen atom. The replacement of the double bond by an electron-donating group has, as expected, the opposite effect [189], so that in a compound such as $CH_3COOHgC_6H_5$ the carbonyl frequency falls as low as $1580 \, cm^{-1}$. Similarly, a compound such as 4-thiapyrone can be expected to show a particularly low carbonyl frequency because of the very enhanced resonance which results from the interaction of the sulphur electrons with the ring. The fact that this is so can be well shown by comparing the carbonyl frequencies of this compound and of the corresponding sulphone, in which the ability of the sulphur atom to donate electrons to the ring has been eliminated. The former absorbs at $1600 \, cm^{-1}$ and the latter at $1667 \, cm^{-1}$, which is a normal frequency for an $\alpha\beta$, $\alpha'\beta'$-unsaturated ketone.

With a postulate of competitive effects working in opposition in this way it is, of course, possible to account for any observed frequency, and these observations do not in themselves prove that the proposed mechanisms are true. General support is given by the fact that the frequency shifts are always in the directions that our chemical knowledge of the impact of these effects would lead us to expect. However, the main basis for these generalizations is the quantitative relationships which have been found in many cases between shifts in vCO and changes in some other property which is accepted as arising from changes in inductive and resonance effects. Many such relationships have been described, and they have been reviewed by Bellamy [43] and by Rao [44]. The commonest examples are in aromatic compounds, in which vCO values of acids, esters, amides, etc., have been correlated with good precision with the Hammett σ values of substituents in the *meta* or *para* positions. In earlier studies it was normal to seek a correlation between the frequencies and simple Hammett σ values, but more recent studies have used the dual parameter equation $v - v_0 = \rho_1\sigma_1 + \rho_R\sigma_R$ in which the inductive and resonance components are separated. The σ_R values used can also be varied from amongst σ_R, σ_R^+, σ_R^- or σ_R^0. Laurence and Wojtkowiak [299] have demonstrated many correlations based on this principle. The overall relationships have been reviewed by Brownlee *et al.* [300] who conclude that in the *meta* substituted series the discrimination between these various substitution constants is not important but that in the *para* substituted series the best relationships are realised using σ_R^+. They have also shown that relationships using σ_R are valid in cases in which the aromatic ring is separated from the carbonyl by a double bond, or a triple bond showing that the substituent effects are relayed through the conjugated system. Relationships with Hammett values can even be realised in aliphatic systems in which the carbonyl group is conjugated, and in which the substituents attract or donate electrons to the double bond in the same way that they do with an aromatic ring. Thus 3-substituted *cyclo*hex-2-ene-1-ones correlate in this way [301].

Other properties that have been related to vCO values include the pKα values of acids [50], ionization potentials, half-wave potentials, electronegativities, pKβ values [214] and Taft σ^* values. Relationships with actual reaction rates have also been described, as in the work of Otting [252] on acetyl heterocyclic compounds. However, the very multiplicity of these relationships has caused this evidence to be questioned [38, 43], if only because these different physical properties show little quantitative agreement among themselves as measures of inductive and resonance effects. If, therefore, one accepts a quantitative correlation with any one of these as evidence for the relation between shifts of vCO and chemical effects one must at the same time reject all the others. This difficulty is primarily a problem of chemistry itself and is not limited to spectroscopy, but it does seem that in induction, for example, the relative effectiveness of individual atoms or groups is not a unique property of those atoms or groups which can be carried over into any environment. Indeed, it would seem that they can be altered, at least to some degree, by the environment in which they are placed. The most useful correlations seem to be those with the Taft σ^* values particularly when these are split into σ_1 and σ_R components in a dual parameter approach. Brownlee and Topsom [302] have reviewed the literature and discussed the statistical significance of the data. As with the Hammett relationship, the best correlations are obtained with the dual parameter system using σ_R^+ values. The Taft values correlate well with the carbonyl frequencies in cases in which the variable substituent is on the α methylene group, but, as with many other systems the correlation is much less reliable when the changing X group is directly attached to the vibrating group (i.e. to the C=O).

There have also been some interesting attempts to bridge the gap between the aromatic Hammett σ and the aliphatic Taft σ^* relationships. Peters [303, 304] has developed a linear free energy relationship of the type $v = v_0 + \rho\gamma^+$ where the group constants γ^+ are characteristic of the entire group, aromatic or alkyl. The γ^+ values for aromatic substituents are the same as the σ^+ constants, whilst that for hydrogen is determined as 2.53. This enables the carbonyl frequency of aromatic compounds to be predicted with reasonable precision from the observed frequency of the corresponding aliphatic aldehyde, and vice versa.

A second and more detailed approach is that of Seth, Paul and Duyse [305]. This uses a group electronegativity concept whereby the carbonyl frequency is proportional to the substituent constants according to the equation $vCO = 1583 + 38.2 \, (X(R') + X(R'')) \, cm^{-1}$. These group electronegativity values $X(R)$ are then related to the Taft σ^* values in aliphatics by the expression $0.482\sigma = X(R) - X(Me)$, and to the Hammett values in aromatics by the expression $\beta\sigma/10 = X(R) - X$ (phenyl). The slope β depends upon the type of substitution (*meta* or *para*) and on the nature of the substituents (electron withdrawing or donating). Although this approach does include some empirical terms it does correlate with some 450 different corbonyl frequencies and it allows the prediction of $vC{=}O$ values with reasonable accuracy. The standard errors found, range from $7.55 \, cm^{-1}$ for acid halides to $1.76 \, cm^{-1}$ for benzoic esters.

These various correlations between the carbonyl frequencies and reactivity parameters do provide a good deal of support for the concept that $vC{=}O$ values are determined by inductive and resonance parameters by showing that there is a quantitative as well as a qualitative relationship. However, it must be recognised that the existence of these relationships is not evidence that there is no coupling of the carbonyl vibration. In a series of esters, for example, the vCO values will relate closely to the rates of hydrolysis, but within this series the bond angles, and the masses and nature of the substituents, are also constant, so that it is not surprising that any changes in vCO can be correlated wholly with chemical factors. It must not be assumed that the frequency shifts which occur, for example, on passing from an acid chloride to an ester can equally be regarded as arising wholly from chemical forces.

However, some studies on the basicity of carbonyl compounds do offer some reassurance on this point. If one is seeking to establish that the shifts of vCO on passing from one type of compound to another are primarily related to changes in the electron distribution within the bond (i.e. to chemical effects) rather than to coupling effects, it is necessary to look for some independent measure of the electron distribution which can be applied to all types of carbonyl compounds. The most suitable possibilities are the ionization potentials of the oxygen atoms or their basicities. The former have been studied by Cook [46, 47] but have disadvantages in conjugated systems, in which it is often difficult to distinguish between the ionizations of the electrons of the oxygen atom and of the double bond. The basicity measurements can be easily made either through the lowering of vCO on the attachment of Lewis acids, such as BF_3, or by measurements of the strengths of hydrogen bonds formed by standard proton donors [38, 48, 49].

If a wide range of different carbonyl compounds are separately dissolved in an inert solvent and pyrrole [43] or phenol [48] is added in small amounts, hydrogen bonds are formed between the OH or NH groups and the carbonyl oxygen atom. The frequency shift of the XH bond provides a comparative measure of the polarity of the carbonyl link. These values can then be compared with the values of vCO for the unassociated compounds. If the latter are truly dependent only on chemical factors there should be a smooth relationship between the two. It is found in practice that such a smooth-curve relationship does exist, both for associations with phenol and with pyrrole. However, certain reservations are necessary. Compounds with abnormal angles show changed carbonyl frequencies for the reasons discussed earlier. No alterations in the CO force constants are involved, so that it is not surprising to find that the basicities do not change significantly in parallel with the alterations in vCO [38, 49]. More surprising at first sight is the fact that conjugated carbonyl compounds also fail to obey the simple frequency/basicity relationship just described. There can be little doubt that the lowering of vCO on conjugation is due to real change in the carbonyl force constant, but this is not reflected in the basicity, which, for example, remains essentially unchanged throughout the series acetone/acetophenone/benzophenone. It has been suggested that this is due to the fact that the basicity measurements are determined by the state of hybridization of the lone-pair electrons of the oxygen atom, and that this will not necessarily change as a result of the delocalization of π electrons in a plane at right angles. This emphasizes the point that a single carbonyl frequency, or force constant, is not in itself sufficient to characterize uniquely the electron distribution within the bond. Two compounds may well have the same carbonyl force constants and frequencies, but in one case we may have vCO raised by a small inductive effect, and in the other altered by a much larger inductive effect, which is partially offset by some resonance. The frequencies would then be the same, but the electronic configurations different.

The impact of conjugation on the carbonyl frequency varies with the polarity of the conjugating group, and is much reduced when the latter has its dipole in the same direction as the carbonyl itself. In biacetyl for example the mean C=O frequency is 1718 cm^{-1} in the liquid state, indicating that there is neither any significant delocalisation nor coupling. Similarly the carbonyl frequency of carbonyl cyanide is 1712 cm^{-1}, whereas that of diethynylketone is 1669 cm^{-1} in the vapour state [306]. It would seem that the opposition of the dipoles prevents or at least much reduces delocalization in the carbonyl cyanide.

The impact on the frequency of conjugation by an acetylenic triple bond, a *trans* olefinic bond or an aromatic or pyridine ring is essentially the same in all cases. Even a *cyclo*propyl group has a closely similar effect and cyclopropyl-ketone absorbs at $1690\ cm^{-1}$ as compared with acetophenone at $1685\ cm^{-1}$ [307]. *Cyclo*propylpyridylketones absorb close to benzophenones. However, conjugation with a furyl or thieny group leads to greater delocalisation and significantly lower frequencies. Thus 2 : 2'-difuryl ketone absorbs at $1632\ cm^{-1}$ and 2 : 2'-dithienyl ketone at $1615\ cm^{-1}$ [308]. In both cases it has been shown by ultraviolet spectra that this is due to increased conjugation rather than to any other effect.

With $\alpha\beta$ unsaturated compounds the carbonyl frequency varies with the conformation (*s.cis* or *s.trans*) and also with the degree of substitution on the double bond. There has been much discussion on whether these changes originate in differences in coupling or in differences in the degree of delocalisation. With the *s.trans* forms it would seem that the coupling is very small, as only the carbonyl frequency changes on ^{18}O substitution or on hydrogen bonding with proton donors. With *s.cis* compounds however both C=O and C=C frequencies show some sensitivity to solvents, Taylor [309] regards both the C=O and C=C bands in both conformers as in part representing symmetric and antisymmetric modes of the whole system, and points out that the mean of the two frequencies does not change with the conformation. He therefore suggests that the differences arise from greater coupling in the *s.cis* case than in the *s.trans* and do not reflect any alteration in the degree of conjugation. This is almost certainly the correct interpretation, and it is supported by ultraviolet work. However, it is doubtful if there is any significant degree of coupling in the *s.trans* systems. The two rotamers are usually differentiated by the separation of the C=O and C=C bands which is significantly greater in the *s.cis* compounds. However, it must be remembered that the C=C frequency rises as the alkyl substitution on the double bond is increased, and the C=O falls. This is normal behaviour for the C=C bond, but the fall in the carbonyl frequency is unexpected. It is extremely unlikely that this is due to force constant changes and is most likely to arise from a widening out of the carbonyl bond angle due to steric repulsions. Thus an unsubstituted *s.trans* compound can show a carbonyl band at much the same frequency as a fully substituted *s.cis* compound and can have a larger separation of the C=O and C=C bands. However, when comparably substituted compounds are compared the separation in the *s.cis* is invariably greater [310] in ketones. Acrylyl chloride appears to be exceptional in that the *s.trans* form has the higher carbonyl frequency and the greater separation between the C=O and C=C bands. This is unlikely to be due to increased coupling and must arise from some type of dipolar interaction.

The fact that *s.cis* conjugated compounds have normally markedly higher frequencies than the *s.trans* can give rise to confusion in what has been called the negative conjugation effect. For example *NN*-dimethylacetamide absorbs at $1652\ cm^{-1}$ and *NN*-dimethylcrotonamide at $1665\ cm^{-1}$, an apparent rise of 13 cm^{-1} as a result of the conjugation. In reality this is due to the fact that the latter exists in the *s.cis* form in which the carbonyl is raised by the coupling. Any comparison of the ketone or amide with the *s.trans* form will show the normal carbonyl shift due to conjugation. If the remaining hydrogen atom on the double bond of *NN*-dimethylcrotonamide is replaced by a methyl group the resulting conformation is *s.trans* and the carbonyl band then appears at 1633 cm^{-1} [311]. Similar effects are found in alkylstyrylketones with bulky groups which lead to *s.cis* conformations [312].

5.6. Field effects in carbonyl compounds

It is now generally accepted that field effects occur between a carbonyl oxygen atom and another polar atom (usually oxygen or a halogen) which is close to it in intramolecular space. The exact nature of these effects is not known, but they can probably be regarded as simple electrostatic effects which lead to alterations of the polarities of both atoms. In this case they should persist at distances considerably greater than the van der Waals' radii, and there is some limited evidence that this is so [41]. However, the vast majority of recognized examples of this effect involve halogen or oxygen atoms at distances which are sufficiently close to allow the possibility of lone-pair/lone-pair repulsion effects of the type envisaged by Sheppard [51] as being responsible for the *cis* configuration of esters. Such interactions would alter the hybridization of the carbonyl oxygen atom and so change the frequency.

Whatever the mechanism of interaction, solvent studies have shown that a change occurs in the polarity of the carbonyl bond. In cyclic ketones this field effect affords an explanation for the higher *v*CO frequencies of equatorial α-halogen substituted compounds as compared with their axial counterparts. In open-chain ketones with α-halogen atoms the presence of two separate carbonyl bands is consistent with the fact (known from dipole moment studies) that rotational isomers coexist in solution. As will be seen from the detailed discussion below, the response of various kinds of carbonyl groups to the degree of halogen substitution varies considerably. Ketones and esters behave similarly, but acid chlorides are anomalous, in that the highest carbonyl frequency falls as the degree of halogen substitution is increased. In amides the introduction of the first halogen atom has no effect. There is some rise in secondary amides in dilute solution when two halogens are present, but there is only a single band. Similarly substituted tertiary amides, show two bands. These differences can be satisfactorily explained on the basis of simple field effects, but difficulties remain with aldehydes and acids, which show only single carbonyl absorptions, and with thioesters, in which the introduction of α-halogen atoms leads to a second band at lower and not higher frequency. All of these various classes are discussed in more detail below.

Field effects are not limited to halogen interactions, although these form by far the largest class of known examples. Interactions with oxygen atoms are well substantiated, and there is evidence for similar effects with both nitrogen and sulphur. Normally field effects arise from α-polar substituents, but several exceptions are known which involve interactions with groups farther along the chain, although they are not necessarily further removed in intramolecular space. ortho-Substituted aromatic ketones fall into this class, as do the transannular effects described by Leonard. The raised vCO value of esters of the type $RCOOCH_2CF_3$ also suggests a near approach of the fluorine and carbonyl oxygen atoms, made possible by the cis configuration of the ester group.

Some authors have preferred to explain the differing carbonyl frequencies directly in terms of the difference in the degree of coupling that could arise from the different geometry [52]. However, it has been shown that the basicity of the carbonyl group changes smoothly as a function of the frequency, suggesting that there are real changes in the carbonyl force constants. This is to be expected also from the chemistry of these compounds. For example, the strong tendency of halogenated aldehydes and ketones to add water across the carbonyl bond provides evidence of a real change in bond properties. The impact of orbital interaction effects must also be considered, but these seem unlikely to provide a satisfactory alternative explanation. The fact that there is frequently no further rise in the higher carbonyl band on increasing the halogen substitution at the α-carbon atom is a good indication that the part played by inductive effects is small. Further the presence of the very electronegative nitro group in the α-position in nitroacetophenone does not alter the carbonyl frequency from that of the parent compound, presumably because the nitro group is not suitably oriented to produce a field effect.

5.6.1 α-Halogen interactions

(a) Ketones

The original recognition of field effects sprang from the observation that vCO in α-halogenated sterols was raised when the halogen was substituted equatorially but unaffected when the substituent was axial. Since that time very extensive studies have been made on cyclic ketones, and particularly on α-chloro- and bromo-cyclo-hexanones [54–61, 263]. The evidence that it is the equatorial form that has the higher carbonyl frequency rests on measurements of the relative proportions of the two forms in α-chlorocyclohexanone, and on the way these change with alterations of phase, temperature and solvents. The assumptions are made that the proportion of the more polar form will increase as the polarity of the medium is increased, and that the proportion of the less stable form will increase with temperature. Dipole moment studies in different media and phases support these assumptions, and there is little doubt that the carbonyl frequency is raised when the oxygen atom is eclipsed by the halogen. Parallel changes occur in the C—Cl stretching frequencies.

In open-chain compounds similar solvent and dipole moment measurements support the view that the frequency rise is associated with a close approach of the halogen and oxygen atoms. Only in this way can a satisfactory account be given for the pattern of behaviour as successive halogen atoms are introduced. The introduction of the first halogen atom results in two carbonyl bands, one at a raised frequency and the other in the original position. A second halogen atom on the same carbon does not affect these frequencies, although the relative intensities change. A third halogen atom eliminates the lower-frequency band. This is consistent with the fact that only one halogen atom can be eclipsed with the oxygen, so that the others do not raise the frequency further. However, the frequency can be raised further by halogen substitution on both sides of the carbonyl group. As expected, three bands are then found which correspond to the three possibilities eclipsed/eclipsed, eclipsed/*gauche* and *gauche/gauche*. The frequency shifts following α-bromo substitution are usually a little smaller than those from chlorine, and those from fluorine substitution are a little higher. Griffin [63] has presented data on the frequencies of a large number of perfluoroalkyl ketones. The spectrum of perfluoroacetone is described by Berney [265], and variously fluorinated acetones have been studied by Crowder *et al.* (313–315). In the liquid state fluoroacetone has two bands at 1740 and 1725 cm⁻¹, and intensity changes with solvent polarity have identified the 1740 cm⁻¹ band as arising from the form in which the fluorine is *cis* to the oxygen atom. *Sym*difluoroacetone appears to exist only in two of the three possible isomers, *gauche/gauche* and *gauche/cis*. The corresponding carbonyl bands around 1750 cm⁻¹ are not fully resolved.

(b) Esters

New data on the carbonyl frequencies of halogenated esters have been given by Josien [64], Radell and Harrah [65] and by Brown [66], who has also studied the band intensities and estimated the rotational barriers between the *cis* and *gauche* forms (*cis* with respect to the carbonyl oxygen atom and the halogen). The pattern of behaviour with chlorine or bromine substitution is the same as that of ketones, but some differences occur with α-fluorine substitution, and these are not properly understood. In ethyl monofluoroacetate there are two bands, as expected. One is at 1775 cm⁻¹ and the other at 1746 cm⁻¹. The latter, which corresponds to the *gauche* form, is similar to that of ethyl acetate itself (1742 cm⁻¹). However, with ethyl α-difluoroacetate there is a small (5 cm⁻¹) further rise in the higher-frequency band, and, very surprisingly, a substantial rise (20 cm⁻¹) in the lower-frequency band. The trifluoro compound has a single band at 1789 cm⁻¹. As only one oxygen atom at a time can be eclipsed with a fluorine atom, the origin of this effect is difficult to see.

The results of thermodynamic studies are also interesting. They show that the *cis* form is slightly more stable than the *gauche*, and that the energy difference between the two forms is slightly greater with fluorine than with chlorine. One would have expected much stronger dipole repulsions between the oxygen atoms and fluorine than with chlorine, and it seems that this is not so. It may be that the greater repulsion is offset by a corresponding increase in the interaction between the fluorine and the ester oxygen in the *gauche* configuration. An increase in the degree of fluorine substitution beyond the α-carbon atom has little effect [65]. Perfluoroaryl esters have been discussed by Filler *et al.* [264]. Katon and Sinha [316] have studied methylchloroacetate, and although they find the normal twin carbonyl bands they do not find any temperature dependence. This has led them to suggest that although rotational isomerism does occur in this compound the carbonyl frequencies do not provide a good method for its identification. They quote in support of this the work of Charles *et al.* [317] who found only a single carbonyl frequency in methyl cyanoacetate although they did establish the presence of rotational isomers. However, in this last case the isomerism does not involve different orientations of the carbonyl oxygen and the carbon atom of the nitrile. On balance therefore it does seem likely that the carbonyl doublet in chlorinated esters does arise from field effects.

An interesting anomaly is also found in thioesters [67]. As will be seen from Table 5.2 (p. 154), mono- and di-α-halogen derivatives show two carbonyl bands, but the new additional band appears at lower frequencies. No explanation is available for this at present.

Field effects are also observed in anhydrides [22] and, as is to be expected, these alter the positions of both carbonyl bands, even though the halogen may only influence one of the two groups directly. The frequencies of trifluoro acetic anhydride ($CF_3 \cdot CO \cdot O \cdot CO \cdot CH_3$) therefore fall midway between those of acetic anhydride and its perfluoro derivative.

(c) Acid halides

These compounds have been studied by Bellamy and Williams [69], and by Tanabe and Saeki [318], and the rotational barrier in CF_3COCl has been measured by Berney [70]. As Table 5.2 shows, there are again two bands in the mono- and di-halo derivatives and one in the trisubstituted compound. The gradual fall in the higher-frequency band as the degree of halogen substitution is increased has been attributed to a second-field effect, this time between the two chlorine atoms in the *gauche* configuration. This has the effect of reducing the polarity and the electronegativity of the chlorine atom directly attached to the carbonyl carbon, with a consequent frequency fall. The existence of the two postulated forms has in these cases been confirmed by dipole moment and electron diffraction studies, and it has been shown unequivocally that the form giving the higher carbonyl frequency is that with the halogen *cis* to the oxygen atom. Tanabe and Saeki [318] have estimated the energy differences for the rotational isomers of chloroacetyl chloride and bromoacetylbromide by the absolute intensity method.

(d) Amides

Studies on amides need to be made in very dilute solutions if one is to avoid the appearance of multiple carbonyl bands due to hydrogen bonding effects. Studies of this kind have been made by Letaw and Gropp [71] and by Nyquist [72, 73], with very interesting results. Very clear-cut differences between mono- and disubstituted amides appear as a result of α-halogen substitution. Neither shows any change in the CO frequency on the introduction of the first halogen atom. However, when a second halogen atom is introduced the tertiary amides show two peaks corresponding to rotational isomers, whereas the secondary amides show a single peak at a slightly raised frequency. The absence of rotational isomerism in the secondary amides is attributed by Nyquist [72, 73] to the formation of an intramolecular hydrogen bond NH . . . Cl, which locks the halogen atom in a *cis* configuration with respect to the nitrogen atom. This suggestion is strongly supported by the behaviour of the NH stretching frequencies. Any additional halogen atoms would then have to take up a skew position with respect to the carbonyl oxygen, where they would exert a reduced field effect. A progressive frequency rise would then occur as successive halogens were introduced. The behaviour of these compounds may well be different in the solid state or in concentrated solutions, as the intramolecular bonds are weak and would be expected to be replaced by intermolecular links. Unfortunately this situation has not been studied in any detail. It is certainly the case that multiple carbonyl peaks are shown under these conditions, but their origins are not certain, as they are shown also by α-tri-halogenated secondary amides.

Primary amides with α-halogen substituents have been less fully studied, although Brown [74] has given some data on both frequencies and intensities. A single α-chlorine atom does not affect νCO, but there is some evidence of doubling in α-dichloroacetamide, in which the band centre is raised 21 cm^{-1} above the value of the mono-substituted compound. A further rise of 16 cm^{-1} occurs on the introduction of a third chlorine atom, so that these compounds appear to behave similarly to the secondary amides.

Field effects can also occur in secondary amides with a halogen atom substituted on to the nitrogen atom. These can then exist in two forms in one of which the halogen atom is *cis* to the oxygen and in another in which it is *trans*. De Klein [319] has shown that in N-chloroacetamide there are two carbonyl bands at 1728 and 1715 cm^{-1} in dilute solution, and that the higher frequency band originates in the form in which the oxygen and chlorine atoms are *cis*. N-bromoacetamide behaves similarly in showing two bands but N-chlorobenzamide appears to exist only in the *cis* form (oxygen, chlorine) and has a single band at 1714 cm^{-1}.

(e) *Acids*

Under normal conditions of resolution, acids do not appear to show multiple carbonyl bands due to rotational isomerism. Thus Barcello [75, 76] reports single bands due to the monomer and to the dimer in the series $CH_3 \cdot COOH$, $CH_2Cl \cdot COOH$, $CHCl_2 \cdot COOH$ and $CCl_3 \cdot COOH$. There is some disagreement in the literature over the precise values, but there is a steady upward displacement of νCO as the degree of halogen substitution is increased. However, Barcello notes that few of these bands are symmetric, and it may be that the breadth of the bands is too great to allow the separate peaks from the rotational isomers to be resolved. This is certainly the case with $CH_2F \cdot COOH$, which has been studied under high resolution [76]. In carbon tetrachloride this shows five carbonyl bands which are assigned to the five possible rotational isomers of the monomer and dimer. The position is further complicated by the fact that whilst fluorine and chlorine at the α carbon atom give a frequency rise, this does not appear to be the case with bromine or iodine. Katon, Carll and Bentley [320] quote values of 1734 cm^{-1} for chloroacetic acid, 1725 cm^{-1} for bromo, and 1680 cm^{-1} for the iodo derivative. They also find that bromopropionic acid absorbs at 1710 cm^{-1} regardless of which of the carbons of the ethyl group is substituted. They conclude that bromine does not affect the frequency and that iodine lowers it. No explanation of these observations is available at this time.

(f) *Aldehydes*

α-Halogenated aldehydes do not appear to exhibit rotational isomerism, although this phenomenon is known to occur in furfuraldehyde [77], which shows two CO bands corresponding to the two possible configurations of the carbonyl group in relation to the ring oxygen. With halogenated aldehydes the successive introduction of α-halogens results in a steady upward drift in νCO [69], as shown in Table 5.2. No explanation is available for the absence of multiple peaks. With CF_3COH the barrier to rotation is very low [321], as indeed it is with CF_3COOH, and this may possibly be the explanation of the abnormal behaviour of the acids and aldehydes, as compared with other carbonyl compounds. However, we do not know sufficient about the rotational barriers in other halogenated aldehydes to enable us to reach any firm conclusions.

5.6.2. Field effects with other atoms or groups in the α-position

Field effects occur with several other elements at the α-position. There is, for example, ample evidence for the occurrence of field effects with α-oxygen substituents. Josien [64] has found twin carbonyl bands in substituted phenoxy acetates, and Brown [66] has confirmed this with other esters. Morris and Young [78] also found twin peaks in α-epoxy esters, and although these were at first attributed to dimerization effects, it has been shown by House [79] that field effects are responsible. Interactions between carbonyl and α-methoxy groups have also been reported by Stradling and Tarbell [80].

Interactions with α-nitro groups can also occur if the geometry is suitable. It has already been noted that there is no interaction in ω-nitroacetophenone, but nitro acids [81] show increases in vCO of about 30 cm^{-1} above the values for the parent compounds, and this has been attributed to a dipolar interaction. Similarly, in compound (I), examined by Nejland et al. [82], there is only a single carbonyl band, whereas compound (II) has two bands at 1715 and 1748 cm^{-1}, indicating a strong dipolar effect. Interactions with an adjacent nitrogen atom are found in aziridylketones [322]. These occur in cisoid and transoid forms. The former in which the nitrogen atom is near to the oxygen absorb near 1710 cm^{-1} and the latter near 1696 cm^{-1}.

Field effects occur also with α-CN groups, at least to the extent that there is a rise in vCO in α-substituted ketones [83] and esters [66], but in neither case are there any multiple bands. It has therefore been assumed that the CN group is eclipsed with the carbonyl link. Interactions with α-sulphur or selenium atoms have not been described, but the data on ortho-substituted aromatic ketones given overleaf suggests very strongly that such effects will occur.

(I) (II)

5.6.3. Interactions with polar groups not at the α-position

Normally, halogen substitution at the β or γ positions has little effect on vCO because the interatomic distances are too large. However, this is not always so, and situations do arise in which such substituents come sufficiently close to interact. The commonest cases are the ortho-substituted aromatics, in which halogen or nitro substituents, ortho to a carbonyl group, produce twin bands corresponding to the two possible configurations of the carbonyl group. The same substituents in the meta or para positions show only one band. The effects in these cases are a little smaller than in the α-halogen ketones due to the larger distances of separation. Double carbonyl bands are also shown when the COC$_2$H$_5$ group is introduced at the ortho position of furan [79].

The most dramatic effects of this kind occur with ortho-substituted sulphur or selenium atoms, which themselves carry polar substituents. Only a single carbonyl frequency is shown, and it appears at a considerably lower frequency. This is attributed to the interaction of the sulphur and oxygen in a *cis* configuration [85]. The interaction has been studied in ketones, acid chlorides, thiol esters, selenoesters and amides. With benzaldehyde (vCO 1690 cm^{-1}) an *ortho* SCN group reduces vCO to 1670 cm^{-1} and an SeCN to 1650 cm^{-1}. However, the corresponding SeCl and SeBr derivatives absorb at 1590 cm^{-1}. The alteration in the direction of the frequency shift as compared with the chlorine/oxygen interaction is to be expected in view of the polarity of the sulphur and selenium atoms, but the magnitude of the effect is surprising.

Interactions with atoms farther away than the β position are very rare. An interesting case occurs with fluorine substitution on an ester link. The compound $CF_3 \cdot CH_2 \cdot COOCH_3$ has a normal ketonic carbonyl frequency, but if the terminal methyl group is replaced [65] by CH_2CF_3, vCO rises by about 20 cm^{-1}. No further rise follows an extension of the CF_3 chain. This must originate in the *cis* configuration of the ester link, which allows the fluorine atom to approach closer to the carbonyl oxygen atom. It is possible that a similar effect is responsible for the high carbonyl frequency reported for CH_3COOCH_2Cl. This absorbs at 1770 cm^{-1} which is exceptionally high for an alkyl ester. Only a single carbonyl band is shown [323], but the *cis* ester arrangement would allow the chlorine to approach close to the carbonyl oxygen.

Interactions have also been reported between two carbonyl groups in the 1,4-positions [33, 86] in sterols. These occur only when the geometry is such, as in 16,22-steroids, that the carbonyl atoms approach each other closely. Finally, transannular effects in large ring systems occur between carbonyl groups and oxygen or sulphur atoms which, although remotely situated along the chain, are in fact close in terms of the intramolecular distances. Several examples of this kind have been reported by Leonard [87]. These follow the general pattern of behaviour of the nitrogen analogues which have been known for some time.

5.7. The effects of changes of phase or of association

There is always a change in vCO on passing from the vapour to the condensed phase. This probably originates largely in dipolar interactions between carbonyl groups, although dielectric effects may also play some part. Many years ago Wheland explained the fact that acetone is a liquid whereas propane is a gas in terms of loose dipolar associations of the carbonyl groups to form chains of the type

$$R_1R_2CO \cdots \overset{\textstyle >}{C}O \cdots \overset{\textstyle >}{C}O$$

One would therefore expect that the size of the frequency shift that accompanied a change of state would be determined by the bond dipole of the carbonyl group. The shifts would then be least in those compounds in which the carbonyl bond was largely covalent, and greatest in those in which it was highly polar. This is true, at least to some extent, and the νCO vapour/liquid shifts of acetyl chloride (15 cm^{-1}) and phosgene (13 cm^{-1}) are smaller than those of acetone (21 cm^{-1}) or of acetaldehyde (23 cm^{-1}), while these in turn are smaller than the shift in dimethylformamide (50 cm^{-1}).

Other factors which can affect the situation are the dielectric constant of the condensed phase, hydrogen bonding and association effects in acids and amides, and steric effects when these are sufficiently large that they prevent the approach of the carbonyl dipoles to their otherwise natural distances. The effects of internal association and of dimerization will be considered separately in the sections dealing with the various types of carbonyl compounds. However, studies on the basicity of the carbonyl group and on the frequency changes which it shows with various proton donors are dealt with below, as they follow naturally from a discussion of solvent effects.

5.7.1. Solvent effects on νCO

A good deal of work has been done on the nature and extent of the solvent shifts shown by carbonyl groups. A simple dielectric constant approach based on the Kirkwood–Bauer–Magat expression is known to be entirely in-adequate, and evidence has accumulated in favour of the alternative view that the shifts arise from localized interaction effects. In the extreme cases these would be hydrogen bonds, but similar weaker dipolar interactions are postulated in other systems. Some interesting attempts have been made to bring these two views together, and to derive equations which would allow quantitatively for both dispersion forces and for polar interactions. Equations of this kind have been put forward by Buckingham [90], by Pullin [91] and others, and their experimental applications to carbonyl frequencies have been studied by Thompson [92, 93] and by Hallam [94, 95]. The results are not wholly decisive. Thompson concludes that equations of this kind are not useful in the prediction of experimental values, whereas Hallam accepts that dispersion forces are significant and that their magnitude can be assessed in this way. Some indirect support for Hallam's view is given in the papers of Kagarise [96], in which he concludes that dielectric constant effects do play some part in determining the extent of frequency shifts in carbonyl groups. Perhaps the most decisive evidence that dispersion effects do play some part in the measured carbonyl frequency comes from the observation [324] of a frequency difference of 6 cm^{-1} between the carbonyl frequencies of formaldehyde in the gas phase and when isolated in a nitrogen matrix. This cannot arise from any localised interaction and it represents about a quarter of the total shift observed when passing from the gas phase to solution in an associating solvent such as chloroform.

Many of these discrepancies have their origins in the lack of a clear definition of just what is meant by a solvent effect. It is usual to assess the magnitude of the frequency shifts by reference to the vapour frequency. The overall shift therefore includes any changes resulting from the alteration of the environment of the carbonyl group from a state of complete isolation to one in which it is entirely surrounded by solvent molecules. This will be additional to any further shifts which are produced as a result of the polarity of the solvent. These two effects will not be controlled by the same factors, and in the case of XH dipoles at least, there is good evidence that this is so. Thus the mean NH stretching frequency of aniline changes considerably on passing from the vapour to hexane solution, and the shifts are comparable with those of pyrrole under the same conditions. However, when these two compounds are compared in solvents of different polarity very great differences appear. The vNH bands of aniline show only small shifts in basic solvents, but the NH bands of pyrrole show substantial shifts. In most XH systems the shifts which occur on passing from the vapour to hexane solution are very small compared with the shifts that occur in solvents such as ether. Any discrepancies which may arise from the inclusion of the former in the total solvent shift are therefore minimized. In the case of the carbonyl group, however, the shifts arising from the phase change are of the same order of magnitude as those which arise from subsequent changes of the solvent. Any assessment of the total solvent shift based on the vapour frequency as the datum point might well lead to the conclusion that dielectric constant factors have made a significant contribution. An assessment based on the shift from the hexane frequency would probably lead to the opposite conclusion and the assignment of the whole of the frequency shift to localized dipolar interactions. If the evidence of Kagarise [96] is viewed in this light it will be seen that this is a very reasonable conclusion, and this is also supported by some results of Tschulanowskij [97].

Detailed discussions of the extents of solvent shifts in various kinds of carbonyl compound will be found in references [13, 92–96, 266–269, 309] and in papers by Jakovleva et al. [98] and by Ito [99, 100].

One useful observation in this area is that of Bellamy and Williams [13], who showed that all carbonyl groups respond to solvent changes in the same way. The order of solvent effectiveness in lowering vCO is therefore always the same, and a quantitative relationship exists between the effects of one solvent and another. Thus, the relative frequency shifts $(\delta v/v)$ of any one carbonyl group in a series of solvents can be plotted directly against the values for some other carbonyl group in the same solvents, to give a straight line. This is of direct value in the identification of carbonyl groups and in the recognition of interaction effects which can lead to deviations from linearity.

Carbonyl frequencies have also been differentiated from C=C stretching bands by this technique, as in pyridones [101] pyrones [102] and tropolones [270]. The use of this method has been questioned in compounds where the carbonyl group is involved in strong vibrational coupling [268, 309, 325], and Smith and Taylor [325] have shown that it does indeed have serious limitations in situations such as the aminocrotonates and other strongly coupled systems.

5.7.2. Interactions of the carbonyl group with hydrogen donors

The changes in vCO on hydrogen bond formation with standard donors, such as hydrogen chloride, methanol, phenol, pyrrole and phenylacetylene, have been extensively studied, and much detailed information is available [13, 46–49, 68, 103–107, 120, 271–272]. The significance of much of this data has already been discussed in part in Section 5.5.1. For unstrained, unconjugated carbonyl groups the fall in vXH is a measure of the relative basicity and good relationships exist between this and the unassociated vCO values or with the carbonyl ionization potential [46]. This experimental finding has been shown to be predictable on the basis of calculations using both the Hückel theory and CNDO/2 treatments [326]. For strained systems δvXH still provides a good measure of the basicity, but this is no longer related to vCO for the reasons already given. However, such measurements are useful, as, for example, in demonstrating that the low vCO value of di-*tert*-butyl ketone is due to angle effects and is not a consequence of force-constant changes in the carbonyl group [108]. Useful relationships between δvXH and other properties of the carbonyl group have also been reported. The δvNH values of indole on association with amide carbonyl groups have been shown to be a linear function of the Taft σ^* values of the carbonyl substituents.

It is interesting to note that there is no corresponding relationship between δvXH and δvCO which is applicable over a range of different systems. There are substantial frequency shifts in the δvCO values of esters and of amides (15–25 cm^{-1}) on association with phenol, whereas the shifts for aldehydes and ketones are much smaller (3–10 cm^{-1}). In the δvOH results, however, ketones produce shifts intermediate between those of esters and amides.

The fact that conjugated compounds show much the same basicities as the corresponding saturated compounds is also interesting, and finds a parallel in the fact that these compounds do not follow the ionization potential relationship either but fall on a separate line of their own [46]. It has been suggested that conjugation affects the π clouds and need not necessarily alter the basicity which is mainly determined by the hybridization of the lone-pair electrons. However, there are differences in the carbonyl shifts as distinct from the XH shifts. In 3-keto-steroids for example, vCO shifts by 14 cm^{-1} on passing from hexane to chloroform solution, whereas with Δ^4 3-keto-steroids the carbonyl shift is 20 cm^{-1}, reflecting the increased polarity of the bond. However, when the conjugation is further increased, as in the $\Delta^{1,4}$ 3-keto-systems, The shift is not increased and indeed is slightly less than that of the saturated sterol [327]. There is therefore much uncertainty as to the real significance of these shifts.

5.7.3. Carbonyl complexes with Lewis acids

In hydrogen bonding studies the shifts of vCO are small compared with those of vXH of the donor. An alternative approach, and one which is attractive because it measures a direct property of the carbonyl bond, is to measure the large shifts in vCO which occur on complex formation with Lewis acids.

This possibility has not yet been very fully explored, partly because of the complications that sometimes arise from the formation of ion-pair complexes such as $(CH_3CO)^+AlCl_4^-$. However, these are relatively uncommon in solution, although the $(CH_3CO)^+$ ion has been observed in $(CH_3CO)BF_4$ [109] and in $(CH_3CO)AlCl_4$ [109, 110]. More generally vCO shifts by a large amount to lower frequencies corresponding to the formation of the complexes such as $CH_3COX \cdot AlCl_3$. The shifts are then of the order of 70–180 cm^{-1}, depending upon the carbonyl compound involved and on the Lewis acid. Lappert [111] has used values of vCO in such compounds to obtain a quantitative measure of the acceptor properties of the acids. It is important in assessing the size of shift to determine whether the complex is 1 : 1 or 2 : 1. Taillandier *et al.* [328] have shown that in complexes of BF_3 with methanol and with acetic acid, the 1 : 1 complex forms stronger bonds than does the 2 : 1. This is parallel to the behaviour of hydrogen bonded complexes. The oxygen atom which has donated one pair of electrons is more resistant to donation of a second pair, and the bonds are then correspondingly weaker.

Bystrov and Filimonov [112] have studied complexes of alkyl formates and acetates, Archambault and Rivest [113] complexes with formamide and dimethylformamide, Paoloni and Marini Bettolo [114] those with aromatic aldehydes and ketones, and Cook [115] has looked at the case of benzoic anhydride. Aldehydes and esters have been studied by Meaume and Odiot [329], Liquier *et al.* [330] and by Taillandier *et al.* [331, 332]. In addition, several papers by Susz and his collaborators [116–118] deal with complexes of acetone, acetophenone and benzophenone. These show the very interesting result that unlike the δvXH measurements reported earlier there is a stepwise increase in δvCO as one passes down the series from acetone to benzophenone. For complexes with BF_3 the δvCO values are acetone 70, acetophenone 107 and benzophenone 112 cm^{-1}. For complexes with $AlBr_3$ the corresponding values are 85, 130 and 142 cm^{-1} respectively. This approach therefore offers yet another way whereby the relative availabilities of the lone-pair electrons of the oxygen atoms of different carbonyl compounds may be compared. A detailed study of the differences between the results of these measurements and those from hydrogen bonding studies would be particularly rewarding, and could well throw new light on the nature of the association mechanisms involved.

Certainly, the extent of the shifts of vCO appears to follow the general trend of the carbonyl basicity, as would be expected from chemical considerations, and in the cases of *para*-substituted acetophenones and benzophenones it can be shown that the $\delta\nu CO$ values of Lewis acid complexes follow the Hammett σ values of the substituents [118, 119]. The whole subject of the Friedel–Crafts complexes of carbonyl compounds is well reviewed and documented by Cook [153]. An alternative to the measure of donor strength through carbonyl shifts is through the measurement of the low frequency modes of the HgI_2 molecule on complexation. This has been used by Joly and Nicolau [333] to establish an order of donor strengths for various solvents.

5.8. Carbonyl frequencies in specific classes of compound

Table 5.2. gives the carbonyl frequencies of many different compounds. The data have been selected from a wide range of sources and represent what are probably the best values available at the time of writing. As they represent the real frequencies of specific compounds, they are likely to prove more generally useful than the correlation charts in indicating the likely frequency range of a given class of compound. The frequencies are measured in carbon tetrachloride unless otherwise stated.

Table 5.2. Carbonyl frequencies I

Effects of Halogens

X

Y	CH_3	CH_2Cl	$CHCl_2$	CCl_3	CH_2Br	CF_3	F	Cl	CHF_2	OCH_3
X	1719	1746	1774	1830		1825	1928V	1813		1832
	1730	1764	1751							
H	1730	1748	1742	1768		1784V	1837V			
CH_3	1719	1752	1743			1765	1872V	1806		
		1726	1724							
C_6H_5	1692	1716	1715	1718	1709		1812	1773		
		1692			1688			1736		
OCH_3	1748	1773	1775	1775	1764			1786		
	1749		1755		1749					
OC_2H_5	1742	1767	1772	1769	1761	1789		1779	1780	1780
	1742	1750			1743				1766	
NH Butyl	1688	1684	1705	1726	1681	1736			1718	
NBu_2	1647	1656	1684			1692			1686	
			1656						1667	
Cl	1806	1821	1810	1803	1802	1810V	1868V	1813		1806
		1785	1779		1773L					
F	1872V					1901V	1928V	1868V	1874V	
SButyl	1695	1699	1703	1699	1691	1710				
		1671	1682		1669					
SC_6H_5	1711	1725	1736	1711	1710	1722				
		1691	1700		1695					
OH	1769m	1791m	1784m	1788m	1772m	1810m			1756d	
	1715d	1735d	1743d	1754d	1726d	1787d				
ONa		1600				1687				
Solid		1420S				1457S				
$OCH_2CH{=}CH_2$	1746	1768	1773	1770						
		1746	1752							
NH_2	1678	1695S_1	1716S_1	1732S_1		1750S_1				
	1702		(double)							

All in carbon tetrachloride except

V	= Vapour	m	= Monomer
L	= Liquid	d	= dimer
S	= Solid	t	= *trans*
S_1	= chloroform solution	c	= *cis*
S_2	= acetonitrile solution	k	= keto
S_3	= CS_2	e	= enol

Table 5.2.—*Continued* Carbonyl frequencies II

Saturated and Unsaturated Ketones, Aldehydes and Esters

X

Y	H	CH₃	C₂H₅	C₆H₅	OCH₃	OC₂H₅	OH	Y
C₆H₅	1710	1692	1693	1667	1727	1720	1695	1667
CH₃CH=CH	1700	t. {1701 / 1682 / c. 1699		1699 / 1678	t. 1726 / c. 1721S₃	1724	t. 1694d / t. 1692d	1660
CH₃(CH=CH)₂⁻	1667S₁			1670	t.t. 1716 / c.t. {1715S₃ / c.c. {		t.t. 1702S / c.t. 1683 / c.c. 1691S	
CH₂=CH	1703	1706 / 1686	1707 / 1690		1734	1730		
C₆H₅·CH=CH	1652L	c.t. 1699 / t.t. 1678	1701 / 1675L		1724		t. 1699d / c. 1711d	1652L
CH₂=C(CH₃)—	1702	1684			1727	1722		
CH₃C≡C					1718		1684	
HC≡C					1719			
SButyl	1675	1695	1691	1685				
SC₆H₅	1693	1711	1710	1685				
OCH₃	1735	1748	1746	1727	1758	1756		1758
OC₆H₅		1749	1767	1743	1755	1757		1786
OOH	1780V	1760V	1760V	1732				
OC₂H₅	1734	1742	1736	1720		1748		1748

Carbonyl frequencies III

Amides, Urethanes, Anhydrides etc.

X

Y	H	CH₃	C₆H₅	OCH₃	OC₂H₅	CF₃	Y	C₂H₅
NH₂	1722	1714m / 1690d	1768S₁	1733 / 1700S	1725S₁	1750	1686 / 1630S	1687S₁
NHCH₃	1666L	1700 / (1653L)	1660S₁		1731		1695	
N(CH₃)₂	1687 / (1670L)	1653			1684		1640	
NHC₆H₅		1688S₁	1679S₁	1707	1725 / 1701S	—	1632S	
N(C₆H₅)₂		1679						
NHC₂H₅		1686m / 1647d	1651S₂					
N(C₂H₅)₂	1684	1652	1640S₁					
NHOH	1650S	1665S	1660					
OCOX	1833 / 1764	1801 / 1740				1880 / 1814		
OOCOX	1820 / 1797	1797 / 1777			1818 / 1799			
CH₂COCH₃		1727 / 1717 } k / 1616e	1724k / 1600e		1733 / 1709 } k / 1645e			
CH₂COC₆H₅		1724k / 1600e	1600e		1698L			
C₂H₅	1738	1722 / 1763	1693	1745	1742	1761		
OCH=CH₂		1763				1800		
NHCOCH₃		1714 / 1690			1754 / 1704S₁			

Table 5.2.—*Continued* Carbonyl frequencies IV

Cyclic systems

Ring	Type	CH_2—CO—CH_2	CHCl—CO—CH_2	CHBr—CO—CH_2	CH_2—CO—O	CH_2—CO—NH	CO—O—CO	NH—CO—NH	CO—NHCO
4	Saturated	1775							
5	Saturated	1742	1755	1750	1841 / 1770	1706	1876 / 1799	1661S	1770
	αβ C=C				1784 / 1742 / 1790		1855 / 1784	1687 (C_3H_7)	1757 (N.Bu)
	βγ C=C (benzo structure)	1721			(γCH_3) 1778	1725 / 1708S_1	1860 / 1795	1722S_1	1775 / 1735 / 1727 / 1637 (N Methyl) / 1724–1709 / 1690–1660 (N—R)
6	Saturated	1719	1745 / 1726	1732 / 1719	1750S_1	1690	1822 / 1780	1692S	
	αβ C—C	1691			1743	1675S_1 (NCH_3)			
	αβ, βγ C=C				1752 / 1731 / 1775S_1	1669	1785 / 1735S_1		
7	Saturated (lactam NH structure)	1706	1718 / 1709	1712		1685S_1 / 1669		1650S	
8	Saturated	1704	1725 / 1714	1710		1670			
10	Saturated	1705	1718	1713					
12	Saturated	1713				1635S			

Table 5.2.—*Continued* Carbonyl frequencies V (aromatics)

Substituent 1	COOH (monomer)	COOCH$_3$	COCH$_3$	NHCOCH$_3$	OCOCH$_3$	CHO
m-N(CH$_3$)$_2$	1740	1727				
m-OCH$_3$	1741	1728	1695	1694c	1773	1709 ⎱ 1686 ⎰
m-CH$_3$	1742	1727		1692c	1770	1708 ⎱ 1686 ⎰
H	1744	1730				1708
m-F	1748	1733				1716 ⎱ 1700 ⎰
m-Cl	1748	1735	1696	1695c	1770	1708
m-Br	1748	1734			1770	1719 ⎱ 1708 ⎰
m-NO$_2$	1752	1738	1701	1706d	1779	
m-COCH$_3$		1733		1709	1773	
p-OH			1686	1686c		1716 ⎱ 1702 ⎰
p-OCH$_3$	1737	1723	1684	1684c	1770	1702 ⎱ 1686 ⎰
p-CH$_3$	1740	1728	1690	1691c		
p-F	1745	1732				1719 ⎱ 1707 ⎰
p-Cl	1745	1731	1694			1708
p-Br	1746	1734	1695	1698c		
p-NO$_2$	1752	1737	1700	1712d	1779	1713
p-CN				1706c		
p-COCH$_3$		1734		1715	1773	
p-CHO				1715	1773	
p-C$_6$H$_5$			1692	1689c	1776	
o-OCH$_3$	1760, 1751	1736, 1718				1703 ⎱ 1685 ⎰
o-F	1755, 1739	1741, 1726				1714 ⎱ 1696 ⎰
o-Cl	1756, 1738	1744, 1727				
o-Br	1757, 1738	1744, 1727				1706
o-I	1753, 1736	1740, 1727				1714 ⎱ 1701 ⎰
o-NO$_2$	1760	1747				
o-OCOCH$_3$	1747	1733				
o-CH$_3$	1742	1728				1707

c, Chloroform solution; d, Dioxan solution.

5.8.1. Alkyl, aryl and conjugated ketones

Little new is available on the frequencies of the carbonyl group in simple alkyl ketones. The more recent determinations of the frequencies in this series merely serve to confirm that vCO is relatively stable and remains close to 1720 cm^{-1} in carbon tetrachloride solution. Only in special cases, such as when the bond angle is opened beyond 120° by steric effects, is any significant departure from this value observed [121]. Methyl *tert*-butyl ketone has vCO at 1709 cm^{-1}, as does pentamethylacetone. Hexamethylacetone absorbs at 1697 cm^{-1}.

In the acetophenone series a number of studies have been made on the effects of substitution at the α-methyl group and in the ring. Substitution at the methyl group follows the same pattern as the alkyl ketones, and only very minor changes result from chain branching [39] unless the groups are sufficiently large to open the C—CO—C bond angle. The frequency shift even then is not large, and α-trimethylacetophenone absorbs at 1680 cm^{-1}, 11 cm^{-1} below the value of acetophenone itself. Substitution of polar groups introduces the possibility of rotational isomerism and of field effects. These occur with α-halogen or α-oxygen substitution and have already been discussed in Section 5.6.2, where the appropriate references are given. Otherwise polar groups on the α-carbon atom have little effect on vCO. This can be seen from the fact that the frequencies of the *gauche* isomers of ω-haloacetophenones are essentially the same as those of the unsubstituted compounds. Even an α-nitro group has little effect [53].

Some further data are available on the frequencies of ring-substituted acetophenones. This confirms the earlier observation that a good linear correlation exists between vCO and the Hammett σ values of the substituents [84, 122, 123, 300] in *meta*- and *para*-substituted compounds. *Ortho* substituents shown deviations from this relation, due either to field effects or to angle changes. If the substituent is sufficiently large the COCH$_3$ group is twisted out of the plane of the ring and the carbonyl frequency rises to that of the unconjugated ketone. Substitution with *ortho*-OH or -NH groups leads, of course, to intramolecular hydrogen bonds which also lower vCO. Hambly [126] has discussed the case of the *ortho*-aminoacetophenones. Similar Hammett σ type relationships exist for the benzophenones, and further data on these and on the benzils have been given by Graf *et al.* [124], by Rao [125] and by Korver [275]. Substituted acetyl pyrroles have been studied by Khan and Morgan [178].

Studies on the $\alpha\beta$-unsaturated ketones have been primarily concerned to establish the identities of the s-*cis* and s-*trans* forms. This is most readily accomplished by a comparison of the relative intensities of the vCO and vC=C bands [127–131]. The recognition of these two conformers has already been discussed in detail in Section 5.5.1. Tables listing much useful data on the CO and C=C frequencies of variously substituted s.*cis* and s.*trans* ketones are given by Barlet *et al.* [310]. Some anomalies in the spectra of $\alpha\beta$ unsaturated ketones have been discussed by Sobolev and Alexsanyan [132]. Data on α-allylic ketones are given by Chouteau *et al.* [191], and on α-acetylenic ketones by Lopez *et al.* [192].

Conjugation with a nitrile group or with another carbonyl group has little effect on the frequency. Conjugation with a cyclopropyl group has an effect comparable with that of an aromatic ring. Conjugation with furyl or thienyl rings is more effective than with aromatic rings, and 2 : 2'-dithienyl ketone absorbs at 1615 cm^{-1}. Conjugation by the diazo group also appears to be particularly effective in lowering vCO. Diazoacetone absorbs at 1640 cm^{-1} [334].

(a) Intensity studies on alkyl and aryl ketones

Thompson [123, 133] has studied the frequencies, intensities and half-bandwidths of a great variety of carbonyl compounds, including many alkyl and aryl ketones. Although there are often large differences between the various types of carbonyl function which can be useful as an aid to identification, there seems to be only very small intensity variations within any one class. The gradient of the curves of log A plotted against Hammett σ values was zero for propiophenones and benzophenones and only 0.05–0.08 for benzaldehydes, acetophenones and benzoates. Similar measurements on aromatic ketones have been reported by Morcillo et al. [134–136]. Some intensity data on cycloalkanones have been given by Cetina and Mateos [137, 138], and on sydnones by Borod'ko and Syrkin [139]. Flett has also summarized a good deal of intensity data on various types of carbonyl compound [166].

(b) β-Hydroxy or amino αβ-unsaturated ketones

In enolic β diketones and similar systems, the carbonyl frequency is lowered both by the conjugation and by the very strong hydrogen bonding. This brings it very close to the double bond frequency, and by analogy with the $\alpha\beta$ unsaturated ketones one would expect to find that in the cis conformation at least, there would be very strong coupling between the two, throwing the frequencies apart. Open chain systems of this kind have been extensively studied (141–144, 335–338), and it comes as a considerable surprise to find that the carbonyl and double bond frequencies are merged into a very intense band in the range 1620–1580 cm^{-1}. The fact that the double bond absorptions appear here has been neatly established by the preparation of the corresponding formylphosphonate esters in which chelation of comparable strengths occur, but which lack a carbonyl group. In the cis form these absorb near 1600 cm^{-1} [336]. The fact that the enol form of acetylacetone shows a very strong band near 1610 cm^{-1} in the Raman spectrum, in which any carbonyl band would be expected to be weak, also supports this assignment.

The origins of this near identity of the carbonyl and double bond frequencies have been studied by deuteration techniques which enable the potential energy distribution to be determined [338]. It is found that these vibrations are indeed strongly coupled but that the separation which would otherwise result is eliminated by further coupling with both the OH out of plane and in plane bends. When the hydrogen of the OH is replaced by deuterium, the C$=$O band appears in the 1620–1600 cm^{-1} region, but the C$=$C now occurs between 1520 and 1490 cm^{-1}. The higher frequency band now has 85% C$=$O character, whereas it was previously extensively mixed. Ketoenols of this kind take the expected *cis* conformation in dilute solutions, forming strong intramolecular hydrogen bonds. However, in the solid, even stronger intermolecular hydrogen bonds are possible with the *trans* conformation, and this is generally found. This change is reflected by considerable alterations in the OH stretching region, and by an upward shift of the carbonyl/double bond band which occurs near 1640 cm^{-1} but usually remains unresolved. Nakamoto [140] has given an extensive review of the spectra of metallic chelates of these systems and identified the frequencies of the ionic form.

With aromatic compounds such as *ortho*hydroxyacetophenone the ring breathing bands are not significantly shifted by coupling with the C$=$O, but the latter still appears at much the same frequencies, as a very intense band in the 1620–1590 cm^{-1} range.

With ring systems such as cyclohexane 1 : 3-diones, the enol is locked in the *trans* form and this results in changes in both the OH and C$=$O stretching regions. The coupling would be expected to be somewhat less than in the *cis* form, and in some instances the carbonyl and double bond bands have been resolved [31, 82, 145, 146, 335]. Two bands appear in the 1600 and 1630 cm^{-1} region in the spectra of associated *trans* enols. The lower frequency band is the stronger, and for this reason is usually identified with the carbonyl absorption. This is probably the case, but Taylor *et al.* have shown that in related systems with extensive coupling it is possible for the C$=$C band to appear more intense than the carbonyl [339].

Campbell and Gilow [149] have investigated the influence of ring size on the degree of tautomerism. In general, it would seem that five-membered ring systems do not enolize to any significant extent [28, 29].

The behaviour of $\alpha\beta$-unsaturated β-amino ketones is broadly similar. They usually exist wholly in the *cis* cyclized hydrogen bonded arrangement, and vCO then appears at 1640–1600 cm^{-1} [147, 150]. Dabrowski [151, 152] has made a detailed study of eight compounds of this type and of their deuterated analogues. He has prepared crystalline samples of the *cis* and *trans* forms and assigned the individual frequencies. In the *cis* series the carbonyl band near 1620 cm^{-1} is regarded as a coupled mode associated with the CO and C$=$C bonds, and a second enamino ketone band is assigned in the 1520–1470 cm^{-1} range. A third band at intermediate frequencies is assigned to the NH$_2$ deformation mode. Dabrowski [268] has also studied the rotational isomerism of N-dialkyl derivatives. A particularly interesting feature of these systems is the fact that the low frequencies of vC$=$O and vC$=$C persist even in *N*-di-substituted compounds, although the shifts are a little smaller than in compounds with hydrogen bonds. This confirms that much of the shifts are due to the strong coupling between the C$=$O and C$=$C bonds. Taylor has pointed out that these compounds are not only vinylogues of amides, but that their chemical properties are those of superamides. He and his coworkers have carried out some very extensive studies on compounds of this kind [309, 325, 339], including alkyl and acylenaminoketones, and 2-substituted thiazolid-4-ones. They conclude that the coupling is so strong that it is better to regard the two bands as symmetric and antisymmetric modes of the $C{=}O/C{=}C$ system. This is supported by the fact that both bands are solvent sensitive and that the strongest band is not always to be associated with the carbonyl mode. They show that *s.cis* and *s.trans* conformers are best distinguished by plotting the changes in frequencies of the principal two bands in different solvents, one against the other. The two forms behave very differently and the differentiation is better than can be achieved by the normal solvent plot of the carbonyl absorption.

Dabrowski and Katcka [341] have also studied amide vinylogues, and have assigned the $C{-}O$ and $C{=}C$ frequencies for the *s.cis* and *s.trans* forms. They have also examined the adducts of a number of such compounds with Lewis acids. Surprisingly, the bands assigned to the carbonyl do not show a major fall on complex formation. For example the compound $HCOCH{=}CHN(CH_3)_2$ absorbs at 1668 and 1585 cm^{-1} (*cis*), whilst the complex with $AlCl_3$ absorbs at 1654 and 1582 cm^{-1}. This may well reflect the coupling between the CO and $C{=}C$ modes.

(c) Quinones

The carbonyl frequencies of quinones have been studied in great detail, and although some of the original anomalies have been explained, others remain unsolved. The obvious discrepancy is the fact that many *para*-quinones show multiple carbonyl bands where only one would be expected on symmetry grounds, whereas many *ortho*-quinones which would be expected to show two strong bands have only a single carbonyl absorption. The spectra of *para*-benzoquinones have been studied by several groups [154–157, 340]. Isotopic studies and measurements on solvent effects have shown conclusively that when multiple carbonyl bands appear, Fermi resonance effects are responsible. A very thorough study of the halogenated p. quinones has been made by Girlando and Pecile [340] covering the entire series of chloro substituted derivatives and many of their perdeuterated analogues. These have led to definitive vibrational assignments for the series.

Brown [155] lists the carbonyl frequencies and intensities of a number of different quinones. Among these it is interesting to note that 1,5-di-chloroanthraquinone has a carbonyl frequency only 6 cm^{-1} higher than that of anthraquinone itself, whereas the 1,8-dichloro derivative has two bands at 1692 and 1674 cm^{-1}. 4,4'-Diphenoquinones have been examined by Gordon and Forbes [158] and shown to have much lower frequencies. The parent compound absorbs at 1630 cm^{-1}, and alkylated derivatives have values as low as 1599 cm^{-1}

Polycyclic quinones have been reported on by Durie *et al.* [159] and by Baudet *et al.* [160]. There is a small but real rise in the carbonyl frequencies as the number of fused rings is increased. This is surprising, as bond-order calculations would indicate that the bonds should become progressively weaker due to the increased conjugation [160].

A number of measurements have been made on chelated anthraquinones with very strong hydrogen bonds. Bloom *et al.* [161] measured the spectra of 59 anthraquinone derivatives and correlated the positions of vCO with the number and positions of the hydroxyl groups as follows:

	vCO, cm^{-1}
No OH	1678–1653
1 OH	1675–1647 and 1637–1621
1,4 or 1,5(OH)$_2$	1645–1608
1,8(OH)$_2$	1678–1661 and 1626–1616
1,4,5(OH)$_3$	1616–1592
1,4,5,8(OH)$_4$	1592–1572

These results are confirmed by further measurements by Tanaka [162] on 80 different anthraquinones. Hadzi [163] has reported on the alterations that occur in the spectra with changes in the crystal form of 2,5-dihydroxy-benzoquinone.

(d) Carbonyl functions in heterocyclic rings

This topic has been well reviewed by Katritzky *et al.* [164, 352], who give numerous references. Many systems of this kind, such as lactones, anhydrides

Table 5.3. Carbonyl frequencies in heterocyclic compounds. vCO values in cm^{-1} for carbon tetrachloride solution

(A) Sulphur-containing compounds

Five-membered rings

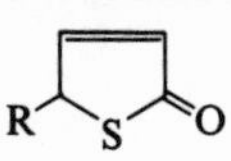

~1675	~1715	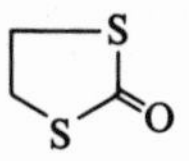 1638 (solid)	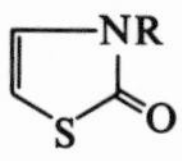 1640

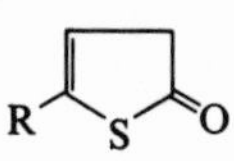

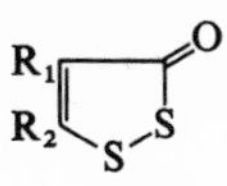

~1635	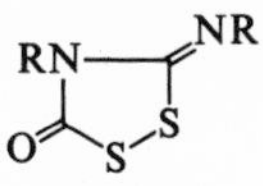 1720–1705	~1710	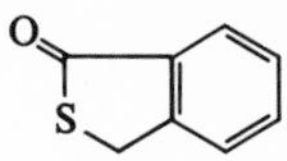 1680 (solid)

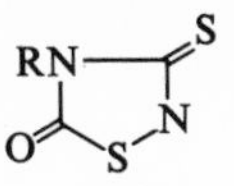

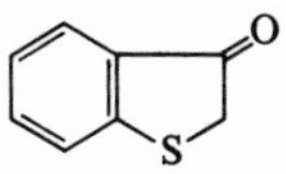

1750	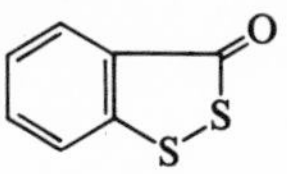 1665

Six-membered rings

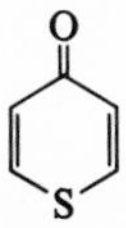

1643	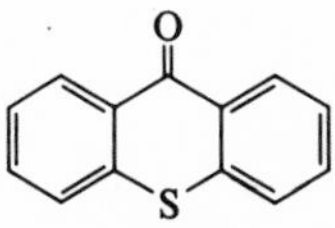 1645	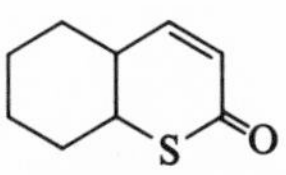 1683

Table 5.3—*continued*

(*B*) *Oxygen-containing compounds*

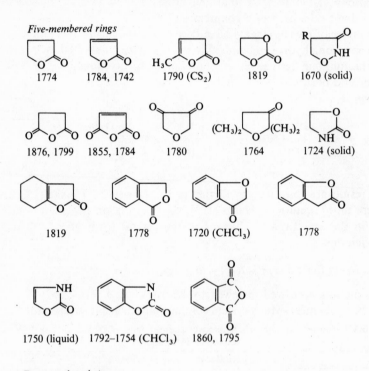

Five-membered rings

1774   1784, 1742   1790 (CS$_2$)   1819   1670 (solid)

1876, 1799   1855, 1784   1780   1764   1724 (solid)

1819   1778   1720 (CHCl$_3$)   1778

1750 (liquid)   1792–1754 (CHCl$_3$)   1860, 1795

Four-membered rings

1841

Six-membered rings

1724 (CS$_2$)   1678, 1657   1660 (CS$_2$)   1650 (solid)

~1725 (CS$_2$)   1745 (solid)   1822, 1780   1743 (CHCl$_3$) 1750 (CHCl$_3$)

Table 5.3—*continued*

Six-membered rings—Continued

1752, 1731   1700   1793   1730 (solid)

(*C*) *Nitrogen-containing compounds*

Five-membered rings

1706   1690, 1660   1661 (solid)   1776, 1718   1792–1751
                                                        (CHCl₃)   (KBr)
                                                                             1736–1686

1724 (solid)   1670 (solid)   1640 (solid)   1684–1677   1740 (solid)
                                                                  (solid)

1758–1700 (CHCl₃)   1772–1755   1792–1754   1715–1705
Various Aromatic   1750–1734   (CHCl₃)   (solid)
Ring Substituents   Various Aromatic   Various Aromatic
                      Ring Substituents   Ring Substituents

1722   1735   1750 (liquid)

Table 5.3—*continued*

Six-membered rings

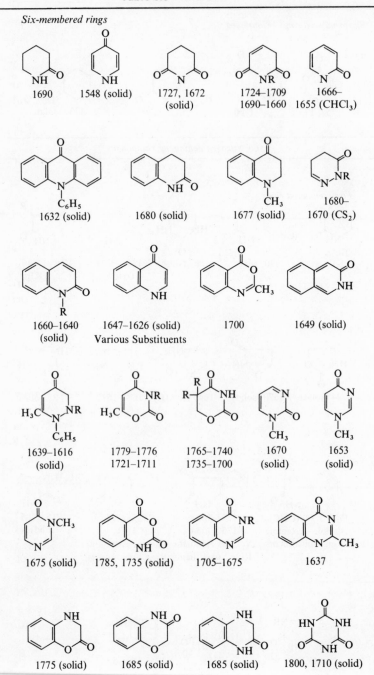

1690   1548 (solid)   1727, 1672 (solid)   1724–1709 1690–1660   1666–1655 (CHCl₃)

1632 (solid)   1680 (solid)   1677 (solid)   1680–1670 (CS₂)

1660–1640 (solid)   1647–1626 (solid) Various Substituents   1700   1649 (solid)

1639–1616 (solid)   1779–1776 1721–1711   1765–1740 1735–1700   1670 (solid)   1653 (solid)

1675 (solid)   1785, 1735 (solid)   1705–1675   1637

1775 (solid)   1685 (solid)   1685 (solid)   1800, 1710 (solid)

and lactams, are of course covered in the appropriate places in this present text. For the remainder, which include the less common situations, it is not possible within the limits of this book to provide all the relevant data. However, a series of typical carbonyl frequencies of characteristic classes of heterocyclic ketones are given in Table 5.3, and this illustrates very well the wide variations that can occur with structural changes in this series. It should be noted that the data are collected from a wide variety of sources, and the frequencies given do not all relate to a common phase. In general, values in carbon tetrachloride or carbon disulphide are given where these are available, but even in these solvents it is likely that some of the measurements on hydroxy or amino compounds actually relate to the associated forms. In addition to the Katritzky review, much useful data on different types of cyclic imides is given in a paper by Bassignana *et al.* [165].

5.8.2. Aldehydes

Publications on aldehydes include the effects of ring substituents on vCO in benzaldehydes [167, 168, 279, 342], pyrrole-aldehydes [169] and pyridine-aldehydes [170]. A good deal of attention has been paid to the steric and hydrogen bonding effects of *ortho* substituents in benzaldehyde. Forbes [171] discusses *o*-nitrobenzaldehyde, and there have also been extensive studies of salicylaldehydes and their derivatives [172–177]. Data on α-halogenated aldehydes are very limited [69, 343] and have been discussed in Section 5.6.2. Sanicki and Hauser [179] give some data on simple aliphatic aldehydes. Fruwert *et al.* [344] have measured the absolute intensities of the carbonyl bands in a series of unbranched alkyl aldehydes. Within this series they find a linear relationship between the intensities and the Taft σ values of the alkyl groups. However, it must be said that the slope of the line is very small and that the intensities change only by small amounts along the series. Rather larger changes are shown by the corresponding acids.

5.8.3. Esters and lactones

The carbonyl frequencies and intensities of a large number of esters of all kinds have been given by Thompson [133], and these are supplemented by similar measurements by Flett [166] Brown [66], Fruwert *et al.* [344] and Mateos [180]. It would seem that the carbonyl intensities of esters are remarkably constant and that they change little with conjugation. Nor can any relation be found between the band intensities and the Hammett σ values of the substituents of benzoates, despite the fact that a good relationship occurs with the corresponding frequencies. Fruewert does find a relation with the Taft values in the alkyl esters but the intensity changes are relatively small [344].

One general finding of considerable interest is that there is a good linear relationship between the stretching frequencies of the single and double carbon oxygen bonds. This appears to hold well for all systems except the formates, and is characterised by the equation

$$\nu C—O = 4112 - 1.625\ \nu C{=}O$$

This has a correlation coefficient of 0.987. Similar findings have been reported earlier for specialised systems such as the acetoxysteroids, and for perfluorinated esters, but this is the first time a general relationship has been reported [345]. This same paper lists some carbonyl frequencies of unusual compounds such as FCOOF (1930 cm^{-1}), FCOOSF$_5$ (1900 cm^{-1}), but the data used for carbonyl frequencies do not extend below 1750 cm^{-1}. The relationship has not therefore been tested on conjugated or aromatic esters. However, if as the authors suggest, the relationship is due to the resonance equilibrium between the two carbon oxygen bonds, it should remain valid for all frequencies.

Measurements on dialkyl esters [181, 182] and on unsaturated esters [182] have been made over a wide variety of compounds, and the results agree well with the values quoted by Thompson and others. Variations in the nature of the alkyl groups result in only small changes in νCO, which remains in the range 1750–1737 cm^{-1}, with slightly lower values for the formates. In chloroform solution [182] rather lower values are obtained. The crotonates [183], acrylates and other conjugated esters show lower values, as expected. Alkyl aryl esters have also been further studied. Eglinton *et al.* [173, 184, 213] have examined the influence of the size of the alkyl group in alkyl benzoates. Although the differences are small (13 cm^{-1} from methyl to *tert*-butyl), there is a regular movement of νCO towards lower frequencies as the size of the alkyl group is increased. This parallels the relative inductive effects of the alkyl groups. Similar results were found in the intramolecularly bonded salicylates and 2,6-dihydroxybenzoates.

The effects of changes in the ring substituents of alkyl benzoates have been studied [133, 166, 182]. Parallel measurements on esters of substituted pyridines have been made by Katritzky [185]. Dewar and Grisdale [42] have shown that νCO in substituted methyl naphthoates is a linear function of the pK$_a$ values of the free acids, and similar results have been reported for benzoate esters [190]. The frequencies of the methyl esters of diphenylacetic acid, fluorene- and anthracene-carboxylic acids have been reported by Bowden [186]. Freedman [122] has made very extensive studies on substituted phenyl acetates, but the frequency range is small (1779–1769 cm^{-1} in carbon tetrachloride). In contrast, changes in the ring substituents in methyl esters of carboxyferrocenes lead to large frequency shifts when the polar groups are introduced into the other ring [187]. The overall range is 1723–1696 cm^{-1}.

Diesters such as malonates and oxalates have been studied by Abramovitch [32], and geminal diesters by Guthrie [188]. The latter show rather higher frequencies than usual and sometimes appear as a doublet, possibly due to field effects. 1,1-Diacetoxypropane absorbs at 1761 cm^{-1} in the liquid state.

Finally, mention must be made of the studies of Freeman [189] on esters CH_3COOX, where X is an element other than carbon. Most of the compounds listed involve attachment to nitrogen, and νCO then falls in the wide range 1810–1710 cm^{-1}. The frequency reflects the polarity of the nitrogen atom, and is therefore highest in compounds such as CH_3COONO_2 (1798 cm^{-1}) and $CH_3COON(COCH_3)_2$ (1810 cm^{-1}), where the nitrogen is strongly electronegative. Lower frequencies arise in compounds such as o-$NH_2 \cdot C_6H_4 \cdot COONH_2$ (1710 cm^{-1}), where the polarity of the nitrogen is reduced, although hydrogen bonding also plays some small part in this. This same dependence on the polarity of X is shown by the high νCO values of peroxyesters, and by the low ones of esters attached to silicon or to metals. $(CH_3)_3SiOCOCH_3$ absorbs at 1715 cm^{-1}, and both $(C_4H_9)_2Sn(OCOCH_3)_2$ and $C_6H_5HgOCOCH_3$ near 1580 cm^{-1} [189].

Work on lactones has largely confirmed the correlations previously known. Hall and Zbinden [36] and Kucherov [196] list the carbonyl frequencies of some simple lactones, and Jones has discussed the spectra of steroid lactones very fully [19, 193]. Unsaturated lactones have been reported on by Jones [18], Kovalyov et al. [148] and Korte et al. [197] (unsaturated six-membered ring systems), Olsen and Russwurm [194] (β-Unsaturated lactones) and Horak [195] (conjugated methylene lactones). Some data on phthalides are given by Graf et al. [124].

5.8.4. Acid halides

Recent measurements on simple carbonyl halides include COFBr, COBrCl [199], COF_2 [199, 69], HCOF and DCOF [200]. The spectra of α-chlorinated acetyl halides have been discussed by Bellamy and Williams in relation to their rotational isomerism, and the spectra of CF_3COCl [70], CF_3COF [201], and CH_2FCOF [315] have been remeasured. Al Jallo and Jalhoom [346] have reported the frequencies and intensities of the carbonyl bands of 40 aromatic and heterocyclic acid halides. Neither bears any relationship to the aromatic substituent constants. The same authors have studied $\alpha\beta$ unsaturated acid halides [280] and discussed the influence of conformation on the frequencies. The problem of the doubling of the carbonyl band in benzoyl chloride has already been discussed in Section 5.3.1, and is covered by references [14, 15, 18, 278].

5.8.5. Chloroformates   (chlorocarbonates)   and   related compounds

XCOHalogen, where X is an element other than carbon.

(a) Chloroformates, ROCOCl

Several workers have examined the carbonyl frequencies of this class. Alkyl derivatives have been studied by Ory [198], Nyquist and Potts [202] and Katritzky *et al.* [182]. The results confirm that vCO falls in a relatively narrow range 1780–1775 cm^{-1}, although α-halogen substitution gives higher values. β-Substitution has no effect [203]. Slightly lower values are given in chloroform solution. The effect of a multiple bond attached to the oxygen atom has not been fully studied, but it appears to raise vCO just as in the vinyl esters. Thus allyl chloroformate absorbs [198] at 1799 cm^{-1} and phenyl chloroformate at 1784 cm^{-1} [203].

(b) Thiol chloroformates, RSCOCl

Only two alkyl and two aryl thiol chloroformates have been examined [48, 202]. The alkyl derivatives absorb between 1772 and 1766 cm^{-1} and the aryl compounds between 1775 and 1769 cm^{-1}. Methyl thiolchloroformate has vCO at 1782 in the vapour phase [202], but this is attributable, at least in part, to Fermi resonance effects.

(c) Carbamoyl chlorides, NR$_2$COCl

The carbonyl frequencies of one alkyl and one aryl derivative are given by Nyquist and Potts [202], and Buder and Schmidt [347] give the spectrum of *N*-methylcarbamoyl chloride. In dilute solutions these absorb near 1780 cm^{-1}, but like the amides, association effects reduce this considerably in the solid state. They then absorb in the 1750–1740 cm^{-1} range.

5.8.6. Anhydrides and peroxides

The main features of this group have already been discussed at length in Section 5.3.2. Tabulated data on the frequencies and solvent sensitivities of many anhydrides are given in reference [21], and other data are available in references [23, 62, 204, 209, 282 and 283]. Thiophthalic anhydride has been studied by Bigotto and Galasso [285]. This absorbs at 1742 and 1707 cm^{-1}, and is less strongly coupled than the normal anhydrides.

Little new is available on the carbonyl frequencies of aroyl peroxides, although a small number of compounds are discussed in reference [21], and in the paper by Seucanka *et al.* [205]. The compound F·CO·O·O·CO·F has been studied by Arvia [206]. In the vapour phase this shows bands at 1934, 1905 and 1899 cm^{-1}.

5.8.7. Carbonates, thiolcarbonates and dithiolcarbonates

Small numbers of alkyl carbonates have been examined by Katritzky *et al.* [182] and Gatehouse *et al.* [207], and rather larger numbers by Hales *et al.* [203] and by Thompson and Jameson [133]. The latter also give intensity data, from which it appears that the carbonyl intensity is considerably greater than it is in esters. The whole, together with some unpublished data of their own, is summarized by Nyquist and Potts [202]. They quote thirteen alkyl carbonates as absorbing between 1741 and 1739 cm^{-1}, seventy-two alkyl aryl carbonates between 1787 and 1757 cm^{-1} and four diaryl carbonates between 1819 and 1775 cm^{-1}.

The inclusion of the carbonate residue in a five-membered ring system causes the carbonyl frequency to rise due to the narrowing of the bond angle at the carbonyl group. Hales *et al.* [203] list a number of instances of such compounds absorbing between 1809 and 1833 cm^{-1}. Further studies of cyclic carbonates have been made by Sarel *et al.* [208], by Hough *et al.* [210, 211] and by Pethrick and Wilson [348].

Halogen substitution at the α-position of substituent alkyl groups can lead to multiple peaks, and in the case of the compound $CCl_3 \cdot O \cdot CO \cdot O \cdot CCl_3$ the carbonyl frequency rises to 1833 cm^{-1} as compared with 1750 cm^{-1} for the dimethyl derivative. A similar effect is found in substituted ethylene carbonates [348]. 4-methyl, and 4-chloromethylethylene carbonate absorb at 1800 cm^{-1}, but the 4-chloro derivative absorbs at 1816 cm^{-1} and the 4 : 5-dichloro derivative at 1842 cm^{-1}. It is possible that although the chlorine is not on the α carbon atom, it is nevertheless sufficiently near in space to the $C{=}O$ (due to the *cis* conformation) to produce a field effect similar to those discussed in Section 5.6.

Thiolcarbonates $R \cdot S \cdot CO \cdot O \cdot R$ have not been much studied, but a few compounds have been described by Baker [48] and by Nyquist [202]. Alkyl thiolcarbonates absorb in the range 1710–1702 cm^{-1}. The replacement of an alkyl group by a phenyl ring raises this to 1731–1714 cm^{-1} if the aryl group is attached to sulphur and to 1739–1730 cm^{-1} if the attachment is to oxygen.

Even fewer dithiolcarbonates have been examined. One dialkyl compound is reported by Baker [48] and three by Nyquist [202]. These absorb in the 1655–1640 cm^{-1} range, showing the trend towards lower frequencies that is also shown when one passes from esters to thiolesters. Surprisingly two diaryl dithiolcarbonates absorb in the 1718–1714 cm^{-1} range. This seems a remarkable jump for so small a change in chemical structure.

5.8.8. Thiolesters

A substantial number of thiolesters have been examined by Nyquist and Potts [67], and a lesser number by Baker and Harris [48], who have also carried out basicity measurements. Dialkyl thiolesters absorb in the relatively narrow range 1698–1690 cm^{-1}.

Alkyl aryl thiolesters of the type $R \cdot CO \cdot S \cdot C_6H_5$ absorb near 1710 cm^{-1}. In both these and the dialkyl thiol esters α halogen substitution at the alkyl group results in multiple carbonyl bands which must arise from rotational isomerism. This is confirmed by the observation that only single bands occur when the substitution is increased to give CCl_3 or CF_3 groups. Similar doubling effects are also found in o-halogenated aryl thiolesters.

Aryl substitution at the carbonyl group lowers vCO, just as in normal ketones. Thiolesters of the type C_6H_5COSR absorb between 1665 and 1670 cm^{-1}, depending on the nature of the ring substituent. However, $ortho$-halogen substituents give higher frequencies. Similar $ortho$ effects occur in diaryl thiolesters, which otherwise absorb close to 1685 cm^{-1}. A few selenoesters (COSeR) have been studied, and details are given by Renson and Draguet [274].

5.8.9. Carboxylic acids

The carbonyl frequencies of monomeric and dimeric alkyl carboxylic acids have been measured by Josien $et\ al.$ [181], and of substituted benzoic acids by Eglinton [213], Josien [50], Flett [166] and Gonzales Sanchez [215]. The first three of this latter group report solution measurements, and the last two deal with solids when, in general, only dimers are present. In addition, Horak and Exner [235] give vCO values for fifty carboxylic acids in dioxane solution. In both the alkyl and aryl series there is a reasonably constant difference between vCO of the monomers and dimers of about 45 cm^{-1}. Eglinton and Josien have both been interested in the relationship between vCO and the pK_a values. Such relationships, within limited series, had been shown previously to exist for the vOH (monomer) values, so that it was reasonable to expect a parallel behaviour in vCO. Apart from the special cases of the $ortho$-substituted benzoic acids, the agreement is remarkably good, and Josien [50] suggests that for unassociated acids (i.e. monomers without OH or NH substitution) the carbonyl frequency can be derived from the formula vCO $= 1785.5 - 10.5$ pK_a. Toluic acids are exceptional and follow a relation of their own, vCO $= 1779.8 - 10.3$ pK_a. Because of the reasonably constant differences between monomeric and dimeric frequencies, the values for the latter can be predicted in the same way. The monomer values used are those in carbon tetrachloride. Significantly lower values are observed in chloroform solution. Morgan [68] and also Josien [107] have studied the variations in vCO of carboxylic acids in different solvents. The values for dimers are remarkably constant and are little affected by either the solvent or the phase. Thus the dimer values in solution are closely similar to those reported by Flett [166] for KBr discs.

The effects of *ortho* substitution in benzoic acids have also been extensively studied. Doubling of vCO occurs in *ortho*-halogenated acids. This was at one time attributed to intramolecular hydrogen bonding. However, parallel studies in which both vOH and vCO are measured have shown [213] that rotational isomerism is involved and that a field effect occurs which raises vCO in that conformation in which the carbonyl oxygen atom is close to the halogen. It is interesting that this effect should be so clear-cut in these compounds while it remains so difficult to detect in the α-halogenated alkyl acids [75, 76, 320]. Ferrocenecarboxylic acids have been discussed by Kazicyna [187] and α-nitrato acids by McCallum and Emmons [81].

Carboxylic acids nearly always occur as cyclic dimers, and substantial proportions of this form persist, even at high dilutions in solution or at temperatures below 150° in the vapour phase. However, in some instances, including acetic and oxalic acids, long-chain polymers can occur, and the hydrogen bonds of these are of a different and weaker strength than those of the cyclic systems [218, 219, 349]. This is very well shown by the α and β forms of anhydrous oxalic acid, which are known from x-ray work to take the open and cyclic forms respectively. Measurements of vOH and OD and of the corresponding bending frequencies show conclusively that the bonding is weaker in the α open-chain form. Despite this, the vCO value is found to be lower than that of the cyclic form. This apparent contradiction is readily understood if one considers the true nature of the vibrational modes concerned. Open-chain systems have a single vibrational vCO mode which is directly related to the force constant of the bond. In the cyclic dimers, however, two modes will arise which correspond to symmetric and anti-symmetric vibrations of the pair of carbonyl groups. These frequencies are artificially split apart, and it is the mean value of the two which is now a function of the force constant. However, symmetry considerations cause the lower of these two frequencies (the symmetric mode) to be forbidden in the infrared. The direct comparison between the carbonyl frequencies of the open-chain and cyclic associated acids is not therefore a valid one, and it does not tell us anything about the real strengths of the hydrogen bonds.

Another instance in which vCO is reported to change due to the occurrence of open-chain associations is that of acrylic acid [220].

The carbonyl frequencies of monomeric acids, and sometimes even those of dimers, can be considerably altered by intramolecular hydrogen bonding. In cases in which the carbonyl group is directly involved this naturally leads to a fall in vCO, but the opposite effect is observed in those systems in which the acid hydroxyl is involved in a bond which is not to the carbonyl link. A number of authors [184, 221–223] have discussed the spectra of intra-molecularly bonded β-hydroxy $\alpha\beta$-unsaturated acids, of which salicylic acid is a good example. This compound and some twenty substituted derivatives have been studied by Eglinton *et al.* [184]. There are two possible arrange-ments of the hydrogen bond in the monomeric acid, and these are represented by (I) and (II) below, while the corresponding possibilities for the dimers are (III) and (IV). As there is little to choose between the forms (I) and (II) in terms of bond angles and distances, one might well expect form (I) to be preferred on the grounds that the carboxylic OH is the more acidic of the two hydroxyls and the phenolic hydroxyl the more basic. However, another factor enters into this, i.e. the preferred *cis* configuration of the carboxylic acid group. Although this is not established with certainty as it is in the case of esters, it seems almost certain that the same lone-pair/lone-pair repulsions that stabilize the *cis* forms of esters will determine the preferred configuration of acids. In fact, a detailed study of the frequency data shows that (II) is the preferred form of the monomers, indicating that the energy which would be lost by the carboxylic group taking the *trans* configuration is greater than that which would be gained by the formation of the stronger hydrogen bond. Thus in salicylic acid vCO is at 1698 cm^{-1} in the monomer and at 1663 cm^{-1} in the dimer. A comparison of the frequencies in methyl salicylate (form (II)) and of *o*-methoxybenzoic acid (form (I)) enables one to identify the acid itself with form (II).

(I)   (II)   (III)

(IV)

The effects of other substituents in salicylic acids have also been studied. The most interesting effect is the increase in hydrogen-bond strength which follows the introduction of bulky substituents at the 3 or 6 positions. This is the result of a buttressing effect whereby the O . . . O distances are reduced [184]. Parallel studies on chelated amino salicylic acids have been reported by Kellie et al. [224], who have shown that in this series vCO is a function of the Hammett σ values of the ring substituents.

When intramolecular hydrogen bonding does involve the carboxylic acid hydroxyl group the latter is compelled to take the *trans* configuration. This leads to a remarkable upward shift in the carbonyl frequency. *o*-Methoxybenzoic acid is an example of such a compound in which vCO rises to 1751 cm^{-1}. The corresponding *para*-substituted derivative absorbs at the more normal value of 1737 cm^{-1}. Oki and Hirota [225, 226] quote many examples of this effect. In a series of α-substituted phenoxyacetic acids, for example, they find that the carbonyl frequency of the *trans* form in which the carboxylic group is associated through the hydroxyl group is consistently some 30 cm^{-1} higher in frequency than the *cis* form. Pyruvic and other α-keto acids behave similarly [226–228].

The origins of this frequency rise in the *trans* form deserve further study. Other instances of intramolecularly bonded acids of this kind are given by Trubnikov [228, 229] (δ-oxo acids and ketonic acids), and by Eberson [230] (alkylated succinic acids). The high carbonyl frequency of 8-carboxyquinoline (1731 cm^{-1}) quoted by Flett [166] also indicates that this compound is intramolecularly bonded.

Peroxy acids have been examined by several workers [231, 232, 350, 351]. In non-polar solvents these exist as intramolecularly hydrogen bonded systems, but in oxygenated solvents, and in the solid state the bonding is intermolecular. Most peroxy acids show two bands in the carbonyl region, separated by about 20 cm^{-1}. However, 2-nitro-4-chloro-peroxybenzoic acid has only one band at 1748 cm^{-1}. In contrast to this, peroxybenzoic acids with a chlorine atom in the 2 or 5 position show more than two bands. The 2 : 5-dichloro compound has four carbonyl absorptions. Hadzi attributes the normal 20 cm^{-1} splitting to correlation coupling, and the presence of additional bands in the halogen series to non-equivalent hydrogen bonding. Thioacids have been examined in small numbers by Nyquist and Potts [202] and by Rao [233]. These absorb near 1700–1690 cm^{-1}, and in contrast to the dithioacids, they show little tendency to dimerize.

Finally, mention must be made of intensity studies on the COOH carbonyl absorption. Because of the difficulties in obtaining samples wholly in the monomer form, these measurements are very difficult to make, but some values have been given by Wenograd and Spurr [234], while some extinction coefficients are given by Eglinton [213]. The measurements on dimers are somewhat easier, but little is known of the possible effects of the medium (if any) on the intensities in this series. Flett [166] has given a useful tabulation of carbonyl intensities of dimeric acids in potassium bromide discs, and Fruwert *et al.* [344] have measured corresponding values in solution for alkyl acids. They find some sensitivity to the polarity of the substituent, and within the homologous series of unbranched alkyl acids, a linear relationship with the Taft substituent constants.

5.8.10. Amides

(a) νCO in primary amides

Only a limited amount of new data are available on carbonyl frequencies in primary amides. Flett [166] gives values for a number of alkyl and aryl amides in potassium bromide discs. He quotes the general range of 1680–1670 cm^{-1}, as in concentrated solutions, but a number of very abnormal cases were found, including o-cyanobenzamide (vCO 1752 cm^{-1}), and p-aminobenzamide (vCO 1623 cm^{-1}). The intensity data were also obtained, but no relationship was found between the intensities and the chemical nature of the substituents. Brown et al. [74] have also measured the carbonyl frequencies and intensities of some simple amides, this time in very dilute solutions in carbon tetrachloride. The vCO values were somewhat higher, as one would expect, the alkyl amides absorbing at 1690 cm^{-1} with higher values for some α-halogenated compounds. CF$_3$·CONH$_2$ absorbs at 1750 cm^{-1}. In some of the halogenated compounds the carbonyl band was doubled, as would be expected, from rotational isomerism. No satisfactory relation could be found between the changes of frequency and of intensity. However, it was noted that amides appear to behave rather like esters, in that the intensity is markedly reduced when bulky groups are introduced at the cis position with respect to the carbonyl group.

Other studies on primary amides include detailed assignments for oxamide by Scott [236] and for acrylamide by Jonathan [237]. Studies on the ^{14}N/^{15}N substitution in benzamide have been used to show that there is real coupling between the Amide I, II and III bands in this compound, as all three show sizeable shifts on isotopic substitution [7, 238].

(b) Secondary amides

Simple acetamides, formamides and benzamides have been studied by several workers. Jones [239] gives frequencies for a number of small molecules in the vapour state, and Miyazawa et al. [240] have made a normal coordinate analysis of N-methylacetamide from which they conclude that the Amide I band at 1653 cm^{-1} has 80 per cent carbonyl character. Homologous series of N-alkylacetamides have been studied by Beer et al. [241] and by Nyquist [72, 73]. The first group included some ^{15}N and deuteration studies and found that vCO was not affected by isotopic substitution at the nitrogen atom, but was shifted by 20 cm^{-1} on deuteration. They quote the carbonyl frequencies of the series as falling close to 1650 cm^{-1}, but this includes measurements on both liquids and on solutions. Nyquist [72, 73], working at higher dilutions, quotes the narrow range 1687–1690 cm^{-1} for the whole series of N-alkyl acetamides from methyl to t-butyl. N substituted benzamides have been examined by Nyquist [73], by Thompson and Jameson [133], and by Reichel et al. [242]. These are rather more sensitive to changes in the alkyl group, and p-methoxybenzamides absorb between 1676 and 1665 cm^{-1}, while p-chlorobenzamides absorb between 1681 and 1671 cm^{-1}. The carbonyl frequency is also sensitive to the nature of the ring substituents, and Thompson [133] gives some data on the frequency and intensity changes that can then result. It has been shown that the *trans* form predominates in all the alkyl amides [353] and the values above relate to this form.

The impact of α-halogen substitution has already been discussed. Extensive data are given by Nyquist [72, 73]. Oxamides have been reviewed by Spinner [243] and by Desseyn *et al.* [354]. In all cases the carbonyl bonds take a *trans* arrangement with respect to each other and only a single carbonyl band appears. This falls in the range 1675–1660 cm^{-1} in the solid state, and between 1681 and 1671 cm^{-1} in chloroform solution. In the solid state the hydrogen bonding is intermolecular. There are, of course, many other studies of the amide carbonyl band in more complex systems, particularly in polymers and in proteins. These cannot be adequately dealt with in the space available, but useful bibliographies will be found in the reviews by Elliott [244] and by Zbinden [245].

(c) *Tertiary amides*

Measurements on a small number of *N*-disubstituted amides in dilute solutions are given by Thompson [133], and also by Schmulbach and Drago [246]. The frequencies of the *N*-dialkyl compounds are a little lower than those of the mono-substituted amides, *N,N*-dimethylacetamide absorbing at 1653 cm^{-1} and *N,N*-dimethylbenzamide at 1644 cm^{-1}. Speziale and Freeman [247] have studied α-halogen substitution in tertiary amides. The results are parallel to those of the monosubstituted compounds, but the complications of internal hydrogen bonding are now absent. *N,N*-dimethyltrichloroacetamide has vCO at 1689 cm^{-1}, and this represents a somewhat higher value than the monoalkyl compound.

Nyquist *et al.* [355], have studied large numbers of *N,N*-disubstituted oxamides in the solid state. Like the monosubstituted oxamides, these occur exclusively in the form in which the carbonyl bonds are *trans* to each other, and therefore have only a single carbonyl band. This falls in the range 1660–1643 cm^{-1} for the alkyl derivatives, and between 1719–1662 cm^{-1} for aryl, or heteroaromatic derivatives. αβ unsaturated *N,N*-dimethyl acetamides have been studied by Kruk and Spaargaren [311]. These can exist in the *s.cis* or *s.trans* conformations. The *s.cis* compounds have the carbonyl band at higher frequencies than the *s.trans*, the difference being about 20 cm^{-1}. This has led to confusion in the past when studying the effects of conjugation. Thus *N,N*-dimethyl crotonamide absorbs 13 cm^{-1} higher than does *N,N*-dimethylacetamide, giving an apparent negative conjugation effect. This is in fact due to the fact that the frequency in the unsaturated compound is raised because it has the *cis* form. A comparison between a saturated and unsaturated amide in the *trans* form shows the expected frequency fall on conjugation.

Spaargarn *et al.* [356] have studied the substituent effects on the carbonyl frequencies of *N,N*-dimethyl benzamides and cinnamides. The frequencies were correlated with the substituent constants of *meta* and *para* substituents using the Swain and Lupton modification of the Hammett values. They also found a correlation with the carbonyl π bond orders and the oxygen π electron densities as calculated by the HMO method. They also demonstrated two other very interesting relationships. There appears to be a close link between the carbonyl frequency and the amide rotational barriers, giving separate linear relationships for each of the two systems studied. The frequencies rise as the barriers increase. They have also measured the amide bascisity as determined by the OH frequency shift on hydrogen bonding to the carbonyl and shown that this also is a linear function of the carbonyl frequency within each separate series.

(d) Anilides and related compounds

Frequency data for anilides with various substituents in the aromatic ring have been given by O'Sullivan and Sadler [249], Freedman [122], Thompson [133], Flett [166] and by Forbes *et al.* [248]. The frequencies are higher than in the tertiary amides, and this is due to a reduction in the resonance within the amide group because of the competition offered by the aromatic ring for the lone-pair electrons on the nitrogen atom. In chloroform solution acetanilides absorb between 1695 and 1710 cm^{-1}. With *o*-nitro substitution there is some degree of hydrogen bonding with the NH group, and high carbonyl frequencies then persist in the solid state [248]. *o*-Nitroacetanilide absorbs at 1707 cm^{-1} in solution, but has two frequencies in the solid state at 1700 and 1670 cm^{-1}. Benzanilides behave similarly [248]. Additional data on benzanilides are given in papers by Flett [166] and by Reichel [242], while Katritzky and Jones [250] give frequencies for the systems RNHCOCH$_3$, RNHCOR, RN(CH$_3$)COCH$_3$ and RN(CH$_3$)COR, where the R groups are either aromatic rings or variously substituted pyridine or pyridine *N*-oxide rings. They find that the replacement of a hydrogen atom on the nitrogen of acetanilides by a methyl group lowers vCO by 25–46 cm^{-1}, while replacement of the aromatic ring by pyridine raises the frequency by up to 23 cm^{-1}, depending upon the point of attachment in relation to the pyridine nitrogen atom.

The effects of competition for the lone-pair electrons of the nitrogen atom are even more pronounced in *N*-acetyl or *N*-benzoyl compounds, in which the nitrogen atom forms part of a heterocyclic ring. The carbonyl frequency reaches the remarkable value of 1779 cm^{-1} in *N*-acetyltetrazole [251]. Bellamy [251] has shown that there is a smooth-curve relationship between vCO and the resonance energy of the heterocyclic rings. Staab *et al.* [252] report similar results and show that in substituted *N*-benzoyl derivatives there is a linear relationship between vCO and the measured rates of hydrolysis. Reid *et al.* [253] have examined *N*-acetyl-2,5-dimethylpyrazoles and again find abnormally high carbonyl frequencies. With acetylindoxyl compounds the amide carbonyl frequencies return nearer to normality. O'Sullivan and Sadler [254] have differentiated the amide and ester carbonyl functions in diacetyl-indoxyl derivatives on the basis that the former show a linear relationship with Hammett σ values whereas the latter do not. The amide bands in this series fall in the range 1717–$1692 \, cm^{-1}$.

(e) Cyclic lactams

Data on the variations of vCO with ring size are collected in Table 5.1 (p. 139). Most of the available values are due to Hall and Zbinden [36], but additional data are available in papers by Zahn [255] and by Huisgen [256]. The latter has been principally concerned with the effects of the reversion from the *cis* to the *trans* form of the amide group which occurs when the ring size becomes nine-membered or more. This reversion has, of course, a dramatic effect on the amide II band, but has little or no effect upon the carbonyl frequency.

Sorygin *et al.* [257] have given some interesting data on lactams with *N*-vinyl substituents. The effects are somewhat less than might have been expected from the behaviour of the anilides. In 2-pyrrolidone the replacement of an *N*-butyl group by *N*-vinyl raises vCO by $15 \, cm^{-1}$, but the rise in *N*-vinylhexanolactam is only $4 \, cm^{-1}$ above the value of hexanolactam itself. Frequency data on more complex lactams are given in Table 5.3 and in the review of Katritzky [164]. The spectra of cyclic imides have been discussed in detail by Bassignana *et al.* [165].

5.8.11. Imides

The structure CONHCO is planar, and like the anhydrides the carbonyl frequencies are coupled. The extent of the splitting depends on several factors, such as the equivalence or otherwise of the carbonyl groups, their conforma-tion with respect to each other, and on the nature of the substituents. Symmetric dialkyl imides such as diacetamide and dipropionamide have been studied by Uno *et al.* [357–360], they can exist in the *trans/trans* or the *trans/cis* form depending on the crystal form or on the solvent. The *trans/cis* form of diactamide has carbonyl bands at 1736 and $1701 \, cm^{-1}$. However, the carbonyl which is *cis* to the NH is intermolecularly hydrogen bonded in a ring dimer, whilst the *trans* carbonyl is not. The two C=O groups are not therefore equivalent and it is difficult to say whether the splitting is due to this or to coupling. The *trans/trans* structures show a wider separation of the two carbonyl bands but here again there is some doubt on the assignments. In *trans/trans* dipropionamide for example bands appear at 1740 and $1681 \, cm^{-1}$ but there is some doubt on whether the last is a true carbonyl absorption. Data on some unsymmetric imides are given by Macay and Poziomek [361]. Alkyl *N*-formyl-acetamides absorb at 1730–$1720 \, cm^{-1}$ and at 1687–$1670 \, cm^{-1}$, but here again it is uncertain how much of this difference is due to the different carbonyls and how much to the coupling.

With cyclic symmetric imides there is no question that the doubling originates in coupling. In glutarimide [362] the carbonyl bands are at 1730 and 1706 cm^{-1}, but the coupling is enormously increased in a compound such as $3 : 5$-dioxopyrrolizidine [361], when the bands are at 1770 and 1688 cm^{-1}. This must be due to the increased possibilities for electronic coupling in this last compound.

5.8.12. Carbamates (urethanes) ROCONH₂ and ROCONHR, Thiocarbamates

Pinchas *et al.* [258], have classified the various alkyl compounds as follows:

Primary RO·CO·NH₂	1728–1722 cm⁻¹
Secondary RO·CO·NHR	1722–1705 cm⁻¹
Tertiary RO·CO·NR₂	1691–1683 cm⁻¹

These measurements were all made in chloroform solution, and the values are distinctly lower than those of other authors using carbon tetrachloride. Nyquist [73], for example, quotes the range $1738-1730 \text{ cm}^{-1}$ for a series of secondary alkyl urethanes $RNHCOOC_2H_5$. Sato [259] compares a number of saturated and unsaturated urethanes, the unsaturated carbon atom being attached to the nitrogen atom. He finds little difference between vinyl and ethyl urethanes $(CH_2=CH \cdot NH \cdot COOC_4H_9 \ \nu CO \ 1716 \text{ cm}^{-1}$, $C_2H_5 \cdot NH \cdot COOC_2H_5 \ \nu CO \ 1720 \text{ cm}^{-1})$, but his overall range (down to 1680 cm^{-1}) is wider than that of Pinchas. Katritzky and Jones [260] have measured 16 aryl or heteroaromatic urethanes $C_6H_5 \cdot NH \cdot COOC_2H_5$, for which, in chloroform solution, the range quoted is $1739-1719 \text{ cm}^{-1}$. Nyquist quotes $1758-1730 \text{ cm}^{-1}$ for similar aryl/alkyl urethanes in carbon tetrachloride solution. In cases where intermolecular hydrogen bonding occurs this can fall to 1692 cm^{-1} in the solid state [364].

The general run of these frequencies is in the range that would be expected from the chemical structures. Cyclic urethanes have been discussed by Hall and Zbinden [36] and Galabov *et al.* [363] have related their carbonyl frequencies to the NCOO bond angles and to the carbonyl bond order. Thiocarbamates have been examined in small number by Nyquist and Potts [202]. Compounds of the type RSCONH alkyl absorb in the range $1690-1695 \text{ cm}^{-1}$, but *N*-aryl derivatives absorb at lower frequencies $(1699-1662 \text{ cm}^{-1})$. However, these were measured as associated solids, and it is difficult to assess the effects of the hydrogen bonding.

5.8.13. Ureas

Early studies on ureas are given in references [217, 261, 262]. These agree in assigning the amide I band near 1640 cm^{-1} in the solid state. This band is of course coupled with the amide II band in this series and the band therefore shifts to some extent on deuteration. However, in about 30 dialkyl ureas the carbonyl band is found in the range 1640–1625 cm^{-1}, shifting to about 1610 cm^{-1} on deuteration [365]. In the monosubstituted ureas the amide I and II band assignments are less certain. Jose [366], has looked at a number of these compounds and finds that of the two bands near 1650 and 1600 cm^{-1} the deuteration results suggest that the 1600 cm^{-1} band has more carbonyl character so that he assigns the amide II band near 1650 cm^{-1} and the carbonyl band near 1600 cm^{-1}.

Cyclic ureas have been studied by Hall and Zbinden [36] and also by Galabov *et al.* [363], the latter have related the frequency changes with ring size to the changes in the NCN bond angle and also to the C=O bond order.

5.8.14. Amides with an element other than carbon attached to the nitrogen atom

The methylol ureas fall into this class, as the oxygen atom is attached to the amide nitrogen. Parsons [88] has studied *O*-methylformhydroxamic acid, H·CO·NH·OCH$_3$, in which vCO occurs at 1738 cm^{-1} in the vapour phase, but falls to 1675 cm^{-1} in the solid. The acid itself has been studied by Orville Thomas and Parsons [89]. Hadzi and Pevorsch [216] have studied a series of alkyl hydroxamic acids R·CO·NH·OH, which in the solid state absorb near 1640 cm^{-1}.

Compounds in which another nitrogen is attached to the amide nitrogen have been explored by Mashima [35]. The series RCONHNH$_2$ gave very variable frequencies within the range 1700–1640 cm^{-1}, but the compounds R·CO·NH·NH·CO·R gave multiple bands in the regions 1740–1700 and 1707–1683 cm^{-1}.

The carbonyl frequencies of a series of aryl sulphonamides, of the type C$_6$H$_5$·SO$_2$·NH·COCH$_3$, have been reported by Momose *et al.* [22]. In the solid state the frequencies are surprisingly high, and they range from 1720 to 1686 cm^{-1}, depending on the nature of the aryl substituents.

Secondary amides with halogen substituents on the nitrogen atom have been discussed by De Klein and Plesman [319]. The carbonyl frequencies then rise sharply, probably due to a field effect. Thus, *N*-methyl-acetamide absorbs at 1688 cm^{-1} in dilute solution, the *N*-chloro derivative at 1729 and 1715 cm^{-1} and the *N*-iodo derivative at 1714 and 1710 cm^{-1}.

5.8.15. Silyl esters, R·CO·SiR$_3$

A series of compounds of this kind have been examined by Brook and Peddle [40]. In all cases the carbonyl frequency was found at the invariant value of 1618 cm^{-1}. The silicon atom has, of course, a very low electronegativity, and this will lead to a lowering of the frequency, but one would not have expected the size of the shift due to this effect alone to be quite so large.

5.9. The carbonyl deformation frequency

A useful but little used group frequency is that of the out-of-plane skeletal deformation of the carbonyl group. In this mode the oxygen atom and the two substituents move in one direction in relation to the central plane, and the central carbon atom moves in the other. An initial survey of the various carbonyl deformation frequencies was made by Lecomte [212], and this has been extended by Overend and Evans [45, 190] and by Nyquist and Potts [202]. The precise positions of this absorption vary widely, and it occurs as low as 393 cm^{-1} (acetone) and as high as 1040 cm^{-1} (formic acid). It is therefore of limited use for diagnostic purposes, but the real interest lies in the fact that this appears to be an uncoupled vibration whose frequency is therefore controlled wholly by the chemical nature of the substituents. An excellent linear relationship has been found between kCO and the sum of the Taft inductive and resonance substituent constants, giving the empirical relation

$$k = 0.233 + 0.199 \sum_{XY} \sigma_1 - 0.268 \sum_{XY} \sigma_R$$

The particular interest in this frequency lies in the fact that both inductive and resonance factors raise the frequency. In the case of the carbonyl stretching mode these two factors are working in opposition. A combination of measurements on the changes in both frequencies should enable one to quantitatively disentangle the relative impact of these two factors without reference to arbitrary standards such as the σ_1 or σ_R values.

Shimizu and Shingu [273] have also discussed this absorption and give equations relating the frequency with a complex function of the masses, the electronegativities and bond distances. However, they have applied it only to compounds substituted with halogens or methyl groups, and even here a separate relation is found to be needed if a methyl group is present.

Bibliography

1. Karabatsos, *J. Org. Chem.,* 1960, **25**, 315.
2. Halford, *J. Chem. Phys.,* 1956, **24**, 830.
3. Halman and Pinchas, *J. Chem. Soc.,* 1958, 1703.
4. Overend and Scherer, *Spectrochim. Acta,* 1960, **16**, 773.
5. Bratoz and Besnainou, *Compt. Rendu.,* 1959, **248**, 546.
6. Frei and Gunthard, *J. Mol. Spectroscopy,* 1960, **5**, 218.
7. Kniseley, Fassel, Farquhar and Gray, *Spectrochim. Acta,* 1962, **18**, 1217.
8. Rao, Goldman and Lurie, *J. Phys. Chem.,* 1959, **63**, 1311.
9. Nolin and Jones, *Can. J. Chem.,* 1956, **34**, 1382.
10. Jones, *Can. J. Chem.,* 1962, **40**, 301.
11. Welther, *J. Amer. Chem. Soc.,* 1955, **77**, 3941.

12. Nolin and Jones, *Can. J. Chem.*, 1956, **34**, 1392.
13. Bellamy and Williams, *Trans. Faraday Soc.*, 1959, **55**, 14.
14. Garrigou-Lagrange, Claverie, Lebas and Josien, *J. Chim. Phys.*, 1961, 559.
15. Rao and Venkataraghavan, *Spectrochim. Acta*, 1962, **18**, 273.
16. Angell, Kruger, Lauzon, Leitch, Noack, Smith and Jones, *Spectrochim. Acta*, 1959, **15**, 926.
17. Allen, Ellington and Meakins, *J. Chem. Soc.*, 1960, 1909.
18. Jones, Angell, Ito and Smith, *Can. J. Chem.*, 1959, **37**, 2007.
19. Jones and Gallagher, *J. Amer. Chem. Soc.*, 1959, **81**, 5242.
20. Campbell and Gilow, *J. Amer. Chem. Soc.*, 1960, **82**, 5426.
21. Bellamy, Connelly, Philpotts and Williams, *Zeit. Electrochem.* 1960, **64**, 563.
22. Momose, Udea, Shoji and Yano, *Chem. and Pharm. Bull. Japan*, 1958, **6**, 669.
23. Dauben and Epstein, *J. Org. Chem.*, 1959, **24**, 1595.
24. Borisevitch and Khoratovitch, *Optics and Spectroscopy*, 1961, **10**, 309.
25. Taub and McGinn, *Dyestuffs*, 1958, **42**, 263.
26. Uno and Machida, *Bull. Chem. Soc. Japan*, 1961, **34**, 545, 551, 821.
27. Mecke and Funck, *Zeit. Electrochem.*, 1956, **60**, 1124.
28. Gren and Vanag, *C.R. Acad. Sci. U.S.S.R.*, 1960, **133**, 588.
29. Aren and Vanag, *J. Gen. Chem. Moscow*, 1961, **31**, (93), 117.
30. Abramovitch, *Can. J. Chem.*, 1959, **37**, 361.
31. Anancenko, Berezin and Torgov, *Bull. Acad. Sci. U.S.S.R.*, 1960, 1644.
32. Abramovitch, *Can. J. Chem.*, 1959, **37**, 1146.
33. Mazur and Sondheimer, *Experimentia*, 1960, **16**, 181.
34. Schmelz, Miyazawa, Mizushima, Lane and Quagliano, *Spectrochim. Acta*, 1957, **9**, 51.
35. Mashima, *Bull. Chem. Soc. Japan*, 1962, **35**, 332, 1862.
36. Hall and Zbinden, *J. Amer. Chem. Soc.*, 1958, **80**, 6428.
37. Deschamps, *Compt. Rendu.*, 1958, **246**, 2622.
38. Bellamy and Pace, *Spectrochim. Acta*, 1963, **19**, 1831.
39. Adelfang, Hess and Cromwell, *J. Org. Chem.*, 1961, **26**, 1402.
40. Brook and Peddle, *Can. J. Chem.*, 1963, **41**, 2351.
41. Dewar and Grisdale, *J. Amer. Chem. Soc.*, 1962, **84**, 3539, 3541, 3548.
42. Dewar and Grisdale, *J. Amer. Chem. Soc.*, 1962, **84**, 3546.
43. Bellamy, in *Spectroscopy*, Ed. Wells, Inst. Petroleum, 1962, 205.
44. Rao and Venkataraghavan, *Can. J. Chem.*, 1961, **39**, 1757.
45. Overend and Evans, *Spectrochim. Acta*, 1963, **19**, 701.
46. Cook, *J. Amer. Chem. Soc.*, 1958, **80**, 49.
47. Cook, *Can. J. Chem.*, 1961, **39**, 31.
48. Baker and Harris, *J. Amer. Chem. Soc.*, 1960, **82**, 1923.
49. Gramstad and Fuglevik, *Spectrochim. Acta*, 1965, **21**, 341.
50. Peltier, Pichevin, Dizabo and Josien, *Compt. Rendu*, 1959, **248**, 1148.
51. Owen and Sheppard, *Proc. Chem. Soc.*, 1963, 264.
52. Boitsov and Gotlib, *Optics and Spectroscopy*, 1961, **11**, 691.
53. Campbell and Schultz, *J. Org. Chem.*, 1960, **25**, 1877.
54. Allinger and Allinger, *Tetrahedron*, 1958, **14**, 64.
55. Allinger, Allinger, Freiburg, Czaja and Le Bel, *J. Amer. Chem. Soc.*, 1960, **82**, 5876.
56. Dang-Quoc-Quan, *Compt. Rendu*, 1961, **252**, 2247.
57. Kozima and Yamanovchi, *J. Amer. Chem. Soc.*, 1959, **81**, 4159.
58. Meda, *Spectrochim. Acta*, 1958, **13**, 75.
59. Castinel, Chirurdoglu, Josien, Lascombe and Vanlanduyl, *Bull. Soc. Chim. France*, 1958, 807.

60. Leonard and Owens, *J. Amer. Chem. Soc.*, 1958, **80**, 6039.
61. Cantacuzene, *J. Chim. Phys.*, 1962, **59**, 186.
62. Marquarat, *J. Chem. Soc. B*, 1966, 1242.
63. Griffin, *Spectrochim. Acta*, 1960, **16**, 1464.
64. Josien and Castinel, *Bull. Soc. Chim. France*, 1958, 801.
65. Radell and Harrah, *J. Chem. Phys.*, 1962, **36**, 1571.
66. Brown, *Spectrochim. Acta*, 1961, **18**, 1615; *J. Amer. Chem. Soc.*, 1958, **80**, 3513.
67. Nyquist and Potts, *Spectrochim. Acta*, 1959, **15**, 514.
68. Collins and Morgan, *J. Chem. Soc.*, 1963, 3437.
69. Bellamy and Williams, *J. Chem. Soc.*, 1958, 3465.
70. Berney, *Spectrochim. Acta*, 1964, **20**, 1437.
71. Letaw and Gropp, *J. Chem. Phys.*, 1953, **21**, 1621.
72. McLachlan and Nyquist, *Spectrochim. Acta*, 1964, **20**, 1397.
73. Nyquist, *Spectrochim. Acta*, 1963, **19**, 509.
74. Brown, Regan, Schultz and Sternberg, *J. Phys. Chem.*, 1959, **63**, 1324.
75. Barcello and Otero, *Spectrochim. Acta*, 1962, **18**, 1231.
76. Bellantano and Barcello, *Spectrochim. Acta*, 1960, **16**, 1333.
77. Claverie, Garrigou-Lagrange and Das Santos, *J. Chim. Phys.*, 1962, **59**, 1046.
78. Morris and Young, *J. Amer. Chem. Soc.*, 1957 **79**, 3408.
79. House and Blaker, *J. Amer. Chem. Soc.*, 1958, **80**, 6389.
80. Stradling and Tarbell, *J. Org. Chem.*, 1964, **29**, 1170.
81. McCallum and Emmons *J. Org. Chem.* 1956, **21**, 367.
82. Nejland Stradyn and Vanag *Compt. Rend. Acad. Sci. U.R.S.S.*, 1960, **131**, 1084.
83. Jones and Spinner, *Can. J. Chem.*, 1958, **36**, 1020.
84. Jones, Forbes and Muller, *Can. J. Chem.*, 1957, **35**, 504.
85. Renson and Piette, *Spectrochim. Acta*, 1964, **20**, 1847.
86. Bellamy and Williams, *J. Chem. Soc.*, 1957, 861.
87. Leonard, Milligan and Brown, *J. Amer. Chem. Soc.*, 1960, **82**, 4075.
88. Parsons, *J. Molecular Spectroscopy*, 1958, **2**, 566.
89. Orville, Thomas and parsons, *J. Molecular Spectroscopy*, 1958, **2**, 203.
90. Buckingham, *Proc. Roy. Soc.*, 1958, **A248**, 169; *Trans. Faraday Soc.*, 1960, **56**, 753.
91. Pullin, *Spectrochim. Acta*, 1958, **13**, 125; Archibald and Pullin, *Spectrochim. Acta*, 1958, **12**, 34.
92. Caldow and Thompson, *Proc. Roy. Soc.*, 1960, **A254**, 1.
93. Thompson, in *Spectroscopy*, Ed. Wells, Inst. Petroleum, 1962, p. 223.
94. Hallam and Ray, *Nature*, 1961, **189**, 915.
95. Hallam in *Spectroscopy*, Ed. Wells, Inst. Petroleum, 1962, p. 245.
96. Kagarise and Whetsel, *Spectrochim. Acta*, 1962, **18**, 315, 329, 341.
97. Tschulanowskij, *Compt. Rend. Acad. Sci. U.R.S.S.*, 1955, **101**, 457.
98. Jakovleva, Maslennikova and Petrow, *Optics and Spectroscopy*, 1961, **10**, 131.
99. Inuzuka, Ito and Imanishi, *Bull. Chem. Soc. Japan*, 1961, **34**, 467.
100. Ito, Inuzuka and Imanishi, *J. Chem. Phys.*, 1959, **31**, 1694.
101. Bellamy and Rogasch, *Spectrochim. Acta*, 1960, **16**, 30.
102. Katritzky and Jones, *Spectrochim. Acta*, 1961, **17**, 64.
103. Denisov, *Compt. Rend. Acad. Sci. U.R.S.S.*, 1960, **134**, 1131; *Optics and Spectroscopy*, 1961, **11**, 428.
104. Derkosch and Kaltenegger, *Monatsh. Chem.*, 1959, **90**, 645.
105. Aksnes, *Acta. Chem. Scand.*, 1960, **14**, 1475.
106. Gramstad and Fugelvik, *Acta. Chem. Scand.*, 1962, **16**, 1369.
107. Lascombe, Haurie and Josien, *J. Chim. Phys.*, 1962, 1233.
108. Morgan, Private Communication.

109. Susz and Wuhrmann, *Helv. Chim. Acta,* 1957, **40**, 722, 971.
110. Cook, *Can. J. Chem.,* 1959, **37**, 48.
111. Lappert, *J. Chem. Soc.,* 1962, 542.
112. Bystrov and Filimonov, *Compt. Rend. Acad. Sci. U.R.S.S.,* 1960, **131**, 338.
113. Archambault and Rivest, *Can. J. Chem.,* 1958, **36**, 1461.
114. Paoloni and Marini Bettolo, *Gazz. Chim. Ital.,* 1959, **89**, 1972.
115. Cook, *Can. J. Chem.,* 1962, **40**, 445.
116. Susz and Lachavanne, *Helv. Chim. Acta,* 1958, **41**, 634.
117. Chalandon and Susz, *Helv. Chim. Acta,* 1958, **41**, 697.
118. Susz and Chalandon, *Helv. Chim. Acta,* 1958, **41**, 1332.
119. Rossetti and Susz, *Helv. Chim. Acta,* 1964, **47**, 289, 299.
120. Pullin and Werner, *Spectrochim. Acta,* 1965, **21**, 1257.
121. Lascombe, Grange and Josien, *Bull. Soc. Chim. France,* 1957, 773.
122. Freedman, *J. Amer. Chem. Soc.,* 1960, **82**, 2454.
123. Thompson, Needham and Jameson, *Spectrochim. Acta,* 1957, **9**, 208.
124. Graf, Girod, Schmid and Stoll, *Helv. Chim. Acta,* 1959, **42**, 1085.
125. Subrahmanyam, Muralikrishna and Rao, *Current Sci.,* 1964, **33**, 304.
126. Hambly and O'Grady, *Austral. J. Chem.,* 1963, **16**, 459.
127. Mecke and Noack, *Spectrochim. Acta,* 1958, **12**, 391.
128. Mecke and Noack, *Chem. Ber.,* 1960, **93**, 210.
129. Noack and Jones, *Can. J. Chem.,* 1961, **39**, 2201.
130. Erskine and Waight, *J. Chem. Soc.,* 1960, 3425.
131. Noack, *Spectrochim. Acta,* 1962, **18**, 1625.
132. Sobolev and Alexsanyan, *Izvest. Akad. Nauk. S.S.S.R. Otdel Khim Nauk.,* 1963, 1336.
133. Thompson and Jameson, *Spectrochim. Acta,* 1958, **13**, 236.
134. Morcillo, Heranz and De La Cruz, *Spectrochim. Acta,* 1959, 497.
135. Herranz, De La Cruz and Morcillo, *Rev. Univ. Min.,* 9, 1959, **15**, 461.
136. Morcillo, Gallego, Madronero and Trabazo, *Anales real Soc. espan. Fis. Quim.,* 1964, **60B**, 199.
137. Cetina and Mateos, *J. Org. Chem.,* 1960, **25**, 704.
138. Cetina and Mateos, *Bol. Inst. quim. Univ. Nac. Mexico,* 1960, **12**, 63.
139. Borod'ko and Syrkin, *Compt. Rend. Acad. Sci. U.R.S.S.,* 1960, **134**, 1127.
140. Nakamoto, *Infrared Spectra of Coordination Compounds,* Wiley, New York, 1963, pp. 216 *et seq.*
141. Martin, Shamma and Fernelius, *J. Amer. Chem. Soc.,* 1958, **80**, 5851.
142. Mirosnicenko, Evstigneeva and Preobrazenkij, *J. Gen. Chem.,* 1960, **30**, (92), 2533.
143. Nejland and Vanag, *Adv. Chem. Moscow,* 1959, **28**, 436.
144. Charette and Teyssie, *Spectrochim. Acta,* 1960, **16**, 689.
145. De Wilde-Delvaux and Teyssie, *Spectrochim. Acta,* 1958, **12**, 289.
146. Duval and Lecomte, *Compt. Rendu,* 1962, **254**, 36.
147. Weinstein and Wyman, *J. Org. Chem.,* 1958, **23**, 1618.
148. Kovalyov, Prokapecko and Titov, *Ukrain. Khim. Zhur.,* 1963, **29**, 740.
149. Campbell and Gilow, *J. Amer. Chem. Soc.,* 1962, **84**. 1440.
150. Holtzclaw, Collman and Alire, *J. Amer. Chem. Soc.,* 1958, **80**, 1100.
151. Dabrowski and Kamienska, *Roczniki Chem.,* 1964, **38**, 1121.
152. Dabrowski, *Spectrochim. Acta,* 1963, **19**, 475.
153. Cook, in *Friedel–Crafts and Related Reactions,* Vol. I, ed. Olah, Inter-science, New York, 1963, pp. 767 *et seq.*
154. Bagli, *J. Amer. Chem. Soc.,* 1962, **84**, 172.
155. Brown, *Spectrochim. Acta,* 1962, **18**, 1065.

156. Becker, Ziffer and Charney, *Spectrochim. Acta,* 1963, **19**, 1871.
157. Flaig and Salfeld, *Annalen,* 1959, **626**, 215.
158. Gordon and Forbes, *Appl. Spectroscopy,* 1961, **15**, 19.
159. Durie, Lock and Hodge, *Austral. J. Chem.,* 1957, **10**, 429.
160. Baudet, Bertier and Pullman, *J. Chim. Phys.,* 1957, **54**, 282.
161. Bloom, Briggs and Cleverly, *J. Chem. Soc.,* 1959, 178.
162. Tanaka, *Chem. Pharm. Bull. Japan,* 1958, **6**, 18, 24.
163. Hadzi and Stajiljkovic, *Bull. Slovene. Chem. Soc.,* 1958, **5**, 75.
164. Katritzky and Ambler, in *Physical Methods in Heterocyclic Chemistry,* Academic Press, New York, 1963, p. 161.
165. Bassignana, Cogrossi, Franco and Mattiot, *Spectrochim. Acta,* 1965, **21**, 677.
166. Flett, *Spectrochim. Acta,* 1962, **18**, 1537.
167. Mateos, Cerecer and Cetina, *Bol. Inst. Quim. Univ. Nac. Mexico,* 1960, **12**, 59.
168. Padhye and Viladker, *J. Sci. Instr. Res.,* 1960, **19B**, 45.
169. Mirone and Lorenzelli, *Ann. Chim. Roma,* 1958, **48**, 72.
170. Chiorboli, Mirone and Lorenzelli, *Ann. Chim. Roma,* 1958, **48**, 355.
171. Forbes, *Can. J. Chem.,* 1962, **40**, 1891.
172. Yamada, *Bull. Chem. Soc. Japan,* 1959, **32**, 1051.
173. Brooks and Morman, *J. Chem. Soc.,* 1961, 3372.
174. Chiorboli and Mirone, *Ann. Chim. Roma,* 1958, 363.
175. Pinchas, *J. Chem. Soc.,* 1962, 2835.
176. Hoyer and Macdonald, *Zeit. Electrochem.,* 1962, **66**, 269.
177. Hoyer and Hensel, *Zeit. Electrochem.,* 1960, **64**, 958.
178. Khan and Morgan, *J. Chem. Soc.,* 1964, 2579.
179. Sanicki and Hauser, *Analyt. Chem.,* 1959, **31**, 523.
180. Mateos, Cetina, Olivera and Meza, *J. Org. Chem.,* 1961, **26**, 2494.
181. Josien, Lascombe and Vignalou, *Compt. Rendu,* 1960, **250**, 4146.
182. Katritzky, Lagowski and Beard, *Spectrochim. Acta,* 1960, **16**, 964.
183. Dalton, Ellington and Meakins, *J. Chem. Soc.,* 1960, 3681.
184. Brookes, Eglinton and Morman, *J. Chem. Soc.,* 1961, 661.
185. Katritzky, Monro, Beard, Dealney and Earl, *J. Chem. Soc.,* 1958, 2182.
186. Bowden, Chapman and Shorter, *Can. J. Chem.,* 1963. **41**, 2145.
187. Kazicyna, Laksin and Nesmejanov, *Compt. Rend. Acad. Sci. U.R.S.S.,* 1959, **127**, 333.
188. Guthrie, *J. Chem. Soc.,* 1961, 2525.
189. Freeman, *J. Amer. Chem. Soc.,* 1958, **80**, 5954.
190. Overend and Evans, *Trans. Faraday Soc.,* 1959, **55**, 1817.
191. Chouteau, Davidovics, Bertrand, Legras, Figarella and Santelli, *Bull. Soc. Chim. France,* 1964, 2562.
192. Lopez, Labarre, Castan and Mathis Noel, *Compt. Rendu,* 1964, **259**, 3483.
193. Jones and Digorgio, *Can. J. Chem.,* 1965, **43**, 182.
194. Olsen and Russwurm, *Annalen,* 1961, **639**, 1.
195. Horak and Pliva, *Chem. and Ind.,* 1960, 102.
196. Kucherov, Berezin and Nazarov, *Izvest. Akad. Nauk. U.R.S.S. Otdel Khim. Nauk.,* 1958, 186.
197. Korte, Buchel and Gohring, *Angew. Chem.,* 1959, **71**, 523.
198. Ory, *Spectrochim. Acta,* 1960, **16**, 1488.
199. Overend and Scherer, *J. Chem. Phys.,* 1960, **32**, 1296.
200. Stratton and Nielsen, *J. Mol. Spectroscopy,* 1960, **4**, 373.
201. Loos and Lord, *Spectrochim. Acta,* 1965, **21**, 119.
202. Nyquist and Potts, *Spectrochim. Acta,* 1961, **71**, 679.
203. Hales, Jones and Kynaston, *J. Chem. Soc.,* 1957, 618.

204. Grant and Grassie, *Polymer,* 1961, **1**, 125.
205. Seucanka, Zjackou, Al'Dekop and Jal'Nicki, *Bull. Acad. Sci. White Russia R.S.S. Ser. Phys. tech. sci.,* 1961, 50.
206. Arvia and Aymonino, *Spectrochim. Acta,* 1962, **18**, 1299.
207. Gatehouse, Livingstone and Nyholm, *J. Chem. Soc.,* 1958, 3137.
208. Sarel, Potoryles and Ben Shosham, *J. Org. Chem.,* 1959, **24**, 1873.
209. Fayat and Foucaud, *Compt. Rendu. Acad. Sci. France,* 1966, **263**, B860.
210. Hough and Priddle, *J. Chem. Soc.,* 1961, 3178.
211. Hough, Priddle, Theobald, Barker, Douglas and Spears, *Chem. and Ind.,* 1960, 148.
212. Lecomte, Josien and Lascombe, *Bull. Soc. Chim. France,* 1956, 163.
213. Eglinton, Brookes and Morman, *J. Chem. Soc.,* 1961, 106.
214. Liler, *Spectrochim. Acta,* 1967, **23A**, 139.
215. Gonzales Sanchez, *Spectrochim. Acta,* 1958, **12**, 17.
216. Hadzi and Pevorsch, *Spectrochim. Acta,* 1957, **10**, 38.
217. Becker and Griffel, *Chem. Ber.,* 1958, **91**, 2025.
218. Bellamy and Pace, *Spectrochim. Acta,* 1963, **19**, 435.
219. Bellamy, Lake and Pace, *Spectrochim. Acta,* 1963, **19**, 443.
220. Bateuv, Oniscenka, Matveeva and Aronova, *J. Gen. Chem. Moscow,* 1960, **30** (92), 657.
221. Bolard, *Compt. Rendu,* 1963, **256**, 4388.
222. Mori, Omura, Yamamoto, Suzuki and Tsuzuki, *Bull. Chem. Soc. Japan,* 1963, **36**, 1401.
223. Mucke, Geppert and Kipke, *J. Prakt. Chem.,* 1959, **9**, 16.
224. Kellie, O'Sullivan and Sadler, *J. Org. Chem.,* 1957, **22**, 29.
225. Oki and Hirota, *Spectrochim. Acta,* 1961, **17**, 583.
226. Oki and Hirota, *Bull. Chem. Soc. Japan,* 1961, **34**, 374, 378; 1963, **36**, 290.
227. Josien, Joussot-Dubien and Vizet, *Bull. Soc. Chim. France,* 1957, 1148.
228. Pentin, Trubnikov, Shusherina and Levina, *J. Gen. Chem. Moscow,* 1961, **31**, (93), 2092.
229. Trubnikov, Teplinskaya, Pentin, Shusherina and Levina, *Zhur. Obshchei Khim,* 1963, **33**, 1210.
230. Eberson, *Acta. Chem. Scand.,* 1959, **13**, 224.
231. Stephens, Haust and Doerr, *Analyt. Chem.,* 1957, **29**, 776.
232. Wasiljew, Terenin and Emanuel, *Compt. Rend. Acad. Sci. U.R.S.S.,* 1956, 403.
233. Murthy, Rao, Rao and Venkateswarlu, *Trans, Faraday Soc.,* 1962, **58**, 855.
234. Wenograd and Spurr, *J. Amer. Chem. Soc.,* 1957, **79**, 5844.
235. Horak and Exner, *Chem. Listy,* 1958, **52**, 1451.
236. Scott and Wagner, *J. Amer. Chem. Soc.,* 1959, **30**, 465.
237. Jonathan, *J. Mol. Spectroscopy,* 1961, **6**, 205.
238. Luttke, *Zeit. Electrochem.,* 1960, **64**, 1228.
239. Jones, *J. Mol. Spectroscopy,* 1963, **11**, 411.
240. Miyazawa, Shimanouchi and Mizushima, *J. Chem. Phys.,* 1958, **29**, 611.
241. Beer, Kessler and Sutherland, *J. Chem. Phys.,* 1958, **29**, 1097.
242. Reichel, Bacaloglu and Schmidt, *Rev. Roumaine Chim.,* 1964, **9**, 299.
243. Milligan, Spinner and Swan, *J. Chem. Soc.,* 1961, 1919.
244. Elliott, in *Advances in Spectroscopy,* Vol. I, Interscience, New York, 1964, p. 214.
245. Zbinden, *Infrared Spectroscopy of High Polymers,* Academic Press, New York, 1964, p. 242.
246. Schmulbach and Drago, *J. Phys. Chem.,* 1960, **64**, 1956.
247. Speziale and Freeman, *J. Amer. Chem. Soc.,* 1960, **82**, 903.
248. Forbes, Morgan and Newton, *J. Chem. Soc.,* 1963, 835.

249. O'Sullivan and Sadler, *J. Chem. Soc.*, 1957, 2839.
250. Katritzky and Jones, *J. Chem. Soc.*, 1959, 2067.
251. Bellamy, *Spectrochim. Acta*, 1958, **13**, 60.
252. Staab, Otting, and Uberle, *Zeit. Electrochem.*, 1957, **61**, 1000.
253. Reid and Konigstein, *Annalen*, 1959, **625**, 53.
254. O'Sullivan and Sadler, *Spectrochim. Acta*, 1960, **16**, 742.
255. Zahn and Kunde, *Chem. Ber.*, 1961, **94**, 2470.
256. Huisgen, Brade, Walz and Glogger, *Chem. Ber.*, 1957, **90**, 1437.
257. Sorygin, Skurina, Sostakovskij, Sidelkovskaja and Zelenskaja, *Bull. Acad. Sci. U.R.S.S. Sect. Chem. Sci.*, 1959, **12**, 2208.
258. Pinchas and Ben Ishai, *J. Amer. Chem. Soc.*, 1957, **79**, 4099.
259. Sato, *J. Org. Chem.*, 1961, **26**, 770.
260. Katritzky and Jones, *J. Chem. Soc.*, 1960, 676.
261. Spinner, *Spectrochim. Acta*, 1959, **15**, 95.
262. Kutepov and Dubov, *J. Gen. Chem. Moscow*, 1960, **30** (92), 3448.
263. Reisse, Peters, Ottinger, Bervelt and Chiurdoglu, *Tetrahedron Letters*, 1966, 2511.
264. Filler, White, Kacmarck and Solomon, *Can. J. Chem.*, 1966, **44**, 2346.
265. Berney, *Spectrochim. Acta*, 1965, **21**, 1809.
266. Pillai, Ramaswamy and Ghanadeskian, *Austral. J. Chem.*, 1966, **19**, 1089.
267. Figeys and Nasielski, *Spectrochim. Acta*, 1967, **23A**, 465.
268. Dabrowski and Kamienska Trela, *Spectrochim. Acta*, 1966, **22**, 211.
269. Heald and Thompson, *Proc. Roy. Soc.*, 1962, **268A**, 89.
270. Gotz, Heilbronner, Katritzky and Jones, *Helv. Chim. Acta*, 1961, **44**, 387.
271. Minato, *Bull. Chem. Soc. Japan*, 1963, **36**, 1020.
272. Brookes, Eglinton and Hanaineh, *Spectrochim. Acta*, 1966, **22**, 161.
273. Shimizu and Shingu, *Spectrochim. Acta*, 1966, **22**, 1528.
274. Renson and Draguet, *Bull. Soc. Chem. Belges*, 1962, **71**, 260.
275. Korver, Veenland and Deboer, *Rec. Trav. Chim. Pays. Bas.*, 1965, **84**, 310.
276. Colthup and Orloff, *Spectrochim. Acta*, 1974, **30A**, 425.
277. Ortiz, Fernandez Bertran and Ballester, *Spectrochim. Acta*, 1971, **27A**, 1713.
278. Laurence and Berthelot, *Spectrochim. Acta*, 1978, **34A**, 1113.
279. Berthelot, Chabanel and Laurence, *Spectrochim. Acta*, 1976, **32A**, 1771.
280. Al Jallo and Jalhoom, *Spectrochim. Acta*, 1975, **31A**, 265.
281. Dahlquist and Euranto, *Spectrochim. Acta*, 1978, **34A**, 863.
282. Rogstad, Klaboe, Cyvin, Cyvin and Christensen, *Spectrochim. Acta*, 1972, **28A**, III, 123.
283. Rogstad, Cyvin and Christensen, *Spectrochim. Acta*, 1976, **32A**, 487.
284. Konarski, *J. Mol. Structure*, 1972, **13**, 45.
285. Bigotto and Galasso, *Spectrochim. Acta*, 1978, **34A**, 923.
286. Thompson, Leroi and Popov, *Spectrochim. Acta*, 1975, **31A**, 1553.
287. Mackay and Poziomek, *Spectrochim. Acta*, 1969, **25A**, 283.
288. Uno and Machida, *Bull. Chem. Soc. Japan*, **19**.
289. Kuroda, Machida and Uno, *Spectrochim. Acta*, 1974, **30A**, 47.
290. Kuroda, Saito, Machida and Saito, *Spectrochim. Acta*, 1971, **27A**, 1481.
291. Klein, *Spectrochim. Acta*, 1971, **27A**, 93.
292. Juarez, Martin-Lomas and Bellanato, *Spectrochim. Acta*, 1976, **32A**, 1675.
293. Hencher and King, *J. Mol. Spectroscopy*, 1965, **16**, 168.
294. Goubeau and Adelhelm, *Spectrochim. Acta*, 1972, **28A**, 2471.
295. Scott and Wagner, *J. Chem. Phys.*, 1959, **30**, 465.
296. Nyquist, Chrisman, Putzig, Woodward and Loy, *Spectrochim. Acta*, 1979, **35A**, 91.

297. Serck Hanssen, *Acta Chem. Scand.,* 1969, **23**, 2900.
298. Fortunato and Fini, *Spectrochim. Acta,* 1975, **31A**, 1233.
299. Laurence and Wojtkowiak, *Bull. Soc. Chim. France* 1971, 3124, 3833, 3870, 3874.
300. Brownlee, Di Stephano and Topsom, *Spectrochim. Acta,* 1975, **31A**, 1685.
301. Azzaro, Gals, Geribaldi and Novo Kremer, *Spectrochim. Acta,* 1978, **34A**, 225.
302. Brownlee and Topsom, *Spectrochim. Acta,* 1975, **31A**, 1677.
303. Peters, *J. Amer. Chem. Soc.,* 1976, **98**, 5627.
304. Peters, *Spectrochim. Acta,* 1978, **34A**, 1159.
305. Seth Paul and Van Duyse, *Spectrochim. Acta,* 1972, **28A**, 211.
306. Miller, Harver and Tyrrell, *Spectrochim. Acta,* 1971, **27A**, 1003.
307. Forrset, Vilcins and Lephardt, *Spectrochim. Acta,* 1976, **32A**, 511.
308. Fisichella, Librando and Maccarone, *Spectrochim. Acta,* 1976, **32A**, 501.
309. Taylor, *Spectrochim. Acta,* 1976, **32A**, 1471.
310. Barlet, Montagne and Arnaud, *Spectrochim. Acta,* 1969, **25A**, 1081.
311. Kruk and Spaargaren, *Spectrochim. Acta,* 1971, **27A**, 77.
312. Kronenberg and Havinga, *Rec. Trav. Chim.,* 1965, **84**, 17.
313. Crowder and Pruettiangkura, *J. Mol. Structure,* 1973, **16**, 161.
314. Crowder and Smyrl, *J. Mol. Structure,* 1971, **7**, 478.
315. Crowder and Pruettiangkura, *J. Mol. Structure,* 1973, **15**, 197.
316. Katon and Sinha, *Spectrochim. Acta,* 1977, **33A**, 45.
317. Charles, Jones and Owen, *J. Chem. Soc. Faraday,* 1973, **89**, 1454.
318. Tanabe and Saeki, *Spectrochim. Acta,* 1972, **28A**, 1083.
319. De Klein, *ibid,* 687. De Klein and Plesman, *Spectrochim. Acta,* 1972, **28A**, 673.
320. Katon, Carll and Bentley, *Appl. Spectros.,* 1971, **25**, 229.
321. Berney, *Spectrochim. Acta,* 1969, **25A**, 793.
322. Barlet, Barlet, Handel and Pierre, *Spectrochim. Acta,* 1974, **30A**, 1471.
323. Charles, Jones, Owen and West, *J. Mol. Structure,* 1976, **32**, 111.
324. Khoshkhoo and Nixon, *Spectrochim. Acta,* 1973, **29A**, 603.
325. Smith and Taylor, *Spectrochim. Acta,* 1976, **32A**, 1477, 1489, 1503.
326. Paoloni, Patti and Mangano, *J. Mol. Structure,* 1975, **27**, 123.
327. James and Ramgoolam, *Spectrochim. Acta,* 1978, **34A**, 1145.
328. Taillandier, Tochon and Taillandier, *J. Mol. Structure,* 1971, **10**, 471.
329. Meaume and Odiot, *J. Mol. Structure,* 1972, **11**, 147.
330. Liquier, Taillandier and Leibovici, *J. Mol. Structure,* 1972, **12**, 241.
331. Taillandier, Liquier and Taillandier, *Compt. Rend. Acad. Sci.,* 1970, **271B**, 693.
332. Ibid, *J. Mol. Structure,* 1962, **2**, 437.
333. Joly and Nicolau, *Spectrochim. Acta,* 1979, **35A**, 281.
334. Poletti, Paliani, Giorgini and Xataliotti, *Spectrochim. Acta,* 1975, **31A**, 1869.
335. Grens, Grinvalde and Stradins, *Spectrochim. Acta,* 1975, **31A**, 555.
336. Matrosov and Kabachnik, *Spectrochim. Acta,* 1972, **28A**, 191.
337. Wierzchowski and Shugar, *Spectrochim. Acta,* 1965, **21**, 943.
338. Ogoshi and Yoshida, *Spectrochim. Acta,* 1971, **27A**, 165.
339. Taylor, *Spectrochim. Acta,* 1970, **26A**, 153, 165.
340. Girlando and Pecile, *Spectrochim. Acta,* 1975, **31A**, 1187; 1978, **34A**, 453.
341. Dabrowski and Katcka, *J. Mol. Structure,* 1972, **12**, 179.
342. Green and Harrison, *Spectrochim. Acta,* 1976, **32A**, 1265.
343. Lucazeau and Novak, *Spectrochim. Acta,* 1969, **25A**, 1615.
344. Fruwert, Galli and Geiseler, *Spectrochim. Acta,* 1971, **27A**, 1279.
345. Varetti and Aymonino, *Spectrochim. Acta,* 1971, **27A**, 183.
346. Al Jallo and Jalhoom, *Spectrochim. Acta,* 1972, **28A**, 1655.
347. Buder and Schmidt, *Spectrochim. Acta,* 1973, **29A**, 1419.
348. Pethrick and Wilson, *Spectrochim. Acta,* 1974, **30A**, 1073.

349. Villepin and Novak, *Spectrochim. Acta,* 1978, **34A**, 1009, 1019.
350. Kavcic, Plesnicar and Hadzi, *Spectrochim. Acta,* 1967, **23A**, 2483.
351. Hadzi, Kavcic and Plesnicar, *Spectrochim. Acta,* 1971, **27A**, 179.
352. Katritzky and Taylor, in *Physical Methods of Heterocyclic Chemistry* Ed. Katritzky, Vol 4. Academic Press, New York, 1971.
353. Hallam and Jones, *J. Mol. Structure,* 1970, **5**, 1.
354. Desseyn, Jacob and Herman, *Spectrochim. Acta,* 1972, **28A**, 1329.
355. Nyquist, Chrisman, Putzig, Woodward and Loy, *Spectrochim. Acta,* 1979, **35A**, 91.
356. Spaargaren, Kruk, Molenaar-Langeveld, Korver, Van der Haak and De Boor, *Spectrochim. Acta,* 1972, **28A**, 965.
357. Uno and Machida *Bull. Chem. Soc. Japan,* 1963, **36**, 427.
358. Kuroda, Saito, Machida and Uno, *Spectrochim. Acta,* 1971, **27A**, 1481.
359. Uno and Machida *Bull. Chem. Soc. Japan,* 1962, **35**, 1226.
360. Kuroda, Machida and Uno, *Spectrochim. Acta,* 1974, **30A**, 47.
361. Mackay and Poziomek, *Spectrochim. Acta,* 1969, **25A**, 283.
362. Thompson, Leroi and Popov, *Spectrochim. Acta,* 1975, **31A**, 1553.
363. Galabov, Simov and Krustev, *J. Mol. Structure,* 1976, **34**, 235.
364. Nyquist, *Spectrochim. Acta,* 1973, **29A**, 1635.
365. Mido, *Spectrochim. Acta,* 1972, **28A**, 1503.
366. Jose, *Spectrochim. Acta,* 1969, **25A**, 111.
367. Ernstbrunner, *J. Mol. Structure,* 1973, **16**, 499.

6

X=Y Bonds Other than Carbonyl νS=O, N=O, P=O, P=S, C=S and C=Se Vibrations

6.1. The sulphoxide group

The SO bond in sulphoxides differs from the double bond of the carbonyl group in that it is made up of a strong σ S—O link strengthened by two relatively weak bonds at right angles to each other. These are formed through the overlap of the p orbitals of the oxygen atom with the d orbitals of the sulphur. One result of this is that the oxygen atom, although polar, is rather less basic than would be expected, because the p character of the oxygen lone pair is reduced. This link also differs from the carbonyl group in that any double bonds attached to the sulphur atom do not lie in the SO plane, and conjugation effects are thereby much reduced. The vibrational frequencies of the SO link in various chemical environments are well characterized and are summarized in Table 6.1 (p. 200).

6.1.1. Characteristic frequencies of the SO link

(a) *Alkyl and aryl sulphoxides*
Sulphoxides self-associate in the liquid or solid state so the S=O band of dimethyl sulphoxide falls from 1101 cm^{-1} in the vapour to 1058 cm^{-1} in the liquid. There are also sizeable shifts on passing from one solvent to another, particularly if the second solvent is a proton donor.

In open-chain dialkyl sulphoxides νSO carbon tetrachloride occurs in the range 1070–1036 cm^{-1}. However, if one excludes the dimethyl (1070 cm^{-1}) and diethyl (1066 cm^{-1}) derivatives, this range narrows to 1060–1036 cm^{-1}. In chloroform the range is 1055–1010 cm^{-1} overall. Numerical data on specific compounds will be found in papers by Cairns [1, 2], Tamres [3] and Gramstad [4]. Data on cyclic sulphoxides are given by Otting [5], Foffani [6] (derivatives of bicyclo[2,2,1]cycloheptene), Cairns [2], Tamres [3] and Del La Mere [7] (1,4-dithian-1,4-dioxides). In six- and seven-membered rings νSO remains close to 1060 cm^{-1} (carbon tetrachloride). Subsequent changes as the ring size is diminished are small, and the four-membered ring system absorbs at 1092 cm^{-1}. A reduced sensitivity to ring size change as compared with the carbonyl group is to be expected in view of the greater mass and the smaller amplitude of the sulphur atom during the S=O vibration. With folded ring systems such as that shown below, where X is oxygen or sulphur the S=O bond can lie in the axial or equatorial position in relation to the ring [1, 127, 128] and these can be differentiated by the frequencies. The equatorial bonds absorb between 1088 and 1074 cm^{-1} and the axial bonds, which are subject to a strong dipolar field, between 1039 and 1025 cm^{-1}. Moreover, because the axial bond is more polar it is more sensitive to association and these differences are increased in chloroform solution. Even larger differences are found when the spectra of adducts with mercuric chloride are used [128].

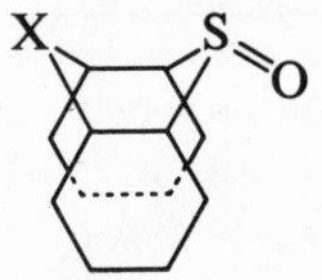

Equatorial 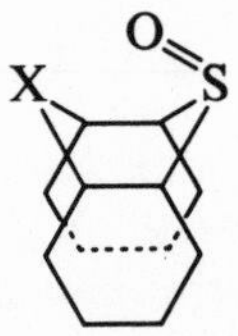   Axial

Aryl sulphoxides have been studied by Pinchas *et al.* [8] (who have been primarily interested in a Fermi resonance effect between vSO and an aromatic band near 1090 cm^{-1}), and by Ghersetti [9, 120] and by Kresze *et al.* [10].

The SO deformation frequencies in these compounds have also been studied by Kresze [10], who places them in the 535–497-cm^{-1} range. However, this particular frequency is very sensitive to the nature of the substituents, and Horrocks and Cotton [11] place it at 530 cm^{-1} in F_2SO, at 382 cm^{-1} in $(CH_3)_2SO$, 344 cm^{-1} in Cl_2SO and 267 cm^{-1} in Br_2SO.

(b) Thiosulphoxides, R·S·SO·R

A substantial number of compounds of this type have been examined by Ghersetti and Modena [12]. The effect of altering the alkyl or aryl groups around the S—SO structure is small, the range for the four possible variants with CH_3 and/or aryl groups being only 1108–1096 cm^{-1}. The effects of substituents in aromatic rings joined either to the sulphoxide group or to the sulphur atom are small, the range for the whole series being no greater than 1114 (p-NO$_2$) to 1099 cm^{-1} (p-OCH$_3$). However, there seems to be a reasonably good correlation between the frequencies and the Hammett σ or Brown σ^+ values. With sulphur atoms on each side of the S=O bond the frequencies remain close to 1105 cm^{-1}.

(c) Disulphoxides

There has been speculation in the literature for some time on the possible existence of these compounds. However, infrared and dipole moment measurements by Grisko and Gur'janova [13] have shown that compounds which might be expected to have the structure RSOSOR exist wholly in the form $R \cdot S \cdot SO_2 \cdot R$.

(d) Sulphites

Simple dialkyl sulphites have been studied by several workers [14, 15, 129, 130]. These absorb near 1200 cm^{-1}. Cyclic sulphites have been more extensively studied in relation to the conformation of six-membered ring sulphites [131–133]. Three possible conformers have been identified, with axial, equatorial and intermediate arrangements, and these can be readily characterised through the S=O frequencies. Although doubling of the bands occurs in some cases due to Fermi resonance, this can be recognised and allowed for by the use of a series of solvents. The different conformers are then found to absorb as follows: axial 1207–1190 cm^{-1}; intermediate, 1220–1230 cm^{-1}; and equatorial 1240–1251 cm^{-1}.

(e) The group RN=S=O

This structure has been studied by Pullin [16] and by Kresze [17]. Two bands are shown in the 1300–1230- and 1180–1100-cm^{-1} regions. It is not surprising that there should be such a major difference from the normal X=Y=Z systems discussed in Chapter 3 if the special nature of the SO bond in this compound is remembered and also the fact that the two multiple bonds constituting the group are no longer colinear. In consequence, the splitting is much reduced, just as it is in sulphur dioxide as compared with carbon dioxide.

(f) Thionyl halides

Studies on the thionyl halides have been made by Long [18] and by Gillespie [19]. Thionyl fluoride absorbs at 1308 cm^{-1}, chloride at 1233 cm^{-1} and bromide at 1121 cm^{-1}. Compounds with one halogen and one other substituent absorb at frequencies corresponding to the sum of the contributions from both substituents. For example CH_3SOCl will absorb midway between the values for dimethyl sulphoxide and thionyl chloride.

(g) Sulphinamides

Sulphinamides have been studied by several workers [134–135]. With two dialkyl groups the S=O frequency is in the range 1110–1120 cm^{-1} which is higher than with carbon substitution due to the lack of resonance. It is, however, a little lower than might have been expected from the electronegativity of the nitrogen. Frequencies for the S=O bond in compounds with one nitrogen substituent and one other, are tabulated by Keat *et al.* [137]. These generally are in line with the electronegativity values of the other substituent. Using electronegativities Steudel [129] has predicted values of 1218 cm^{-1} for the —NSOF group and 1167 cm^{-1} for —OSON. Both are in close agreement with the observed values. Sulphinamides with a hydrogen atom on the nitrogen show two S=O bands at lower frequencies (1060–1040 cm^{-1}). This is probably the result of hydrogen bonding.

6.1.2. The variations of νSO with changes in the substituents

It is well known that alkyl and aryl sulphoxides have their SO stretching frequencies in essentially the same positions. This is due to the nature of the SO link and to the geometric arrangement, which limits the possibilities of electron delocalization such as occurs in carbonyl compounds. In the same way, one can predict that substituents with lone-pair electrons will be less liable to exert a mesomeric effect. It will be seen from Table 6.1 (p. 200) that these expectations are generally followed, and that the value of νSO for a given pair of substituents is largely determined by their electronegativity. Daasch [20] has suggested a linear relationship between νSO and the Pauling electronegativities of the substituents, and this has been extended by Steudel [129]. Some modification of the Pauling values is necessary in the cases on nitrogen and sulphur substituents. However, the additivity of the substituent effects is remarkably constant so that it is usually possible to make reasonably good predictions of a frequency from the values in other compounds. For example SOF$_2$ absorbs at 1310 cm^{-1} and (NMe$_2$)$_2$SO at 1120 cm^{-1}. One would therefore expect (NMe$_2$)$_2$SOF to absorb close to the mean of these values (1215 cm^{-1}), and it actually absorbs at 1218 cm^{-1}. Similar good frequency predictions can be made for any other combination of substituents.

It therefore seems probable that, while induction is the main factor in determining νSO values, there are other modifying influences. Of these the most likely is the possibility of interaction between the d orbitals of sulphur and the π or p orbitals of the substituent group. This is strongly suggested by a comparison of the frequencies of the sulphites and of thionyl chloride. The lower values of the former, despite the higher electronegativity of oxygen, would then be attributed to some kind of pd interaction between the oxygen lone pairs and the sulphur atom. If this is so, there should be a significant change on passing to diaryl sulphites, when the interaction would be reduced by the competitive effect of the rings. This has a parallel in the high νCO values of vinyl esters, which arises in a similar way. In fact, νSO in diphenyl sulphite absorbs at 1245 cm^{-1}, which is some 45 cm^{-1} higher than the dialkyl derivatives, and is also now higher than the value in thionyl chloride. However, it must also be said that in divinyl sulphite vSO is only 1220 cm^{-1}, so that delocalization effects cannot be the sole cause of the high frequency of the diphenyl derivatives.

Some further evidence that the SO bond is susceptible to influences other than simple inductive effects is afforded by the complex pattern of behaviour in solvent and basicity studies. Although vSO hardly alters in dialkyl or diaryl sulphoxides, the δvOD values for the association of d-methanol differ by as much as 56 cm^{-1}. This must correspond to some difference in the state of the lone-pair oxygen orbitals in the two cases [4], and could well be due to some interaction between the ring electrons and the sulphur d orbitals which is not reflected in the simple frequency value. It is also possible that some similar type of interaction is responsible for the surprisingly high values of vSO in the thiosulphoxides.

In view of the hybridization of the oxygen atom in sulphoxides, and of the distances by which it is removed from substituents at the α-carbon atom, there is very much less likelihood of the occurrence of field effects, such as occur in carbonyl compounds. Meyers [21] has assigned some abnormal acidities in hydroxy-aryl sulphoxides to interactions of this type. Leonard [22] has observed some field effects involving sulphur in some transannular interactions with carbonyl groups, and the differences between axial and equatorial S=O bonds in cyclic sulphites must also arise in this way.

6.1.3. Sulphoxides as donors; solvent effects

The coordination of metal atoms at the SO bond has been studied by several workers [23–27, 128, 138–142]. Cotton *et al.* [23] have examined a number of such complexes involving dimethyl sulphoxide. They argued from considerations of bond character that coordination through the oxygen atom would increase the ionic character of the SO bond and lead to a frequency fall, whereas coordination through the sulphur atom would lead to a frequency rise. In fact, both types of shift are observed. In $[Co(DMSO)_6]^{2+}$ vSO fell to 960 cm^{-1}, whereas in platinum complexes, such as $PtCl_2 2DMSO$, vSO rose to 1157–1116 cm^{-1}. Similar results by Cotton and Francis [24] on tetrahydro thiophene oxide complexes led them to conclude that coordination could occur through either the oxygen or sulphur atom.

The S=O frequency shifts on coordination through the oxygen atom are often surprisingly small, and suggest that the weakening of the S=O bond is relatively trivial. With HgI_2 for example, the frequency of dimethyl sulphoxide falls only to 1003 cm^{-1} [142], whilst with $Al(CH_3)_3$ the frequency is 992 cm^{-1}. One of the largest frequency shifts is produced by $SbCl_3$ when the band is at 880 cm^{-1} [140]. A useful tabulation of the data on sulphoxide complexes of this kind and the frequency shifts shown is given by Reynolds

[139]. It would seem that the frequency fall of the sulphoxide bond is a true measure of the reduction of the oxygen p_π—sulphur d_π bonding as it can be shown that there is a linear inverse relationship between the force constants of the S=O and metal—oxygen bonds. Clearly the latter is proportionately strengthened as the electron transfer occurs from one bond to the other [138].

One useful practical application of these shifts on complex formation is in the recognition of different conformers of cyclic sulphites. It has already been stated that there are differences in the S=O frequencies in the different forms, but these differences are accentuated in the complexes so that the individual types are more readily recognised [128].

Table 6.1. νSO in XSOY compounds, cm^{-1}

	CH$_3$	CL	OCH$_3$	N(CH$_3$)$_2$	F
CH$_3$	1050	1150	1130		
Cl	1150	1239	1216		
OCH$_3$	1130	1216	1209	1164	1253
OPhenyl			1220		
N(CH$_3$)$_2$		1199	1164	1120	1218
F		1253	1218	1310	

The SO stretching frequency is extremely sensitive to solvent effects [28, 29], especially where proton donors are involved, and the general pattern of behaviour is very similar to that of the carbonyl group. There is a marked difference between the solvent sensitivities of diphenyl and dimethyl sulph-oxides [28], despite the similarity of the original frequencies. This must reflect some real difference in the electronic make up of the bonds and may well form a useful basis for the further study of the nature of the differences themselves. Differences in the behaviour of some sulphoxides on passing from carbon tetrachloride to chloroform solution have been noted. The shifts are always substantial and provide a useful confirmatory test for the recognition of the SO stretching band.

An alternative approach is the measurement of $\delta\nu$OH or OD when an alcohol or phenol is allowed to associate with the sulphoxide. This has been used by Tamres [3] (CH$_3$OD) and by Gramstad [4] (phenol), and the larger shifts measurable in this way allow a more precise relative measurement of the basicities. Thus one can detect a difference in the basicity of four-membered ring sulphoxides ($\delta\nu$OD methanol 128 cm^{-1}), as compared with larger ring systems (155–167 cm^{-1}). Gramstad's data [4], using phenol as the donor, also show subtle basicity changes following even minor structural alterations. Figueroa et al. [122] give comparable data for variously sub-stituted aryl sulphoxides.

6.2. The XN=O bond, nitrites, nitroso compounds nitrosamines and N-oxides

6.2.1. Bond characteristics

The N=O bond lies in the same plane as the substituent atoms on either side, and in this respect it is similar to the carbonyl group. It is therefore sensitive to mesomeric or conjugation effects in just the same way as carbonyl absorptions. Indeed, it has been shown that a simple linear plot [30] can be constructed in which vNO of XN=O systems is plotted against the corresponding vCO values of the CH_3COX compounds, provided the comparison is made on similar states or solvents. The similarity extends even to the abnormality that despite the difference in electronegativity, the vNO values of NOCl (1799 cm^{-1}) and NOBr (1801 cm^{-1}) are closely alike. The same effect is, of course, seen in Cl_2CO and Br_2CO. Sulphur-substituted NO compounds also absorb at lower frequencies than the organic nitrites, just as thioesters absorb at lower values than esters.

Perhaps the only essential differences between the two classes are the wider range of polarity possible for the N=O bond, the ability of XN=O compounds in certain cases to take up *cis* and *trans* forms and their ability to take a canonical structure $(NO)^+Cl^-$. This last feature shows up particularly in solvent effects, etc. Thus NOCl is one of the few compounds known in which the multiple-bond frequency actually rises on passing from the vapour into solution, presumably due to the increase in the contribution of the more polar canonical form in the more polar medium.

However, NO group frequencies as a class do raise a number of problems which are not at all understood and which deserve further study. One such is the tendency for $\geqslant$C—N=O compounds to dimerize unless they are prevented from so doing by steric effects. No parallel for this is found in carbonyl compounds, and it must relate to some intrinsic difference in the bond character. If one regards vNO as an index of bond polarity, it is even more surprising to find that this tendency to dimerization is limited to the nitroso compounds and is not shared by the nitrites (higher frequencies) or the thionitrites (lower frequencies). There is some doubt about the situation with nitrosamines, in which Looney et al. [31] believe they have detected some evidence of dimerization, as the later work of Williams et al [32] suggests that this is not so. In any event, such dimerization that does occur in this series must be on a very limited scale.

A second problem is the ability of nitrites to exist in *cis* and *trans* forms, whereas esters are always found in the *cis* configuration. This has been neatly dealt with by Owen and Sheppard [33], using the principle that lone-pair electrons exert greater repulsive forces on other lone pairs than on bonding pairs. The *cis* configuration of esters is then explicable in terms of the fact that the lone pair/lone pair repulsion in the *trans* form is greater than the lone pair/bonding pair repulsion in the *cis* configuration (I and II on p. 202).

In the case of nitrites the presence of the additional lone pair on the nitrogen atom reduces the energy difference between the two configurations (III) and (IV), and both can coexist. However, this explanation does not account for the relatively large differences (up to 60 cm^{-1}) that are found between the νNO values of the two forms. If this difference originates wholly in the differences in the lone-pair repulsion terms these must have a remarkably large effect. The position is made the more complicated by the preliminary observation that the N=O link in *cis*-methyl nitrite is less basic than that of the *trans*-isomer, despite the fact that the latter has the higher frequency and might be supposed to be the less polar. It may well be that basicity measurements on various kinds of X—N=O systems may lead to a better understanding of the availability of the lone-pair electrons, and so of the bonding arrangements themselves. Gramstad [4] has made some studies on the association of phenol with nitrile oxides when large shifts of νOH are found, and the extension of such measurements to other NO bond types would be very informative. At the present time no satisfactory interpretation of these differences between the two configurations is possible.

6.2.2. Group frequencies

Table 6.2 gives frequency values for νNO in various chemical environments. As indicated earlier, there has been little recent interest in the spectra of compounds of this type and the most valuable compilations on nitrites and nitroso compounds remain those of Tarte and of Luttke, which were quoted in the present author's earlier volume. The data on nitroso dimer frequencies given in the table are from Gowenlock [35]. Values for the N=O frequencies of variously substituted nitrosobenzene dimers have been given by Gruger and Le Calve [168, 169]. Specific papers of interest are the application of the Urey Bradley force field to the nitrosyl halides [36], the examination of a small number of thio nitrites [37] and some studies on nitrosamines [31, 32]. The latter raise some points of interest in connexion with the question of whether or not dimerization or rotational isomerism can occur.

Looney [31] investigated a number of nitrosamines by infrared and nuclear resonance techniques and studied the rotational barriers. If these are sufficiently high two forms should exist in unsymmetrically substituted

Table 6.2. νN=O frequencies cm^{-1} (carbon tetrachloride solution)

X	X—O—N=O Monomers		X—N=O Dimers		X$_2$NN=O Monomers	XSN=O Monomers
	cis	trans	trans	cis*		
CH$_3$	1625	1681	1290	1387	1460	1534†
C$_2$H$_5$	1621	1675	1222	1426, 1370	1454	1534†
n-C$_3$H$_7$	1621	1672	1210	1431, 1406 1381	—	1534†
iso-C$_3$H$_7$	1615	1667	1212	1426, 1408, 1382	1438	1534†
n-C$_4$H$_9$	1618	1669	1211	1426, 1385	—	—
iso-C$_4$H$_9$	1618	1669	1218	1418, 1382	—	—
sec-C$_4$H$_9$	1615	1665	—	1420, 1384	1437	—
tert-C$_4$H$_9$	1610	1655	—	—	—	—
sec-C$_5$H$_{11}$	1618	1664	1193	1408, 1377	—	—
tert-C$_5$H$_{11}$	1613	1653	—	—	—	—

* All solid in potassium bromide discs.
† Multiple bands, suggested as originating in coupling with CH deformation modes.

Other N=O frequencies:
  FN=O 1844 vap.   CH$_3$N=O monomer 1564
  ClN=O 1799 vap.   (CH$_3$)$_3$CN=O monomer 1546
  BrN=O 1801 vap.   CH$_3$C$_6$H$_5$NN=O 1476
  IN=O 1809 vap.   (C$_6$H$_5$)$_2$NN=O 1480

nitrosamines, and there is some evidence of their existence from NMR studies. However, in unsymmetrically substituted compounds Williams [32] could find little alteration in the relative intensities of the various bands with solvent polarity, such as would be expected if there were two forms present in equilibrium. He also observed that the band assigned by Looney to NO monomer absorption was solvent insensitive, whereas that assigned to the dimer followed a typical X=O solvent pattern. If dimerization occurs at all it does not seem to be extensive.

There has been rather more interest in the identification of the NO stretching absorption in heterocyclic N-oxides, such as those of pyridine, pyrazine, etc. Shindo [38] and Katritzky [39] have studied this absorption in a large number of pyridine N-oxides. In non-polar media it falls in the 1319–1230 cm^{-1} region, the precise frequency depending on the degree and nature of the ring substitution. The frequency is lowered by electron donor substituents (p-OCH$_3$ 1240 cm^{-1}) and raised by electron attractors (p-NO$_2$ 1303 cm^{-1}), and it follows, as would be expected, a reasonably good linear relationship with the substituent Hammett σ values. These systems have also been studied by Mirone [40] and by Tsoucaris [41], and Katritzky [42] and Quagliano [43] have discussed their electron donor properties.

Pyrazine N-oxides have been studied by Shindo [44] and by Klein and Berkowitz [45]. The parent compound has its νN → O stretching band at 1318 cm^{-1}, which is some 54 cm^{-1} higher than in the pyridine compound.

This is attributed to the electronegative nitrogen atom at the 4 position. Otherwise the behaviour is parallel with that of the pyridine oxides, with electron donor substituents having lower frequencies and electron acceptors higher values. Pyrimidine-1-oxide absorbs at an intermediate frequency (1279 cm^{-1}), but in pyrazine-1,4-dioxides the N—O band shifts to higher values. This may be due in part to an electronic effect, but an apparent frequency rise is to be expected, as in this compound vNO will be split into assymetric and symmetric modes and only the former will be infrared active. As this is usually the higher frequency of the two, some high-frequency shift is to be expected.

In all of these compounds additional bands are found at lower frequencies which appear to be characteristic of the compounds as a whole and which are sometimes also assigned to an NO stretching vibration. It is difficult to see how this can be so, but the presence of these bands may be a useful aid to identification. In pyridine N-oxides this second band is found in the range 1190–1150 cm^{-1}. A second band is described as occurring in the range 1040–990 cm^{-1} in pyrazine N-oxides. This may be an aromatic-type band enhanced in intensity in some way. Klein et al. [45] also identify a band near 850 cm^{-1} as characteristic of these systems. In nitrile oxides the NO stretching band is found near 1300 cm^{-1}; these have been studied by Califano [34].

6.3. The P=O stretching frequency

In contrast to the paucity of data on the N=O group, the phosphoryl group has been very extensively studied. Thomas and Chittenden [46, 47] have recently reviewed the whole of the published spectra in this area, including their own extensive collection, and the summarized data relate to about 900 different compounds. They rightly point out the great difficulty in the comparison of so many results from different laboratories. These arise partly from small calibration errors, but principally from differences in the physical state in which the specimens were examined. As will be seen, the P=O link is particularly sensitive to association effects, and shifts of as much as 65 cm^{-1} can arise from a change of phase. The great majority of the recorded data relate to liquid films or to solids measured in Nujol or in discs, and the values given in the tables relate to this state. The P=O band often appears as a doublet, and the reasons for this have been discussed by several workers [48, 49, 121, 136, 137]. In many cases this has been shown to be due to rotational isomerism. This is, for example, the case in triphenyl phosphate. The compound α chloroethylphosphono dichloride has been shown to have three rotational isomers [136] and two P=O bands [1295 and 1282 cm^{-1}]. This does not however arise from any field effect between the oxygen atom and the chlorine such as occurs in carbonyl compounds. These atoms are too far apart in space, and indeed two isomers occur in methyl phosphonodichloride [137]. In all these cases the P=O band separation is small. In a few instances a larger separation of about 50 cm^{-1} has been reported, but this is believed to be due to Fermi resonance interaction.

6.3.1. P═O group frequencies in compounds other than acids or amides (phosphates, phosphonates, phosphinites, phosphine oxides, pyrophosphates, etc)

Table 6.3 lists the P═O frequencies of a range of R_3P═O compounds with a single R substituent. It will be seen that the impact of the various groups follows approximately, but not precisely, the inductive effects of the substituents as measured by their electronegativity. This aspect is discussed in more detail in Section 6.3.3. Data on phosphate esters are given by Thomas [47], and in papers by Ketelaar [51] and Popov [52]. Goubeau and Lentz [143] have measured the frequencies and assessed the force constants of a number of series of compounds X_3P═O as the X group is systematically replaced by Y, i.e. X_2YP═O, XY_2P═O and Y_3P═O. The stepwise frequency changes are of the same order, but are not identical. For example the frequency falls by 21 cm^{-1} on passing from OP(OCH$_3$)$_3$ to OP(OCH$_3$)$_2$(SCH$_3$), by a further

Table 6.3. νP═O cm^{-1} condensed phase

Three identical groups *Group*	(*O*-Alkyl)$_2$ and I group *Group*	Alkyl$_2$ and I group *Group*
O-Alkyl 1258–1286	*C*-Alkyl or Aryl 1232–1265	OH 1191–1139
O-Aryl 1290–1314	H 1266–1250	OH (R═Aryl) 1205–1087
C-Alkyl 1151–1183	Cl 1280–1309	Alkyl 1183–1151
C-Aryl 1197–1145	Br 1282	*O*-Alkyl 1220–1181
S-Alkyl c. 1202	F 1290–1312	H 1157 (R Alkyl)
S-Aryl c. 1209	F 1330–1325 (R aryl)	H 1170–1182 (R Aryl)
NHR* 1215–1227	SR 1247–1269	Br 1250 (R Aryl or alkyl)
NR$_2$* 1191–1245	NHR 1198–1258	Cl 1215 (R Alkyl)
F 1414	NH$_2$ 1220–1250	Cl 1235 (R Aryl)
CL 1269	NR$_2$ 1253–1274	SR 1198
Br 1252	O—P═O 1282–1307 | X OH 1250–1210	NHR 1180–1156

* Small number of examples only.

29 cm^{-1} on passing to OP(OCH$_3$)(SCH$_3$)$_2$, and by 31 cm^{-1} on passing to OP(SCH$_3$)$_3$. With trimethyl phosphate, the frequency rise on replacing one methyl by a chlorine is 5 cm^{-1} greater than the effect of replacing all three. This indicates that strict additivity of inductive effects does not occur.

With intensity measurements however, the limited amount of data available do show that substituent groups do contribute in an additive manner.

Goldwhite and Previdi [144] have shown that for sixteen different P=O compounds the individual substituent groups can be assigned values which can be added for the three groups to yield the square root of the absolute intensities. They have also studied the relationships of the intensities to the substituent constants σ^*, σ_i, σ_m, etc. They conclude that reactivity constants which relate wholly to inductive effects (e.g. σ^*, σ_i) correlate only poorly with $\sqrt{A}$, whilst those such as σ_m and σ_p, which contain some contribution from resonance, correlate well. It would seem that resonance effects do therefore contribute to the absolute intensities. A different approach is that of Gramstad et al. [145] who have correlated P=O intensities with the basicities of the bond as measured by the frequency shifts of proton donors forming hydrogen bonds. This effectively relates the intensities to the P=O polarities. Mathis Noel et al. [53] have given values for intensities in some esters and chlorides of phosphoric acid.

Cyclic phosphates have been examined by Katritzky et al. [57] who found that a change in ring size from a six- to a five-membered ring did not affect the P=O frequency. This continues the trend already noted for the cyclic sulphoxides, and is due to the smaller amplitude of the phosphorus atom as compared with the carbon of the carbonyl group, and the reduced coupling with the adjacent links that results. Cyclic pholphoramidates have been examined by Arnold [58] and compounds of the type below by Haring [59].

Pyrophosphates and systems are interesting in that unlike the anhydrides of carboxylic acids, there is no coupling between the two X=O bonds [2, 62]. Thus there is no splitting of the P=O band in symmetrical pyrophosphates, and two bands are only found in unsymmetrically substituted compounds, when each corresponds closely to the value expected from the particular substituent concerned. The values are in fact those of the two parent symmetrical pyrophosphates. This confirms that there is no vibrational interaction between the two components.

The normal frequency range for these systems is given as 1307–1206 cm^{-1}, but this covers a wide range of different substituents, and for tetra-alkyl compounds the range narrows to 1238–1206 cm^{-1}. In general, the frequencies follow the same pattern of change with substituents as the compounds listed in the tables. Mixed, P=O and P=S anhydrides have also been studied [2, 61]; these show normal phosphoryl frequencies.

6.3.2. Group frequencies of phosphorus acids and amides

The spectra of the various acids of phosphorus show a number of interesting features, and have been extensively studied by Peppard and Ferraro [63–67], and by Thomas [46, 47, 68]. The P=O stretching band is always broadened and shifted to a lower frequency as a result of hydrogen bonding. Because of the extreme difficulty in breaking these very strong bonds on dilution in inert solvents, it was at one time thought that the association must be intra-molecular, but it is now known that this is not so. The monobasic acids associate as dimers with cyclic rings similar to those of carboxylic acids. The dibasic acids associate as polymers in large rings of about six units [63].

The P=O absorption in acids is usually about 50 cm^{-1} lower than the value in the corresponding esters, and most of this shift must be attributed to hydrogen bonding. Typical ranges for various classes of acid in the solid state, are as follows:

(RO)$_2$P(OH)=O	1210–1250 cm^{-1}
(RO)HP(OH)=O	1200–1212 cm^{-1}
(RO)RP(OH)=O	1170–1215 cm^{-1} (R alkyl)
	1205–1220 cm^{-1} (R aryl)
RRP(OH)=O	1139–1205 cm^{-1} alkyl or aryl
RHP(OH)=O	1136–1174 cm^{-1}
ROP(OH)$_2$=O	1250 cm^{-1}

Correlation ranges for phosphonates and for phosphinates are also given in Table 6.3. It will be seen that they follow the same general pattern of behaviour as the phosphates. Aryl groups on the oxygen atoms lead to higher frequencies than alkyl groups, and an OH group on the α-carbon atom again results in a large fall in vP=O due to hydrogen bonding.

Diesters of phosphonous acid and monoesters of phosphinic acid exist

wholly in the form $\overset{\diagdown}{\underset{\diagup}{\underset{H}{\overset{|}{P}}}}$=O, and there is no evidence of the existence of any

OH group, [51, 54–56, 60, 71]. However, this is not the case with (CF$_3$)$_2$POH. This has been shown to have an OH rather than a P=O group, and indeed exhibits two OH stretching frequencies as it exists in two rotational forms [50].

It will be seen that there is a general lowering of the phosphoryl frequency as the alkoxy groups are successively replaced by hydrogen atoms or by alkyl groups. This is similar to the behaviour found in the esters. The magnitude of the P=O shift is somewhat less than might have been expected from the vOH bands, which show the characteristic ABC pattern of very strong hydrogen bonds [70]. However, the extent of the P=O shift does not appear to be a particularly good index of the strengths of the hydrogen bonds involved. Thus if phosphine oxides are allowed to associate with pentachlorophenol vP=O shifts by 40 cm^{-1}, which is not much less than in many acids. But the frequency shift of the vOH band is very much smaller than in the acids, and there is no evidence of any splitting into a band series [72]. It is also significant that the P=O shifts in the dimeric monobasic acids are comparable with those of the polymeric dibasic acids, despite the change in structure and the absence of the C band from the OH bands of the latter.

As vP=O falls it seems likely that the polarity of the bond increases and the sensitivity to hydrogen bonding will also increase. However, any effects of this sort on the frequencies are probably partly offset by the increase in coupling that must inevitably occur as the P=O bond approaches nearer and nearer towards the pure single-bond polar form. In the extreme case the PO_2^- ion gives two separate bands, due to the symmetric and anti-symmetric vibrations of the oxygen atoms. However, it is interesting to note that in some salts the PO_2^- ion frequency is higher than that of some of the hydrogen-bonded acids. Dibutylphosphoric acid, for example, has vP=O at 1205 cm^{-1}, whereas in sodium dibutylphosphate the main PO_2^- band is at 1242 cm^{-1}. Some authors [69] have argued from this that the ion retains some double-bond character in the P—O links and that this is greater than in the associated acids. However, it must be remembered that the 1242-cm^{-1} band is only one of a pair of frequencies, and any comparison that can be made at all must be with the mean of both rather than with the value of the anti-symmetric mode. Phosphoramidic or phosphonamidic acids have not been considered in the above discussion, as these exist wholly in the ionic form.

Phosphorus compounds containing nitrogen substituents have been studied by several groups of workers [2, 73–77, 143], and the results have been summarized and reviewed by Thomas [46, 47]. The P=O frequencies show a considerable scatter, even among closely related compounds, so that it is particularly difficult to predict their likely position in any one case. In the dialkoxyphosphonamides, which have been more extensively studied than most other groups, the overall frequency ranges are as follows:

Primary	1220–1244 cm^{-1} alkoxy substitution
	near 1250 cm^{-1} aryloxy substitution
Secondary	1198–1258 cm^{-1}
Tertiary	1235–1274 cm^{-1}

When the P=O is substituted with three N-dialkyl groups it absorbs near 1210 cm^{-1} [143]. This is substantially higher than results from substitution with three methyl groups, and indicates the much reduced importance of resonance as compared with the carbonyl compounds. However, the frequency is lower than would have been expected from electronegativity considerations.

The phosphoryl frequency in primary and secondary amides is almost certainly lowered by hydrogen bonding with the amide hydrogen atoms, and there is evidence from the NH frequencies that this is so. This is probably a contributory factor to the wide frequency ranges often encountered. Thus, in compounds of the type $(R)(NHR)_2P\!\!=\!\!O$ the phosphoryl frequency ranges from 1163 to 1220 cm^{-1}

6.3.3. The systematics of the P=O frequencies in relation to the substitution pattern

As with the S=O link, the P=O bond cannot lie in the same plane as the multiple bonds of any substituents, so that it can be expected to be—and indeed is—largely independent of conjugation effects. The inductive effects of the substituents would then be expected to be the dominant factors in determining the frequencies, and this is the case. In this connexion Ketelaar [51] has noted that the changes in vP=O with substitution, parallel the energies of activation for hydrolytic reactions. The activation energies fall as the frequencies rise. He ascribes this to the changing polarity of the P=O bond and the effect of this on the facility with which an OH group can approach.

Relationships between vP=O and the summed Pauling electronegativities of the substituents were suggested many years ago, but Goubeau and Lentz were able to show that the frequencies depended upon the position of the substituent atoms in the periodic table as well as on their electronegativities [143]. Griffen [78] and Zingaro [90] proposed a relation with Taft σ values which appeared to be more satisfactory. Thomas [46, 47] has reviewed the whole of the data from this point of view and concluded that niether is wholly satisfactory, and has gone on to develop an improved relationship of a kind suggested earlier by Bell. If the P=O frequency is plotted against the summed electronegativities of the halogens in the various phosphoryl trihalides a straight line is obtained corresponding to the equation

$$v\text{P}\!\!=\!\!\text{O} = 930 + 40\Sigma x$$

where x is the Pauling electronegativity. Using this line as a datum, a series of electronegativity values for various substituents has been obtained, the numbers being chosen to give the best possible fit over the greatest number of compounds. It is recognised that these are simply empirical numbers, and the process is used solely to enable one to arrive at a reasonable estimate of the P=O frequency in a given instance. They do not correspond to real electronegativities unless it is the case that this frequency is determined only by the inductive effects of the substituents, and this is probably not the case. Thomas recognizes this by giving them the general title of phosphorus inductive or π constants. A selection of these π values (which are given at greater length by Thomas [46, 47]) are included in Table 6.4, and they will be found to be very useful in the prediction of phosphoryl frequencies. The observed values for over 900 compounds were checked against this relation, and good agreement (within 12 cm^{-1}) was found in most cases. In phosphates and phosphonates, for example, vP=O was predicted within these limits in 277 compounds, and only 15 showed a greater deviation. In thiolates the ration was 100 : 1. The utility and accuracy varies with the class of compound, and π values are least useful in phosphine oxides and amidates. All phosphine oxides with aromatic substituents were found to fall outside the predicted range, and there were 86 failures in the amidates out of a total of 241. The phosphine oxides have particularly low phosphoryl frequencies corresponding to very polar P=O links, and it may be that these are influenced by dipolar interactions in the crystal, and possibly by coupling with low-frequency modes. The amidates are liable to give disturbed values because of the additional hydrogen-bonding effects.

Table 6.4. Some π constants (after Thomas [46, 47])

CH_3	2.1	OCH_3	2.9	Br_3	8.2	NH_2	1.85
CH_2	2.0	$OCH_2C_6H_5$	2.7	Br_2	5.5	NHR	2.0
CH	1.8	$OCH=CH$	3.1	Br	3.1	NR_2	2.2
CO	2.5	OC_6H_5	3.0	Cl_3	9.0	SR	2.4
CH_2Cl	2.7	OCO	3.4	Cl_2	6.3	CN	3.5
CCl_3	3.0	$OP=O$	3.3	Cl	3.4	H	2.5
CH_2Br	2.55	C_6H_5	2.4	F_3	12.0	CF_3	3.3
$CHCl_2$	2.9						

It is interesting to speculate on the true nature of the π constants. The fact that the values for oxygen and nitrogen substituents are so much lower than the Pauling values for the elements suggests that factors other than simple induction are involved. However, this could equally well imply that the effective charge on these atoms is modified by the substituents, and that the π values do indeed measure the true inductive effect. The fact that different values are required for chlorine or bromine, depending on the numbers present, suggests that this is not so, but it is nevertheless a great pity that the one vibration for which so much data are available should be that in which so many other complications are introduced through the study of the spectra in the solid state. In the absence of solution data it is doubtful whether this useful concept can be refined much further, but it would be very interesting to know whether these π values are unique to the P=O vibration or whether they are a close approximation to true inductive effects, in which case they would be equally applicable to other groups of similar geometry. A preliminary comparison does suggest that there is a close parallel between these values and the variations in the $-SO_2-$ group frequencies. These vary in a similar way, and the OR substituents also give lower frequencies than would be expected from their electronegativities. However, no detailed comparisons are possible in view of the limitations of the data.

6.3.4. Basicity studies on phosphoryl compounds

The phosphoryl bond is a good proton acceptor, and νP=O is more sensitive to solvent effects than is νC=O. A number of workers have studied the efficiency of P=O as an electron donor and the way in which this varies with changes in the substituents. Hanson and Bouck [79] measured the increase in the intensity of the CH stretching bands of chloroform, methylene chloride and other solvents on association with phosphoryl links. They used this increase as an index of the strength of the association assuming that the intensity would increase with the strength of the hydrogen bonds. On this basis they classified the donor properties of a number of different classes of compound as follows:

$$[(CH_3)_2N]_3P{=}O > (C_6H_5)_3P{=}O > (C_2H_5S)_3P{=}O > (C_6H_5S)_3P{=}O >$$
$$(CH_3C_6H_4O)_3P{=}O > [(C_2H_5)_2N]_3P{=}O$$

It is startling to find two compounds which differ by only a CH_2 group at the head and tail of this list.

A more detailed study has been made by Gramstad [72, 80, 81, 146], who has measured $\delta v P{=}O$, $\delta v OH$ and δH values for the association of phosphoryl compounds with phenol, with pentachlorophenol, other alcohols and with chloroform. For each individual proton donor he finds that K_{ass^N}, ΔH, ΔF and ΔS are simple linear functions of $\delta v OH$, a separate line being required for each donor. No similar relation appears to cover the shifts of $v P{=}O$. Thus $HP(OC_2H_5)_2{=}O$ ($v P{=}O$ 1258 cm^{-1}) gives a $\delta v OH$ value with phenol of 310 cm^{-1} and a $\delta v P{=}O$ value of 35 cm^{-1}. However, in the more basic $C_2H_5P(OC_2H_5)_2{=}O$ ($v P{=}O$ 1231 cm^{-1}) the $\delta v OH$ value increases (355 cm^{-1}) but the $\delta v P{=}O$ value falls (20 cm^{-1}). There are also inexplicable variations from one alcohol to another. Triphenylphosphine oxide appears to be more basic than $CH_3PO(OC_2H_5)_2$ as judged by the $\delta v OH$ values of either methanol or α-naphthol. In the case of methanol the $\delta v P{=}O$ values run parallel (16 and 8 cm^{-1} respectively). With α-naphthol, however, the opposite is true ($\delta v P{=}O$ 18 and 25 cm^{-1} respectively), so that the largest shift seems to come from the weaker association. The size of phosphoryl group frequency shifts on association is not therefore a reliable guide to the strength of the bonds.

So far as the overall polarities are concerned, there does seem to be a general trend whereby the higher $v P{=}O$ frequencies correspond to less basic groups as measured by $\delta v OH$ values in the way described above. However, there are minor discrepancies in the order, and there is no smooth relation between $v P{=}O$ and the corresponding $\delta v OH$ values. There is however a linear relation between the OH shift and the P=O intensities [145].

Gramstad [80, 81] has also studied the association of phosphoryl groups with iodine in charge transfer complexes. The associations are very much weaker than those involving hydrogen bonds, at least as judged by association constants, but the P=O shifts are much greater. Shifts of up to 80 cm^{-1} have been found, and this again emphasizes the need for caution in the use of these shifts to judge the strengths of the association. Dahl et al. [147] have also studied the effects of interaction with ICN. The P=O shifts of about

20–40 cm^{-1} are less than with iodine, and there is again no relationship between the P=O frequencies and the equilibrium constants. However, there is a linear relationship between the equilibrium constant and the frequency shifts of the I—C band.

Cotton *et al.* [82, 118, 119] have looked at the shifts of νP=O on coordination. The frequency falls by 70–20 cm^{-1}. Deacon and Green [148] and Joly and Nicolau [142] have studied complexes of phosphoryl compounds with mercury halides, but both have concentrated on the shifts of the mercury—halogen bond rather than on those of the P=O.

6.4. The P=S vibration

This vibration has been extensively studied, but the results are somewhat disappointing [52, 74, 83–88, 123–124]. This band is not strong, and it is difficult to identify, as it falls in a region in which many other bands appear. A careful comparison of pairs of compounds with P=O and P=S links has enabled two bands to be identified which seem to be connected in some way with the P=S structure. Both are absent in the corresponding P=O compounds, and both vanish during the isomerism from phosphorothionates to phosphorothiolates. The overall ranges of these two bands are quite wide,

$$
\begin{array}{ccc}
\text{R} \quad \text{S} & & \text{R} \quad \text{O} \\
\diagdown \diagup\diagup & & \diagdown \diagup\diagup \\
\text{P} & \longrightarrow & \text{P} \\
\diagup \quad \diagdown & & \diagup \quad \diagdown \\
\text{RO} \quad \text{OR} & & \text{RO} \quad \text{SR}
\end{array}
$$

802–658 and 730–550 cm^{-1}, and no satisfactory explanation is available for the fact that there are two characteristic bands. Nor is it known which corresponds to the true P=S band. Many authors [84–87] prefer to regard the lower-frequency bands as due to P=S, mainly because of the better agreement shown with attempts to predict νP=S from force-constant data. Often only one or other of the two bands is discussed in any one publication. Chittenden and Thomas [83] have extracted all the data available on both bands and have tabulated the frequencies for various structures. They have also shown that the bands do not show any change in relative intensity with temperature, thus eliminating one possible explanation in terms of rotational isomerism.

The positions of both bands are sensitive to the nature of the substituents, and as neither of them follows the π type of relationship shown by the P=O band, they cannot be identified in this way. The most useful diagnostic for the P=S band should be the sensitivity to hydrogen bonding effects. When acids of the type $(RO)_2P(SH)=S$ are compared with the esters $(RO)_2P(SR)=S$ the higher-frequency band shows a marked frequency fall, whereas the lower-frequency band is unchanged. The fact that these acids do have remarkably strong hydrogen bonds is well known from the $\delta\nu$SH shifts, which can be as large as 200 cm^{-1}, and this evidence therefore suggests that the higher-frequency band is that which originated in the P=S vibration. There is some further support for this from the work of Zingaro and Hedges [90], who observed frequency shifts of up to 21 cm^{-1} in the higher-frequency band when these compounds were allowed to associate with alcohols or with iodine. Unfortunately they did not study the behaviour of the lower-frequency absorption. Gramstad [72] also refers to shifts in the P=S band on complex formation, but does not quote the frequencies in question. The bulk of the evidence therefore suggests that the higher frequency band is that most strongly linked to the P=S, and this is strongly supported by studies on the thiophosphoryl halides [149–151]. These cover not only the PSX$_3$ compounds but also many mixed halides. The latter all show a medium strength band in the range 770–713 cm^{-1}, whilst SPCl$_3$ absorbs at 770 cm^{-1} and SPF$_3$ at 693 cm^{-1}. However, it is not to be expected that a band at these frequencies will represent a single uncoupled mode, and there is little doubt from potential energy distribution work that this band has major contributions from both the P=S and the P—halogen stretch.

The positions of bands I and II, as tabulated by Chittenden and Thomas, for the solid or liquid phases are listed in Table 6.5. The overall trends in both cases are different from those of the P=O group. This is to be expected in view of the extensive coupling of the P=S mode.

Table 6.5. Characteristic bands of the P=S group

System	Band I, cm^{-1}	Band II, cm^{-1}
(RO)$_3$P=S	844–800	662–602
(RO)$_2$RP=S	803–770	650–595
(RO)R$_2$P=S	792–769	608–580
R$_3$P=S	769–685	596–532
(RO)$_2$SR P=S	833–790	663–645
(RO)$_2$SH P=S	780–730	658–649
R$_2$Cl P=S	775–750	626–593
RCl$_2$P=S	781–775	668–640
(R$_2$N)$_3$P=S	837–790	714–690

Only a very limited amount of work has been done on the intensities of these bands, but Vasil'ev [87] has given some data on both intensities and half-bandwidths.

6.5. The P=Se vibration

This has been little studied, but data on some phosphorus selenium compounds have been given by Quinchon et al. [89] and by Thomas [83]. This likewise gives two bands, both of which seem to be associated with the P=Se bond. These fall in the ranges 577–517 cm^{-1} (band I) and 535–473 cm^{-1}

(band II). However, the number of compounds covered is small, and these assignments must be regarded as tentative. Rojhantalab et al. [152] assign the P=Se absorption as low as 442 cm^{-1} in trimethyl phosphine selenide. The general trends suggest that, like the P=S bands, there is no particular relationship between these frequencies and Thomas's π values.

6.6. The C=S vibration

This group is less polar than the carbonyl link and has a considerably weaker bond. In consequence, the band is not intense, and it falls at lower frequencies, where it is much more susceptible to coupling effects. Identification is therefore difficult and uncertain in the infrared. However, recognition can be considerably helped by the use of the Raman spectrum where the high polarisability of the sulphur atom leads to particularly strong bands from all bonds connected to it. The various classes of compounds for which data are available are discussed below. However, it is very difficult to identify any systematic behaviour of the C=S band with changes in the substituents. The highest frequency, as with the carbonyl group is the difluoride which absorbs at 1368 cm^{-1}, but this is followed by dialkyl thioketones (near 1260 cm^{-1}), by thiocarbonates near 1220 cm^{-1}, and the dichloride at 1121 cm^{-1}. Thioureas take the lowest frequencies near 750 cm^{-1}. This order $F > C > O > Cl > N$ does not follow the order either of the inductive and resonance effects of the substituents or the order of C—X bond strengths. It is in fact a reflection of the electronic effects combined with strong coupling in most cases. It is only to be expected that in the C=S stretch in which the carbon atom moves much more than the sulphur, the influence of angle effects and of the effects of compression of the C—X bonds will be considerably more pronounced than in the carbonyl vibration.

(a) Dithioesters

There is reasonably good agreement that νC=S lies between 1225 and 1190 cm^{-1} in these compounds. Bak et al. [96] place it there in a series of twenty-one dithioesters, and their results have been confirmed by Bellamy and Rogasch [97] using solvent studies. Only one band in the spectra of dithioesters is found to be shifted in proton-donating solvents, and as the pattern of behaviour is similar to that of other X=O groups, this can be assigned to the C=S bond. The trithiocarbonates absorb at lower frequencies in the 1050–1100-cm^{-1} region, as does ethylene trithiocarbonate (1083 cm^{-1}). The appearance of the C=S bond exocyclic to a five-membered ring does not therefore raise νC=S. Complex formation of the thiocarbanato compounds with metals such as nickel, platinum and zinc has remarkably little effect on the C=S frequencies, these fall slightly into the 1010 cm^{-1} region, and show minor variations from one metal to another [153, 154].

(b) *Thioketones*

The tendency for some simple thioketones to dimerise can cause confusion in the identification of the C=S absorption. However, careful preparative work, coupled with the use of the Raman spectra in which the C=S band is very strong has shown that this absorption occurs in the range 1224–1270 cm^{-1} in simple alkyl thioketones [155–157]. The intensity in the infrared is moderate except in thioacetone when it is several times more intense. This frequency range is very close to that which can be calculated from the mass changes from the corresponding carbonyl compounds. This predicts a ratio of vC=O/vC=S of 1.38. However, this is largely fortuitous as force constant calculations show that in thioacetone there is only 53 per cent of C=S character in the 1265 cm^{-1} band, which is strongly coupled with other modes. The band is only slightly sensitive to solvent effects. Andrieu and Mollier [155] have found a reasonable correlation between these frequencies and the Taft values of the substituents.

Conjugated thioketones absorb at lower frequencies, and the data have been reviewed by Rao [91], and other workers [92, 125, 158]. Thiobenzophenones absorb between 1224 and 1207 cm^{-1}, and neither in these nor in the aryl dithioesters is there any correlation between the frequencies and the Hammett σ values of any ring substituents [93]. Heteroaromatic conjugation produces rather larger shifts, as it does with the carbonyl series. *Bis* thienyl-2-thioketone absorbs at 1170 cm^{-1} and aryl-2-thiophenones at 1190 cm^{-1} [158]. Thiopyridones absorb even lower in the range 1150–1100 cm^{-1} [94, 95].

(c) *Xanthates*

Dialkyl xanthates, dixanthogens and heavy metal xanthates show a series of bands [98–100, 159–161] in the ranges 1250–1200, 1140–1110 and 1070–1020 cm^{-1}. All originate in the structure R—O—C=S, but it is difficult to identify any specific band with the C=S absorption. Rao [91] prefers to regard the 1070–1020-cm^{-1} band as originating in the C=S mode and assigns the higher-frequency bands to carbon oxygen stretching modes. However, it is likely that there is extensive mixing and that none of these bands represents a pure vibrational mode. This is supported by normal coordinate calculations on metal thioxanthates [161]. These show that the C=S mode is strongly coupled.

(d) *Other* C=S *compounds* (*except those attached to nitrogen*)

Thiophosgene absorbs at 1121 cm^{-1}. This is significantly less than the values for the alkyl thioketones and suggests that the halogen electronegativity is less effective in raising the frequency than in the carbonyl series. CSF_2 does absorb at 1368 cm^{-1} but both CSFBr and CSClBr absorb at 1130 cm^{-1}. Bellamy and Rogasch [97] attribute this to the lack of polarity in the C=S bond, so that it behaves more like the C=C stretching mode, which also moves to a lower frequency on chlorine substitution. A series of γ-mercaptoazo compounds have also been studied [101] and shown to absorb near 1130 cm^{-1}.

(e) N—C=S compounds

νC=S is strongly coupled in nearly all the compounds in which the carbon atom is directly linked to nitrogen. In consequence, there are a number of different bands, each of which contains a significant contribution from the C=S stretching mode. This accounts both for the difficulty in identification of this band and for the diversity of regions to which it has been assigned. Complete vibrational assignments are helpful here, but no complete answers are possible. Thus, Susuki [102] regards the 843-cm^{-1} band of thioformamide as a pure C=S mode, whereas Davies and Jones [103] assign bands at 1432 and 1287 to the antisymmetric and symmetric modes of the NCS system in this compound.

The data have been well reviewed by Rao [91], who has drawn up a table showing the distinctive movements of each of the bands with structural change. Each has some contribution from the C=S mode, but for diagnostic purposes their use is very limited. Detailed work on individual classes of thioamides include the following: thioacetamide [102, 104, 105, 162], dithio-oxamides [106, 107, 163], thiadiazoles [108] and thiazoles [108], thiohydran-toins [109], thioureas [104, 110, 113, 117], thiosemicarbazones [111] and thioamides generally [97, 112, 115]. All of these types of compound show three bands in the ranges 1570–1395, 1420–1260 and 1140–940 cm^{-1}, whilst most thioamides show one other band in the 700–800 cm^{-1} region. These are normally designated the thioamide I, II, III and IV bands. The first two have little C=S content, and originate mainly in C=N and NH deformation modes but the last two have both a significant C=S content. However, there is strong coupling, as is clearly shown for example in the molecule N-methylthiocarbanate [164]. Due to the considerable double bond character of the C—O link in this compound this can exist in two configurations, with the C=S cis or trans to the NH bond. The cis form has the C=S band at 905 cm^{-1} and the trans at 680 cm^{-1}. The difference must largely arise from coupling differences.

6.7. The C=Se vibration

Little that is useful can be said about this mode, which has not been much studied. However, a number of N—C=Se compounds have been studied. The results of normal coordinate studies show that as with the C=S vibration the C=Se is very considerably coupled [114, 116, 165–167]. As a result there are a number of bands which have some C=Se stretching content and their position varies considerably with structure. In selenoacetamide the band with the highest C=Se character is at 614 cm^{-1} [167], in tetramethylseleno it contributes to two bands at 408 and 381 cm^{-1}, whilst in NN-dimethylseleno formamide, the bands at 895 and 524 cm^{-1} have each about 50% C=Se content [165, 166]. Gingrao et al. [126] discuss this frequency in selenosemicarbazones, which falls between 800–780 cm^{-1}.

Bibliography

1. Cairns, Eglinton and Gibson, *Spectrochim. Acta,* 1964, **20**, 31.
2. Cairns and Eglinton, *Spectrochim. Acta,* 1964, **20**, 159.
3. Tamres and Searles, *J. Amer. Chem. Soc.,* 1959, **81**, 2100.
4. Gramstad, *Spectrochim. Acta,* 1963, **19**, 829.
5. Otting and Neugebauer, *Chem. Ber.,* 1962, **95**, 540.
6. Foffani, Ghersetti and Montanori, *Ric. Sci.,* 1960, **30**, 1010.
7. Del La Mere, Millen, Tillett and Watson, *J. Chem. Soc.,* 1963, 1619.
8. Pinchas, Samuel and Weiss Broday, *J. Chem. Soc.,* 1962, 3968.
9. Ghersetti, *Boll. Sci. Chim. Ind. Bologna,* 1961, **19**, 83.
10. Kresze, Ropte and Schrader, *Spectrochim. Acta,* 1965, **21**, 1633.
11. Horrocks and Cotton, *Spectrochim. Acta,* 1961, **17**, 134; 1960, **16**, 358.
12. Ghersetti and Modena, *Spectrochim. Acta,* 1963, **19**, 1809; *Ann. Chim. Rome,* 1963, **53**, 1083.
13. Grisko and Gur'janova, *J. Phys. Chem. Moscow,* 1958, **32**, 2725.
14. Detoni and Hadzi, *Spectrochim. Acta,* 1957, **14**, 601.
15. Simon and Heintz, *Chem. Ber.,* 1962, **95**, 2333.
16. Glass and Pullin, *Trans. Faraday Soc.,* 1961, **57**, 546.
17. Kresze and Maschke, *Chem. Ber.,* 1961, **94**, 450.
18. Long and Bailey, *Trans. Faraday Soc.,* 1963, **59**, 792.
19. Gillespie and Robinson, *Can. J. Chem.,* 1961, **39**, 2171.
20. Daasch, *Spectrochim. Acta,* 1958, **13**, 257.
21. Meyers, Lombardini and Bonoli, *J. Amer. Chem. Soc.,* 1962, **84**, 4603.
22. Leonard and Johnson. *J. Amer. Chem. Soc.,* 1962, **84**, 3701.
23. Cotton, Francis and Horrocks, *J. Phys. Chem.,* 1960, **64**, 1534.
24. Francis and Cotton, *J. Chem. Soc.,* 1961, 2078.
25. Drago and Meek, *J. Phys. Chem.,* 1961, **65**, 1446.
26. Lappert and Smith, *J. Chem. Soc.,* 1961, 3224.
27. Selbin, Bull and Holmes, *J. Inorganic and Nuclear Chem.,* 1960, **16**, 219.
28. Bellamy, Conduit, Pace and Williams, *Trans. Faraday Soc.,* 1959, **35**, 1677.
29. Biscarini and Ghersetti, *Gazz. Chim. Ital.,* 1962, **92**, 61.
30. Bellamy and Williams, *J. Chem. Soc.,* 1957, 863.
31. Looney, Philips and Reilly, *J. Amer. Chem. Soc.,* 1957, **79**, 6136.
32. Williams, Pace and Jeacock, *Spectrochim. Acta,* 1964, **20**, 225.
33. Owen and Sheppard, *Proc. Chem. Soc.,* 1963, 264.
34. Califano, Moccia, Scarpati and Speroni, *J. Chem. Phys.,* 1957, **26**, 1777.
35. Gowenlock, Spedding, Trotman and Whiffen, *J. Chem. Soc.,* 1957, 3927.
36. Devlin and Hisatsune, *Spectrochim. Acta,* 1961, **17**, 206.
37. Phillippe and Moore, *Spectrochim. Acta,* 1961, **17**, 1004.
38. Shindo, *Chem. and Pharm. Bull. Japan,* 1958, **6**, 117; 1959, **7**, 791.
39. Katritzky, Beard and Coates, *J. Chem. Soc.,* 1959, 3680.

40. Mirone, *Atti. Accad. Naz. Lincei. Rend. Classe Sci. fis. mat. nat.*, 1963, **35**, 530.
41. Tsoucaris, *J. Chim. Phys.*, 1961, **58**, 619.
42. Katritzky, *Rec. Trav. Chim. Pays Bas.*, 1959, **78**, 995.
43. Quagliano, Fujita, Franz, Phillips, Walmsley and Tyree, *J. Amer. Chem. Soc.*, 1961, **83**, 3770.
44. Shindo, *Chem. and Pharm. Bull. Japan*, 1960, **8**, 33.
45. Klein and Berkowitz, *J. Amer. Chem. Soc.*, 1959, **81**, 5160.
46. Thomas and Chittenden, *Chem. and Ind.*, 1961, 1913.
47. Thomas and Chittenden, *Spectrochim. Acta*, 1964, **20**, 467.
48. Maiantz, Popov and Kabacnik, *Optics and Spectroscopy*, 1959, **7**, 108.
49. Gersmann, Physich Chemische Metingen aan organische phosphor verbindung, Thesis, Amsterdam 1956.
50. Dobbie and Straughan, *Spectrochim. Acta*, 1971, **27A**, 255.
51. Ketelaar and Gersmann, *Rec. Trav. Chim. Pays Bas.*, 1959, **78**, 190.
52. Popov, Kabacnik and Majac, *Adv. Chem. Moscow*, 1961, **30**, 846.
53. Mathis Noel, Boisdon, Vives and Mathis, *Compt. Rendu. Acad. Sci. France*, 1963, **257**, 404.
54. Wolf, Mathis-Noel and Mathis, *Bull. Soc. Chim. France*, 1960, 124.
55. Wolf, Miquel and Mathis, *Bull. Soc. Chim. France*, 1963, 825.
56. Goncalves, Mathis and Wolf, *Bull. Soc. Chim. France*, 1961, 1595.
57. Jones and Katritzky, *J. Chem. Soc.*, 1960, 4376.
58. Arnold and Bourseaux, *Angew. Chem.*, 1958, **70**, 539.
59. Haring, *Helv. Chim. Acta*, 1960, **43**, 1826.
60. Miller, Miller and Rogers, *J. Amer. Chem. Soc.*, 1958, **80**, 1562.
61. Coe, Perry and Brown, *J. Chem. Soc.*, 1957, 3604.
62. Lazarev and Akselrod, *Optics and Spectroscopy*, 1960, **9**, 326.
63. Peppard, Ferraro and Mason, *J. Inorganic and Nuclear Chem.*, 1958, **7**, 231.
64. Peppard and Ferraro, *J. Inorganic and Nuclear Chem.*, 1959, **10**, 275.
65. Peppard, Feraro and Mason, *J. Inorganic and Nuclear Chem.*, 1959, **12**, 60.
66. Peppard, Ferraro and Mason, *J. Inorganic and Nuclear Chem.*, 1961, **16**, 246.
67. Ferraro and Andrejasich, *J. Inorganic Nuclear Chem.*, 1964, **26**, 377.
68. Thomas and Clark, *Nature*, 1963, **198**, 855.
69. Smith, *J. Inorganic and Nuclear Chem.*, 1960, **15**, 95.
70. Braunholtz, Hall, Mann and Sheppard, *J. Chem. Soc.*, 1959, 868.
71. Slovochotova, Anisimov, Kunickaja and Kolobova, *Bull. Acad. Sci. U.R.S.S. Ser. Chim.*, 1961, 71.
72. Gramstad, *Acta Chem. Scand.*, 1961, **15**, 1337.
73. Steger, *Zeit. Electrochem.*, 1957, **61**, 1004.
74. Mcivor and Hubley, *Can. J. Chem.*, 1959, **37**, 869.
75. Greckin and Sagidullin, *Bull. Acad. Sci. U.R.S.S.*, 1960, 2135.
76. Sagidullin, *Bull. Acad. Sci. U.R.S.S.*, phys. ser., 1958, **22**, 1079.
77. Kabacnik, Giljarov and Cvetkov, *Bull. Acad. Sci. U.R.S.S.*, 1959, 2135.
78. Griffen, *Chem. and Ind.*, 1960, 1058.
79. Hanson and Bouck, *J. Amer. Chem. Soc.*, 1957, **79**, 5631.
80. Gramstad, *Spectrochim. Acta*, 1964, **20**, 729.
81. Blindheim and Gramstad, *Spectrochim. Acta*, 1965, **21**, 1073.
82. Cotton and Goodgame, *J. Amer. Chem. Soc.*, 1960, **82**, 5774.
83. Chittenden and Thomas, *Spectrochim. Acta*, 1964, **20**, 1679.
84. Hoodge and Christen, *Rec. Trav. Chim. Pays Bas*, 1958, **77**, 911.
85. Popov, Mastrjukova, Rodinova and Kabacnik, *J. Gen. Chem. Moscow*, 1959, **29(91)**, 1998.
86. Rockett, *Applied Spectroscopy*, 1962, **16**, 39.

87. Vasil'Ev, *Zhur. Obshchei Khim.,* 1963, **33**, 874.
88. Tridot and Tudo, *Bull. Soc. Chim. France,* 1960, 1231.
89. Quinchon, Le Sech and Gryszkiewicz-Trochimowski, *Bull. Soc. Chim. France,* 1961, 735, 739; 1962, 169.
90. Zingaro and Hedges, *J. Phys. Chem.,* 1961, **65**, 1132.
91. Rao and Venkataraghavan, *Spectrochim. Acta,* 1962, **18**, 541.
92. Lozach and Guillouzo, *Bull. Soc. Chim. France,* 1957, 1221.
93. Rao and Venkataraghavan, *Can. J. Chem.,* 1961, **39**, 1757.
94. Katritzky and Jones, *Spectrochim. Acta,* 1961, **17**, 64.
95. Katritzky and Jones, *J. Chem. Soc.,* 1960, 2947.
96. Bak, Hansen Nygaard and Pedersen, *Acta Chem. Scand.,* 1958, **12**, 1451.
97. Bellamy and Rogasch, *J. Chem. Soc.,* 1960, 2218.
98. Pearson and Stasiak, *Applied Spectroscopy,* 1958, **12**, 116.
99. Little, Poling and Leja, *Can. J. Chem.,* 1961, **39**, 745.
100. Shankarenaryana and Patel, *Can. J. Chem.,* 1961, **39**, 1633.
101. Spinner, *J. Chem. Soc.,* 1960, 1237.
102. Susuki, *Bull. Chem. Soc. Japan,* 1962, **35**, 1286; 1449, 1456.
103. Davies and Jones, *J. Chem. Soc.,* 1958, 955.
104. Spinner, *Spectrochim. Acta,* 1959, **15**, 95.
105. Kutzelnigg and Mecke, *Spectrochim. Acta,* 1961, **17**, 530.
106. Scott and Wagner, *J. Chem. Phys.,* 1959, **30**, 465.
107. Milligan, Spinner and Swan, *J. Chem. Soc.,* 1961, 1919.
108. Thorn, *Can. J. Chem.,* 1960, **38**, 1439, 2349.
109. Elmore, *J. Chem. Soc.,* 1958, 3489.
110. Suresh, Ramachandran and Rao, *J. Sci. Ind. Research (India),* 1961, **20B**, 203.
111. Sadler, *J. Chem. Soc.,* 1961, 957.
112. Yamada, Omar and Hino, *Chem. and Pharm. Bull. Japan,* 1964, **12**, 244.
113. Becher and Griffel, *Chem. Ber.,* 1958, **91**, 2025.
114. Collard-Charon and Renson, *Bull. Soc. Chim. Belges,* 1963, **72**, 149, 291, 304.
115. Spinner, *J. Org. Chem.,* 1958, **23**, 2037.
116. Jensen, *Acta, Chem. Scand.,* 1963, **17**, 551.
117. Cibisov and Pentin, *J. Gen. Chem. Moscow,* 1961, **31**, 11.
118. Cotton, Barnes and Bannister, *J. Chem. Soc.,* 1960, 2199.
119. Cotton and Goodgame, *J. Chem. Soc.,* 1960, 5267; 1961, 2298, 3735.
120. Ghersetti and Pallotti, *Gazz. Chim. Rome,* 1963, **93**, 1000.
121. Nyquist and Muelder, *Spectrochim. Acta,* 1966, **22**, 1563.
122. Figueroa, Roig and Szmant, *Spectrochim. Acta,* 1966, **22**, 1107.
123. Chen. *Acta. Chim. Sin.,* 1965, **31**, 29.
124. Husebye, *Acta. Chem. Scand.,* 1965, **19**, 774.
125. Korver, Veenland and De Boer, *Rec. Trav. Chim. Pays Bas,* 1965, **84**, 310.
126. Gingras, Supunchuk and Bayley, *Can. J. Chem.,* 1965, **43**, 1650.
127. Lumbroso and Montaudo, *Bull. Chem. Soc. France,* 1964, 2119.
128. Vazquez and Castrillon, *Spectrochim. Acta,* 1974, **30A**, 2021.
129. Steudel Zeit. *Naturforsch* 1970, **25B**, 156.
130. Dorris, *Appl. Spectrosc.,* 1970, **24**, 492.
131. Cazaux, Bastide, Chassaing and Maroni, *Spectrochim. Acta,* 1979, **35A**, 15.
132. Green and Hellier, *J. Chem. Soc.* Perkin, **11**, 1972, 458.
133. Cazaux and Maroni, *Tetrahedron Letters,* 1969, 3667.
134. Smith and Wu, *Appl. Spectrosc.,* 1968, **22**, 346.
135. Keat, Ross and Sharp, *Spectrochim. Acta,* 1971, **27A**, 2219.
136. **Raevsky, Verestichagin, Mumzhieva, Zyablikova, Alexandrova and Arbuzov.** *J. Mol. Structure,* 1977, **36**, 299.

137. Raevsky, *J. Mol. Structure,* 1973, **19**, 275.
138. James and Morris, *Spectrochim. Acta,* 1978, **34A**, 577.
139. Reynolds, in *Progress in Inorganic Chemistry* ed Lippard Wiley New York, 1970, Vol 12, p. 1.
140. Burgard and Leroy, *J. Mol. Structure,* 1974, **20**, 153.
141. Meunier and Forel, *Spectrochim. Acta,* 1973, **29A**, 487.
142. Joly and Nicolau, *Spectrochim. Acta,* 1979, **35A**, 281.
143. Goubeau and Lentz, *Spectrochim. Acta,* 1971, **27A**, 1703.
144. Goldwhite and Previdi, *Spectrochim. Acta,* 1970, **26A**, 1403.
145. Gramstad and Storesund, *Spectrochim. Acta,* 1970, **26A**, 426.
146. Gramstad and Mundheim, *Spectrochim. Acta,* 1972, **28A**, 1405.
147. Dahl, Klaboe and Gramstad, *Spectrochim. Acta,* 1969, **25A**, 207.
148. Deacon and Green, *Spectrochim. Acta,* 1969, **25A**, 355.
149. Muller, Koniger, Cyvin and Fadini, *Spectrochim. Acta,* 1973, **29A**, 219.
150. Cyvin, Vizi, Muller and Krebs, *J. Mol. Structure,* 1969, **3**, 173.
151. Olie and Stufkens, *Spectrochim. Acta,* 1976, **32A**, 469.
152. Rojhantalab, Nibler and Wilkins, *Spectrochim. Acta,* 1976, **32A**, 519.
153. Cormier, Nakamoto, Christophliemk and Muller, *Spectrochim. Acta,* 1974, **30A**, 1059.
154. Burke and Fackler, *Inorganic Chem.,* 1972, **11**, 2744.
155. Garrigou-Lagrange, Andrieu and Mollier, *Spectrochim. Acta,* 1976, **32A**, 477.
156. Andrieu and Mollier, *Spectrochim. Acta,* 1972, **28A**, 785.
157. Andrieu and Mollier, *Tetrahedron Letters,* 1971, 1573.
158. Andrieu and Mollier, *Bull. Soc. Chim. France,* 1969, 831.
159. Ray, Sathyanarayana, Prasad and Patel, *Spectrochim. Acta,* 1973, **29A**, 1578.
160. Coucouvanis, *Progress in Inorganic Chem.,* 1970, **11**, 233.
161. Geetharani and Sathyanarayana, *Spectrochim. Acta,* 1974, **30A**, 2165.
162. Walter and Staglich, *Spectrochim. Acta,* 1974, **30A**, 1739.
163. Desseyn, Jacob and Herman, *Spectrochim. Acta,* 1969, **25A**, 1685.
164. Chaturverdi and Rao, *Spectrochim. Acta,* 1971, **27A**, 65.
165. Anthoni, Neilsen, Borch and Klaboe, *Spectrochim. Acta,* 1978, **34A**, 955.
166. Antoni, Heindriksen, Nielsen, Borch and Klaboe, *Spectrochim. Acta,* 1974, **30A**, 1351.
167. Gayathri Devi, Sathyanarayana, and Volka, *Spectrochim. Acta,* 1978, **34A**, 1137.
168. Gruger and Le Calve, *Spectrochim. Acta,* 1975, **31A**, 581.
169. Gruger and Le Calve, *Spectrochim. Acta,* 1975, **31A**, 595.

7

Stretching Vibrations of XO$_2$ Systems, RSO$_2$, RNO$_2$ and RCO$_2^-$

7.1. The SO$_2$ stretching vibrations

There appears to be very little coupling between the anti-symmetric and symmetric S=O stretching modes and the other vibrations of the molecule to which this group is attached. These bands therefore afford a particularly good system in which to study the impact of the electronic effects that arise from changes in the substituents. Unfortunately, the relative insolubility of many of these compounds has led to their being studied in the solid state or in solution in polar solvents, so that the overall picture is overlaid by association effects. Nevertheless, it is possible to draw some general conclusions from this material, both as regards the variations of the frequencies with structure and with angles. These are presented in more detail in Section 7.1.2, in which the systematics of these frequencies is discussed.

The absence of any significant coupling with other vibrations also leads directly to the simple linear relationship between v_s and v_{as} which was first described by Bellamy and Williams. Robinson [1] has recently applied this relation to a very much wider range of compounds containing the SO$_2$ group, including inorganic ions such as XSO$_3^-$, SO$_4^-$ and to complexes in which the SO$_2$ group is contained in a ring. Despite the fact that not all the data related to the same phase, the overall agreement remained remarkably good. In some cases Robinson has been able to use this relation to correct assignments. However, more recent studies by Butcher et al. [110] and by Engberts [109] have revealed instances in which the relation fails, probably due to coupling in the symmetric mode. Engberts quotes the equation $v\text{SO}_2^{sym} = 0.326\ v\text{SO}_2^{as} - 668$ ($r = 0.60$), but points out that this is considerably improved if one considers only the limited series of the dialkyl sulphones when $v\text{SO}_2^{sym} = 1.256\ v\text{SO}_2^{as} - 519$ ($r = 0.92$).

Both bands, usually but not always, show a multiple structure with sub-bands on the sides of the main peaks. The positions of these sub-bands have been carefully tabulated by several workers. The presence of the structure is useful as an aid to identification, but must be used with caution. The splitting persists in the solid state and does not therefore arise from rotational isomerism. In many instances the splitting of the asymmetric band arises from the close proximity of CH_3 or CH_2 deformation bands. In CH_3SO_2X compounds for example, the symmetric deformation mode of the methyl group attached to sulphur appears near 1320 cm^{-1}, and then appears as a strong shoulder on the side of the SO_2 stretch. The latter band is not split in the deuterated compounds, nor is it in compounds such as FSO_2F, $ClOSO_2F$ or $HOSO_2F$. In CH_3OSO_2Cl, the $asSO_2$ band at 1404 cm^{-1} again appears to be split, but this time it is due to the presence of the OCH_3 deformation at 1433 cm^{-1}.

The splitting of the symmetric band is also variable, and like the antisymmetric band it probably arises from a variety of causes. For example the SO_2 stretch in CH_3OSO_2Cl at 1192 cm^{-1} appears to be double due to the presence of the OCH_3 rock at 1186 cm^{-1} [90].

In the following discussion the characteristic frequencies of these vibrations with various types of substitution is first discussed. This is followed by an account of the structural factors which determine the positions of the bands and their separation, and finally the impact of phase changes and of association effects is discussed. Table 7.1 presents the symmetric and anti-symmetric stretching frequencies of a range of symmetrically substituted compounds. The values for unsymmetrically substituted materials will be found to be very close to the mean value of the two corresponding symmetric parent compounds.

7.1.1. Group frequencies of the SO_2 link

(a) Sulphones

Robinson [1] has summarized the literature values on sulphones up to 1961, and suggested the following frequency ranges:

Dialkyl sulphones 1339–1307 and 1145–1136 cm^{-1}
Alkyl/aryl sulphones 1334–1325 and 1160–1150 cm^{-1}
Diaryl sulphones 1358–1336 and 1169–1159 cm^{-1}

Although these are comparatively narrow ranges, they do in fact include data in both the solid state and in various solvents, so that these ranges are generally applicable, as long as polar solvents are avoided. It will be seen from Table 7.1, which includes some later data from Feairheller and Katon [2], that it is also possible to distinguish between straight-chain and branched-chain alkyl sulphones. The former absorb at higher frequencies (1324–1317 and 1152–1136 cm^{-1}) than the latter. This is parallel to the cases of phosphoryl compounds, in which the branched-chain alkyl derivatives have lower frequencies (lower π values) than the open chains.

Bavin *et al.* [3] have measured a number of fluorene derivatives with sulphonyl groups at the 9 position. In carbon tetrachloride these absorb in the narrow ranges 1328–1318 and 1162–1152 cm^{-1}. These represent only a very small extension of the normal ranges of dialkyl sulphones. In all cases the higher-frequency band shows multiple peaks, and these are usually present also in the lower-frequency band. A complete assignment for dimethyl sulphone has been given by Fujimori [4].

Aryl and diaryl sulphones have been extensively studied by several groups, particularly by Momose et al. [5, 6], by Ghersetti [78, 79], by Marziano et al. [7–9] and by Shinriki [88] and Exner [89]. The effects of conjugation are very small, and it is unlikely that there is any significant interaction between the π clouds of rings or of double bonds and the S=O links. Such frequency shifts as do occur are towards higher frequencies, and this is the expected result if we are primarily concerned with the inductive effects of the substituents. In the same way, SO stretching frequencies are responsive to alterations in the ring substituents, which alter its inductive properties, but are unaffected by substituents which do not change these. The general pattern of behaviour follows the Hammett σ values reasonably well. The range quoted above covers the effects of changes in the ring substituents, but it should be noticed that the presence of multiple peaks, and the occasional presence of other bands in the same spectral regions sometimes makes it very difficult to pinpoint the positions of these bands.

Cyclic sulphones have been examined in small numbers by Bavin et al. [3] and by Neuberger [10]. There seems to be little change in the frequencies as one passes from a six- to a five-membered ring system. This is to be expected in view of the lack of coupling with other modes, and is presumably a reflection of the small amplitude of the heavy sulphur atom, as compared with that of carbon in carbonyl compounds. The impact of hydrogen bonding by amines on sulphones has been discussed by Hambly and O'Grady [11].

Table 7.1. X_2SO_2 stretching frequencies in cm^{-1}

X	ν_{as}	ν_s	X	ν_{as}	ν_s
CH$_3$	1324	1152	p-Tolyl	1328	1158
n-C$_3$H$_7$	1317	1136	NH$_2$	1356	1151 (solid)
n-C$_4$H$_9$	1322	1136	F	1502	1269 (vap.)
n-C$_6$H$_{13}$	1320	1137	Cl	1414	1182 (Raman)
i-C$_3$H$_7$	1308	1130	OH	1365	1170 (solid)
i-C$_4$H$_9$	1304	1138	N(C$_3$H$_7$)$_2$	1320	1147
Vinyl	1324	1136	N(dicyclohexyl)$_2$	1320	1142
Phenyl	1326	1161			

The properties and spectra of β-disulphones and of β-ketosulphones have been studied to determine whether there is any enolization and hydrogen bonding of the kind that commonly occurs in β-diketones. In fact, there is no parallel and the SO$_2$ frequencies of these compounds are normal, as are the carbonyl frequencies in the β-ketosulphones. In the three possible systems

RSO_2—CH_2—COR where R is either alkyl or aryl, the bands do not alter by more than a wave number or so (1329–1330 and 1160–1157 cm^{-1}). The dimethyl disulphones $CH_3 \cdot SO_2 \cdot CH_2 \cdot SO_2 \cdot CH_3$ absorb at 1314 and 1137 cm^{-1}. There is no indication of any coupling between the separate SO_2 groups, and this is to be expected from the molecular geometry.

(b) Halogen-substituted SO₂ groups

Birchall and Gillespie [80] give values for SO_2F_2 and for SO_2FCl. Sulphuryl chloride absorbs at 1414 and 1182 cm^{-1} and the corresponding fluoride [13] at 1502 and 1269 cm^{-1}. These frequency rises are of the order to be expected from the inductive properties of the substituents. Compounds with one halogen and one other group have frequencies which are close to the mean values of the two separate disubstituted compounds. Thus the frequencies of $C_6H_5 \cdot SO_2 \cdot Cl$ are close to the mean values for SO_2Cl_2 and $(C_6H_5)_2SO_2$. Robinson [1] gives the overall range of 1390–1364 and 1185–1169 cm^{-1} for all types of sulphonyl monochlorides, whether aromatic or aliphatic. As with the sulphones, the differences between the latter two classes are very small. Similarly, olefinic substitution has little effect. Freeman and Hambly [14] compared the C=C frequencies of prop-2-ene, prop-1-ene-1-sulphonyl chloride and 2-phenylethylene-1-sulphonyl chloride. No changes were found throughout the series, and the SO_2 frequencies of the second and third compounds remained unchanged.

The most useful compilations of data on the frequencies of sulphonyl chlorides are those of Geiseler and Bindernagel [15, 16] and Malewski and Weigmann [17]. Geiseler has tabulated the stretching frequencies of an homologous series of alkyl sulphonly chlorides, and Malewski has done the same for a series of aryl derivatives. Geiseler and Nagel [91] give values for methyl sulphonyl fluoride, chloride and bromide. The findings generally confirm the overall ranges suggested by Robinson [1]. However, Malewski's results are interesting in showing the marked effects that result from changes in the aryl ring substituents. The observed frequencies in this series ranged from 1401 to 1380 and 1195 to 1168 cm^{-1}. The highest value in each case refers to the *ortho*-nitro derivative. The spectra of these compounds are illustrated in the paper and afford an excellent example of the difficulties in assigning precise single values to the frequencies of the multiple bands. Not only are both bands split but each is often divided into two main peaks of about equal intensity. Any logical discussion of the shifts in terms of Hammett σ values, etc., is therefore very difficult, although the general trends are very clear.

With oxygen as the second substituent Robinson [1] suggests the ranges

$R \cdot O \cdot SO_2 \cdot Cl$ 1408–1452 and 1225–1205 cm^{-1}

$R \cdot O \cdot SO_2 \cdot F$ 1445–1510 and 1230–1260 cm^{-1}

The data are limited but these ranges are supported by a compilation by Christie *et al.* [92] of literature values for a series of compounds of this kind, such as F_2NOSO_2F, $HOSO_2F$ and CH_3OSO_2F.

(c) Sulphonamides and related compounds

New data on sulphonamides have come from a variety of sources [5, 18–23, 31, 93, 94], and include work on sulphonyl modes other than the stretching frequencies, and on the ring modes of aryl sulphonamides and *N*-aryl compounds [18, 19]. The ranges given by Robinson [1] are 1358–1336 and 1152–1169 cm^{-1} for the SO_2 stretching frequencies. This has been subdivided and slightly extended by measurements by Goldstein *et al.* [93] on twenty-five *N*-alkyl and *N*-aryl sulphonamides, they quote the antisymmetric band at 1334–1322 cm^{-1} in *N*-alkyl compounds, at 1355–1336 cm^{-1} in *N*-dialkyl compounds and at 1355–1309 cm^{-1} in aryl-*N*-alkyl compounds. In all three series the symmetric band was in the range 1170–1140 cm^{-1}. Sulphonamides of heterocyclic systems have been studied by Uno *et al.* [81], and by Arcoria *et al.* [94]. These fall in essentially the same ranges as the aryl compounds, but in the case of the thiophene substituted derivatives the symmetric frequency sometimes falls to 1130 cm^{-1}.

Diamides of the type $R_2N \cdot SO_2 \cdot NR_2$ have been examined by Vandi *et al.* [20]. Alkyl and aryl diamides behave similarly and absorb between 1340–1320 and 1145–1140 cm^{-1}. This is interesting in providing an exception to the normal trend. The replacement of the second carbon atom by nitrogen would be expected to raise the frequencies, and this does not appear to occur.

(d) Sulphonates, sulphates and sulphonic acids

Only a limited amount of new information is available on sulphonates and covalent sulphates. Freeman and Hambly [14] studied fourteen sulphonates and found an overall range of 1380–1347 and 1193–1182 cm^{-1}. The differences between aryl and alkyl compounds are small, but methyl methanesulphonate absorbs at lower frequencies (1354 and 1165 cm^{-1}) than the aromatic compounds, and in the latter there is a trend towards higher values when electron-attracting groups are substituted in the *para* position. In all cases v_{as} appeared as a strong doublet, with the higher-frequency peak being the more intense. Some additional data are given by Simon and Kriegsman [24]. The special cases of the sulphonates of carbohydrates have been studied by Guthrie and Spedding [26]. These papers suggest a somewhat wider frequency spread than that given by Freeman, and the overall range is probably as wide as 1372–1335 and 1195–1168 cm^{-1}. However, these variations also take account of the various states in which the compounds were examined, and narrower ranges might well result from a study in a constant solvent. Cyclic sulphonates (sultones) have been examined by

Philbin *et al.* [27] and found to behave exactly like the open-chain compounds. Alkyl thiosulphonates have been examined by Simon and Kunath [32].

Covalent sulphates examined by Detoni and Hadzi [25] conform with the earlier findings and show ranges of 1415–1380 and 1200–1185 cm^{-1}. Lloyd has given data on carbohydrate sulphates [29], and on sulphates of alcohols, amino alcohols and amino acids [28].

Sulphonic acids show bands in the narrower ranges [25] 1350–1342 and 1165–1150 cm^{-1}. These values relate to the anhydrous forms, and it should be noted that these compounds hydrate very readily to give systems with very different frequencies. In fact, the hydrates are believed to exist as hydroxonium sulphonates ($RSO_3^- \cdot H_3O^+$), and this fact has given rise to the misassignments of sulphonic acid frequencies in the past. The hydrates give bands between 1230 and 1120 cm^{-1} similar to that of acid salts.

Metallic salts of sulphonic acids have been studied by Detoni and Hadzi [25], by Norita [30] by Fujimori [31] and others [95, 96]. The overall ranges agree with those quoted above, but for the more limited series of sodium salts of alkyl sulphonic acids this reduces to [31] 1192–1175 and 1063–1053 cm^{-1}.

7.1.2. Factors affecting the positions of the SO_2 stretching bands

It has already been mentioned that these bands show some sensitivity to changes of phase and to association effects. In extreme cases this can produce frequency shifts of up to 20 cm^{-1}. Unfortunately, due to solubility problems, the great mass of data relate to the spectra of solids, and there is therefore some uncertainty in deciding how much of any observed shifts can properly be attributed to substituent effects. The position is further complicated by the multiple structure of the bands themselves, and to the variations in the relative intensities of the various sub-peaks. Thus, in deciding the position of these bands, some authors quote values representing the mean frequency of the complex, while others refer to the frequencies of the most intense member of the set. Despite these difficulties, a clear pattern of frequency behaviour in relation to the substitution pattern can be discerned. Thus Gillespie and Robinson [33] (using the mean values of v_{as} and v_s) have found a smooth-curve relation between the frequencies and (*a*) the S=O bond length and (*b*) the S=O bond order. The mean frequency also appears to follow the changes in the O=S=O bond angles fairly closely.

As will be seen from Table 7.1, the picture is one of dominant inductive effects, with conjugation and resonance playing little or no part in determining the frequency positions. This is well shown by the close similarities between alkyl- and aryl-substituted SO_2 compounds, and the fact that the latter show slightly higher values corresponding to the increased inductive effect of the aromatic ring. Similarly, sulphonamides show higher frequencies than sulphones, corresponding to the greater electronegativity of nitrogen.

This result is to be expected from the geometry of the SO_2 group (which does not lie in the same plane as the bonds linking the other substituents) and from the essentially different character of the $S{=}O$ bond from that of a more normal system such as the carbonyl group. Vibrational coupling with the adjacent bonds will also be less than in the carbonyl group, as the increased mass of the sulphur atom will result in the increased amplitude of the oxygen atoms as compared with the sulphur. For the same reason, changes of ring size can be expected to have less effect on the $S{=}O$ frequencies of cyclic sulphones and sulphites.

The dependence of the frequencies on the substituent inductive effects is mirrored in the relationship between νSO_2 (mean value) and the acidities of the XSO_2OH acids, and in the approximate electronegativity relationship of Daasch [34]. However, as in so many other cases, the Pauling electronegativity values do not always accurately reflect the frequency changes, and they tend to overestimate the effects of oxygen substituents in particular. This raises the important question of whether, in systems such as this, where the geometry eliminates resonance effects, and probably most field effects also, and where there is little vibrational coupling, the frequency shifts do not provide a better relative measure of the intrinsic inductive effects of the substituents than that given either by Pauling electronegativity or Taft σ^* values. As much the same considerations apply to the $P{=}O$ stretching vibration, this could best be explored by a direct comparison of the behaviour of $P{=}O$ and $S{=}O$ vibrations with changes in the substituents. Unfortunately the dearth of reliable values for the frequencies of either of these vibrations in dilute solution makes any accurate comparison impracticable at present. However, a comparison can be made if phase-change effects are ignored. One then simply plots the shifts in $\nu S{=}O$ frequencies in various types of RSO_2R compounds against the π values of the substituents, as derived by Thomas (Chapter 6) from data on $P{=}O$ bonds. The preliminary comparison is very encouraging, and the SO_2 frequencies show a remarkably good parallelism with similarly substituted $P{=}O$ compounds. This even extends to such minor effects as the changes which one finds in $\nu P{=}O$ as attached alkyl groups are altered from primary to secondary and to tertiary. These changes are accurately mirrored in the frequency shifts of the comparable sulphones, both in direction and in relative magnitude. The overall effectiveness of one group as compared with another in raising νSO (mean) is also almost precisely the same as the order derived from $\nu P{=}O$ values. This aspect of the SO_2 group frequencies clearly merits more detailed study.

The degree of coupling between the symmetric and anti-symmetric stretching modes is obviously a function of the bond angles of the $O{=}S{=}O$ group. Vibrational coupling would be at a maximum if the angles were $180°$, and eliminated altogether if they were reduced to $90°$. As the bond angles are also related to the hybridization of the sulphur/oxygen orbitals, it is to be expected that there will also be some relation between the frequencies and the

O=S=O angles. This is indeed so, and Gillespie and Robinson [33] have demonstrated an approximately linear relation between νSO (mean) and the O=S=O bond angles. They have used this to derive these angles in compounds for which the values are unknown. There are no corresponding studies on the relation between the bond angles and the separation of the antisymmetric and symmetric bands. These separations vary widely and are sensitive to structural change, and they might well be expected to provide a useful guide to bond angles.

7.1.3. Basic properties of the SO_2 group

The SO_2 group has basic properties which enable it to form loose associations with proton donors. The frequency shifts which accompany solution in hydrogen bonding solvents are a good indication of this, as are the shifts of XH frequencies in compounds which form hydrogen bonds to the sulphonyl group. The first study of the basicity of SO_2 groups is that of Kartha *et al.* [35]. They measured the $\delta\nu$OH values of pentachloro phenol when this compound was allowed to associate to form I : I complexes with sulphates, sulphonates and sulphones. Unfortunately they did not record the corresponding shifts of the S=O vibrations, but some interesting trends were found. Thus there is a relationship between $\delta\nu$OH and the log of the complex dissociation constant, and also with the Hammett σ values of groups substituted in methyl aryl sulphonates. There is also an inverse relationship between $\delta\nu$OH and the rates of solvolysis of the methyl sulphonates in water.

More recently Engberts and his coworkers [106–109] have made a number of studies on the hydrogen bonding properties of the SO_2 group. They have related the OH frequency shifts of phenol when associating with sulphones to the electron density on the oxygen atoms as measured by the anti-symmetric stretching frequency. They derive a very good linear relation with the equation $\nu SO_2{}^{as} = -0.499\,\Delta\nu + 1398$. It will be seen that the change of basicity with frequency is quite rapid $\Delta\nu$ being 159 cm^{-1} for a ν_{as} value of 1321 and falling to 79 cm^{-1} when ν_{as} is 1363. As with the corresponding studies on the carbonyl group, the basicity increases as the S=O frequency falls. The substituent effect on $\Delta\nu$ OH has been shown to depend on the inductive properties of the adjacent groups and to be related to their electronegativities. The correlation with the S=O symmetric stretching mode is less satisfactory.

7.2. The X—NO$_2$ stretching vibrations

The NO$_2$ group is planar, and unlike the SO$_2$ group, it is therefore responsive to conjugation and resonance effects. Aromatic and ethylenic nitro compounds therefore absorb at lower frequencies than the nitroparaffins. The polarity of the oxygen atoms appears to be relatively low, so that while hydrogen bonding can be shown to occur, it has little apparent effect on the

NO_2 stretching frequencies. Perhaps for the same reason there is little change in the frequencies with changes of state. Many nitro compounds in chloroform solution show both the stretching frequencies within 1 or 2 cm^{-1} of the solid-state values. The higher-frequency band (anti-symmetric mode) appears to be essentially uncoupled, and its position correlates well with the electron-attracting or donating properties of the substituents [86] (i.e. with Hammett σ or Taft σ^* values as appropriate). The symmetric mode, however, is partially coupled with the X—N vibration, and although this band often shows rather larger shifts than v_{as}, the directions of shift and the extents are correspondingly harder to interpret.

Because of this coupling there is no universal relation between the values of the two stretching frequencies, such as have been described for SO_2 groups and others, although, within a limited related series in which the coupling remains constant, such relationships can be found.

7.2.1. The C—NO$_2$ group

(a) Aromatic nitro compounds

The NO_2 stretching frequencies of a very large number of aromatic nitro compounds are now available. Borek [36] deals with the inductive and resonance effects of CH_2X groups in the para position, and Katritzky [37] and also Kingusa [82] with a whole range of different groups in ortho, meta and para positions, and in heteroaromatic nuclei, such as pyridine. Green et al. [97, 98] have given complete assignments for a large number of nitroaromatics. Conduit [38] has also examined a large number of nitro aromatics, including many with multiple nitro substitution. Van Veen et al. [39] have given data on alkyl nitrobenzenes with particular reference to the ortho effects with bulky substituents. The ortho effect has also been discussed by Yamaguchi [40], and Sorygin [41] has discussed the relation between the frequencies and the angle of twist of the nitro group about the C—N bond. Hydrogen bonding usually has little effect on the anti-symmetric frequency, but there are occasionally changes in v_s [42]. The behaviour of the two stretching bands with changes in the substituents is sufficiently different to make it desirable to consider them separately.

(1) The anti-symmetric NO_2 vibration. With single para substituents the position of this band is directly related to the electron donor or acceptor properties of the group. The extreme cases are represented by p-$N(C_2H_5)_2$ (1487 cm^{-1}) and p-NO_2 (1550 cm^{-1}). In all other cases the band is in the narrower range 1535–1510 cm^{-1}. The meta position is less effective in altering the band position, and for single substituents the frequency lies between 1539 and 1525 cm^{-1}. Again the higher frequencies correspond to the more strongly electron-withdrawing groups. With small ortho substituents the range is 1540–1515 cm^{-1}. The heterocyclic aromatics behave similarly.

Normally, therefore, this band will be found between 1540 and 1515 cm^{-1}, and departures from this will usually be the result of either heavy multiple substitution or of steric effects. When more than one nitro group is substituted on the ring there is coupling between the two. With *para* and *meta* substitution this results in minor differences between the infrared and Raman frequencies, but when the nitro groups are on adjacent carbon atoms it results in multiple bands. *ortho* dinitrobenzene has bands at 1550 and 1532 cm^{-1}, and 1 : 2 : 3-trinitrobenzene at 1572 and 1558 cm^{-1}. However, in these cases there could be an additional factor due to the twisting of one or both of the nitro groups out of the plane of the ring. This is shown to have little effect on the antisymmetric frequencies in *ortho*-alkyl nitrobenzenes although the more sensitive symmetric bands are displaced. Thus even in *o-tert*. -butyl benzene the anti-symmetric frequency does not rise above 1530 cm^{-1}. Hydrogen bonding also has little effect on this frequency. Even in *o*-nitrophenol, which has a particularly strong OH . . NO$_2$ bond compared with most nitro group associations, the v_{as} band is at 1537 cm^{-1}. This is actually higher than either the *meta* or *para* derivatives, and is not very different from *o*-nitroanisole (1530 cm^{-1}).

(2) *The symmetric vibration.* This mode is subject to coupling effects which, in the aromatic series, probably involve some ring modes. Changes in the substituents which alter the latter are therefore liable to change this frequency even if there is no change in the force constants or electronic arrangement of the NO$_2$ group itself. The frequencies therefore vary in a somewhat erratic way. In *para*-substituted nitrobenzenes, for example, the frequency range is 1355–1338 cm^{-1}, but the highest value is that of the *p*-bromo derivative, while the *p*-nitro and *p*-methoxy derivatives absorb at essentially the same point (1338 cm^{-1}) despite the very different character of these two groups. Subsidiary bands appear in a few cases, but usually the intensity is low. However, the band is doubled in *p*-nitroaniline.

In *meta* derivatives the overall range is quite small (1355–1345 cm^{-1}), but again there is no relation between the frequencies and the electrical properties of the substituent. *Ortho* derivatives have a similar range, except when bulky groups are present, when the frequencies rise significantly [37–39], and approach a maximum value of 1380 cm^{-1}. In *ortho* dinitrobenzene the bands are doubled due to coupling and appear at 1370 and 1362 cm^{-1} [97]. In hydrogen bonded systems, such as *o*-nitrophenol, v_s falls to 1320 cm^{-1}, but as v_{as} is not altered this may be due to alterations in the degree of coupling. There is no generalized relation between the *s* and *as* frequencies, although one does exist for the limited series of alkyl nitro compounds.

(3) *Association effects in aromatic nitro compounds.* There is no doubt that nitro groups can take part in hydrogen bonding, but with the exception of special cases, such as *o*-nitrophenol, the associations seem to be very weak [42]. Baitinger *et al.* [43] list the δvOH values of methanol and phenol on association with alkyl and aryl nitro compounds. The ranges were only

25–42 cm^{-1} and 46–101 cm^{-1} respectively. Even so, the largest shifts were for *p*-nitro anisole, where it is at least equally likely that the bond is to the ether oxygen atom. The corresponding shifts of the NO$_2$ group are extremely small, and this has led to a good deal of controversy on whether or not weak hydrogen bonds exist in compounds such as *o*-nitroaniline. Danilova and Smakova [44] have discussed intramolecular bonding with OH and NH groups, and Cardinaud has studied both the H and D forms of the nitrophenols [45].

Table 7.2. νNO$_2$ in aromatic nitro compounds (from [37]) CHCl$_3$ solution

Substituent	para		meta		ortho	
	ν_{as}	ν_s	ν_{as}	ν_s	ν_{as}	ν_s
N(CH$_3$)$_2$	1487	1318				
OCH$_3$	1510	1339	1526	1348	1530	1357
OH	1517	1338	1529	1352	1537	1335
Cl	1522	1343	1527⎱ 1523⎰	1350	1537	1357
Br	1527	1355⎱ 1346⎰	1532	1380⎱ 1348⎰	1536	1356
CH$_3$	1520	1346	1531	1350	1527	1354
CH$_2$Cl	1527	1348	1532	1353		
CN	1536	1348	1538	1352		
COOCH$_3$	1528	1348	1532	1348	1537	1353
CHO	1535	1343			1532	1347
COCH$_3$	1530	1342				
NO$_2$	1555	1338	1539	1346		

(b) Alkyl nitro compounds

Studies on alkyl nitro compounds include a number of Russian papers on nitroalkanes [46], α-halogen nitroalkanes [47] and 1,1-dinitroalkanes [48]. Urbanski and others [49–52, 83,] have made some extensive studies of nitroalcohols and amines, and Pickering and Werbin [53] have dealt with the nitro-oestrones. These studies confirm and extend the earlier findings on the effects of substituents such as α-halogen groups on the nitro-group frequencies, and they also confirm the existence of intramolecular hydrogen bonding in the nitroalcohols. Basicity studies have also been made [43].

Further attempts have been made to rationalize the behaviour of these bands in relation to the nature of the substituents concerned. Iogansen and Litovchenko [54] have discussed the effects of coupling on these bands and the consequences of intermolecular interaction. Lunn [55] has produced some remarkable interrelationships between ν_{as} and ν_s within specific series and has discussed their significance.

There are small differences between the anti-symmetric and symmetric frequencies of primary, secondary and tertiary nitrocompounds which allow some differentiation, at least of the tertiary materials. With multiple nitro substitution on the same carbon atom, the anti-symmetric frequencies rise and the symmetric frequencies fall [101]. There is also some doubling due to coupling but this is usually restricted to the symmetric band. This appears at 1305 and 1371 cm^{-1} in trinitromethane and at 1217 and 1348 cm^{-1} in tetranitromethane. The increase in the separation of the *as* and *s* bands must arise in some opening out of the ONO bond angles, which is something of a surprise as the steric repulsions might have been expected to close them down. The normal frequency positions in these various types of alkyl nitro compounds are listed in Table 7.3.

Table 7.3. Normal frequency positions in various types of alkyl nitro compounds

Primary	1554 and 1382 cm^{-1}
Secondary	1550 and 1370 cm^{-1}
Tertiary	1536 and 1349 cm^{-1}
$(NO_2)_2C$	1576 and 1330 cm^{-1} (usually split)
$(NO_2)_3C$	1600 and 1300 cm^{-1} (usually split)

Unlike the *ortho* substituted aromatics the presence of nitro groups on two adjacent carbon atoms does not cause doubling of either of the stretching bands [99], although this does occur if more than one is present on either carbon.

Lunn [55] has related the behaviour of v_{as} over the range 1548 cm^{-1} (simple alkyl substitution) to 1607 (CF_3 substitution) cm^{-1} with the sum of the Taft σ^* values for the substituent groups. A separate relationship, however, is required for tertiary compounds with no hydrogen at the α-carbon atom. Bellamy [56] has discussed the significance of these relationships, and pointed out that it must be limited, as were the original Taft determinations themselves, to compounds with a carbon atom attached to the group concerned. The relationship fails if one attempts to extend it further to include the effects of the direct attachment of a substituent to the nitro group. The Taft σ^* value for chlorine, for example, is only a little higher than that for a CCl_3 group, but the effect of changing one group for the other is entirely disproprotionate.

7.2.2. Covalent nitrates, $RONO_2$

In contrast to the nitro compounds, the covalent nitrates have received little attention, and the only major publications in recent years are those of Guthrie and Spedding [26] and of Carrington [57]. The former workers were largely concerned with carbohydrate derivatives, but their findings have been confirmed by Carrington [57] on simple nitrato-paraffins. In general, the earlier group frequency assignments have been confirmed. In a wide range of open-chain, branched-chain and cyclic nitrato-paraffins, Carrington finds v_{as}

between 1634 and 1626 cm^{-1} and v_s between 1282 and 1272 cm^{-1}. The variations that occur within this range with changes in the substituents are probably too small to have any real significance. However, it is readily possible to recognize secondary alkyl nitrates from the fact that these show v_s as a doublet, with the intensity of each component reduced to half the normal value. The same effect is found in monocyclic nitrates, but not in bicyclic compounds, which have to be treated as special cases. Carrington has also measured the intensity values of both v_{as} and v_s in a series of nitrates, and discussed the use of such measurements in structural diagnosis.

Nitrato complexes in which the third oxygen atom of the NO$_3$ group is coordinated to a metal have been discussed by Gatehouse et al. [58] and by Bannister and Cotton [59]. There is a small lowering of the frequencies as compared with organic nitrates, but the bands appear in the ranges 1530–1480 and 1290–1250 cm^{-1}. Unidentate and bidentate nitro compounds can be simply distinguished by the relative intensities of the three N—O stretching bands in the Raman spectra [100]. With unidentate nitrates the intensity order is $I_{1000} > I_{1250} > I_{1600}$, but with bidentate compounds this changes to $I_{1600} > I_{1000} > I_{1250}$.

7.2.3. XNO$_2$ stretching bands when X is an element other than carbon or oxygen

Nothing new of importance has been published on NNO$_2$ group frequencies, but there have been some interesting Urey Bradley forcefield studies on the nitryl halides by Devlin [60], who has also studied the nitrogen oxides NO$_2$, N$_2$O$_4$ and N$_2$O$_3$ [61, 62]. Miller [35] has studied the compounds FONO$_2$ and ClONO$_2$. Coordinated nitro groups have been studied by Nakamoto et al. [63] and by Puget and Duval [64]. In K$_2$(Pt(NO$_2$)$_4$) v_{as} splits into three components at 1436, 1410 and 1386 cm^{-1}. v_s is at 1250 cm^{-1}. Both bands are at lower frequencies in the nickel and cobalt compounds. Nitroammine complexes have been studied by several groups [65–67] with particular reference to the stereochemistry. Cis and trans isomers can be distinguished by the numbers of bands, as the cis forms have a lower symmetry.

7.2.4. The systematics of the changes in v_{as} and v_s in XNO$_2$ compounds

The changes in both v_s and v_{as} with the nature of the substituents in the series CH$_2$XNO$_2$ have already been discussed. These follow the general pattern of Taft σ^* values with reasonable precision, and the frequency shifts reflect the relative inductive effects of the X groups. As with vCO, an increase in the electronegativity of X leads to a rise in the NO$_2$ stretching frequencies. This can be attributed to a shortening of the N=O bonds as they become more covalent in character. The same qualitative pattern holds for direct substitution in the XNO_2 systems, but there is no longer any quantitative relation. The shifts are usually much greater in this latter series than would be expected from the Taft values, and there is no longer any relation between v_s and v_{as}.

So far as the overall behaviour of the $N{=}O$ bonds are concerned, Johathan [68] has shown that some smooth-curve relations exist which interconnect force constants, frequencies, bond orders and bond lengths. Devlin [60] has also related the $N{=}O$ force constant to a function of the two frequencies, $\sqrt{(v_{as}^2 + v_s^2)}$, so that some relation between the frequencies and the chemical character of the bonds is to be expected. However, it is very doubtful whether any function can be found which will satisfactorily correlate with both the v_s and the v_{as} frequencies. The overall order of the frequencies themselves is a sufficient indication of the difficulty. For v_{as} we have $F > Cl > OR > C {\backsimeq} N$, whereas v_s has $C > F > Cl > OR {\backsimeq} N$. The order shown by the anti-symmetric mode is more in line with the likely impact of inductive and resonance effects than is the order shown by v_s, and it is almost certain that the latter is influenced considerably by vibrational coupling. Nevertheless, even in the *as* mode, the similarity between the values for carbon and nitrogen substituents is surprising, and has no parallel in either electronegativity or Taft σ^* values. Changes in the ONO bond angles will also affect both frequencies which will move apart as the bond angle widens. A simple plot of the separation of frequencies of the NO_2^+ ion (960 cm^{-1} 180°), NO_2, (300 cm^{-1} 134°) and the NO_2^- ion (67 cm^{-1} 115°), is linear and shows that the separation changes by about 14 cm^{-1} per degree of angle change. It could be therefore that the band separation could be used to give some indications of bond angle changes, but this can never be more than an approximation in view of the coupling in the symmetric mode and the consequent contribution of the $N{-}X$ bond to this frequency.

7.2.5. Other characteristic frequencies of the nitro group

There is general agreement in almost all the studies that have been carried out on alkyl nitro compounds, that the $C{-}N$ stretching frequency occurs as a medium to strong band at higher frequencies than any of the NO_2 deformation modes. In primary nitroalkanes it falls in the ranges 915–895 cm^{-1} and 885–870 cm^{-1}, corresponding to the *gauche* and *trans* conformers respectively. In secondary compounds the ranges are about 10 cm^{-1} lower. Wider variations occur in the dihalogenodinitromethanes (1060–830 cm^{-1}) [100] and in the multinitro compounds generally [99]. Because of the splitting due to rotational isomerism these bands are of limited use for diagnosis. However, the symmetric NO_2 deformation which is assigned in the 630–610 cm^{-1} region is generally regarded as reliable.

It is therefore something of a surprise that in the aromatic series a strong band in the 860–845 cm^{-1} region does not appear to arise from the corresponding $C{-}N$ stretch, but rather from the NO_2 deformation. Indeed

Green, who has made a very careful assignment of a large number of aromatic nitro compounds [97, 98], states that there is no band which can be reasonably identified with the C—N vibration. The differences between the N=O stretching frequencies of alkyl and aryl compounds are not so large as to lead one to expect changes in the deformation frequencies of such magnitude, and there is clearly a problem in these assignments which needs to be resolved.

7.3. The ionized carboxyl group CO_2^-

The stretching frequencies of the CO_2^- ion vary with both the nature of the metallic ion and with the substituents on the organic residue. The characteristic frequencies have been reviewed by Nakamoto [102] and by Oldham [103]. Spinner [69] has discussed in some detail the spectra of a wide variety of substituted acetate ions.

In sodium acetate v_{as} occurs at 1583 cm^{-1} and v_s at 1421 cm^{-1}. In sodium propionate the values are 1565 and 1429 cm^{-1}. Conjugation has only a small effect, as shown by sodium acrylate (v_{as} 1562 cm^{-1}) and sodium benzoate (v_{as} 1552 cm^{-1}), but in most other respects, substitution of active groups at the α-carbon atom produces shifts which, for v_{as}, are very similar to, but somewhat larger than, those produced by the same groups on vC=O. Thus on passing from $(CH_3)_3COO^-Na$ to CCl_3COO^-Na v_{as} rises by 126 cm^{-1}, whereas for the corresponding acid dimers vC=O rises by 60 cm^{-1}. The general order of effectiveness is the same in both series, and Spinner quotes the sequence for v_{as} as follows:

t-Butyl(1551 cm^{-1})$<C_2H_5<CH_3$ (1583 cm^{-1})$=CH_2I<CH_2Br<CH_2CN$ $=CH_2Cl<CHBr_2<CH_2F<CHCl_2<CBr_3$ (1659 cm^{-1})$<CCl_3<CF_3$ (1689 cm^{-1}).

The overall frequency range, extending up into what is normally regarded as the covalent carbonyl region, is surprising. In some mono- and di-halogen-substituted compounds multiple C—Halogen bands appear in the Raman spectra of aqueous solutions and allow the relative configurations to be decided. As with carbonyl compounds, it is found that v_{as} rises in that form in which a halogen atom is coplanar and eclipsed with one oxygen atom, while the *gauche* form gives a lower value. In mono- and di-chloroacetic acid salts, and in sodium dibromoacetate, only the high C—Halogen frequencies are found, so that these must exist wholly in the planar, eclipsed form. However doubling of these bands can arise from causes other than rotational isomerism as most dichloroacetic acid salts show splitting of both the symmetric and anti-symmetric stretch bands in the solid state [104]. Monohaloacetic acids do not show this multiplet structure but it is also present in some trihalo compounds [105]. In general the frequency separation between the two bands or between the means of the multiplets is proportional to the change of ionic radius of the metal ions.

The very high anti-symmetric stretching frequencies of compounds such as the trifluoroacetate ion has led Spinner [69] to suggest that the two C—O bonds are no longer equivalent. This is certainly the case in situations involving the trifluoroacetates of group four elements. These form monodentate bonds which are largely covalent. However, some elements can also form bidentate ligands in which the equivalence of the C—O bonds is restored.

Spinner's argument is reinforced to some extent by the fact that the behaviour of the symmetric absorption is not parallel to that of v_{as}. The order found for this vibration is as follows:

CBr_3(1338 and 1355 cm^{-1})$< CCl_3 < CHBr_2 < CH_2CN < CH_2I < CHCl_2 < CH_2Br < CH_2Cl < CH_3$ (1413 cm^{-1}) $< C_2H_5 < CF_3 \doteqdot CH_2F$ (1448 cm^{-1}).

With the strongly electron-withdrawing groups CBr_3 and CF_3 occupying the top and bottom of this range it is difficult to see any connexion with chemical factors. Spinner points to the contrast between this behaviour and that of v_s and v_{as} in the SO_2 group, where these frequencies are directly linked together. However, it is not to be expected that there will be a close parallel in the two cases, because the OCO symmetric stretch will be more strongly coupled to the adjacent C—X bond than will be the case with the sulphones.

Intensity studies on these bands have been made by Flett [70] using mulls in potassium bromide. The results show a surprisingly wide variation with even small changes in structure. Thus the integrated intensity of v_{as} in sodium butyrate is twice that in sodium acetate. Other studies on CO_2^- spectra are reported by Hargreaves and Stevinson [71] (salts of dibasic acids), Vratny et al. [72] and Nakamura [75] (salts of acetic acid) and Green et al. [73] (benzoates and salicylates). A paper by Ellis and Pyszora [74] suggests a complicated function which they believe relates the stretching frequencies with the mass, radius and electronegativity of the metal. However, Warrier et al. [87] have failed to find any relation between the frequency shifts in chloroacetate salts and the E/r function, where E is the electron excitation energy. The subject has been well reviewed by Nakamoto [76], who has also published work in this area [77].

Both v_{as} and v_s show substantial changes with the nature of the metal atom, and as with the organic residues, the larger shifts are shown by v_{as}. However, as Nakamoto has pointed out [76], these changes must be considered in relation to the structure of the complex. Sodium acetate has a structure in which both C—O bonds are of equal lengths and the oxygen atoms are strictly equivalent. In lithium acetate dihydrate this is not the case, and one oxygen atom is nearer to the metal than the other (C—O lengths 1.22 and 1.33 Å). There are other possibilities, such as a bridging arrangement or separate metal atoms linked to each oxygen. These different possibilities will each lead to changes in the stretching frequencies, and some of these are predictable. For example, one would expect compounds such as lithium acetate to show higher v_{as} and lower

v_s values than normal, whereas in bridged systems both bands would move in the same direction, as is indeed found [77]. Other examples of this difference of behaviour of mono and bidentate ligands are given in reference [104].

Bibliography

1. Robinson, *Can. J. Chem.*, 1961, **39**, 247.
2. Feairheller and Katon, *Spectrochim. Acta*, 1964, **20**, 1099.
3. Bavin, Gray and Stephenson, *Spectrochim. Acta*, 1960, **16**, 1312.
4. Fujimori, *Bull. Chem. Soc. Japan*, 1959, **32**, 1374.
5. Momose, Ueda, Shoji and Yano, *Chem. and Pharm. Bull. Japan*, 1958, **6**, 670.
6. Momose, Ueda and Shoji, *Chem. and Pharm. Bull. Japan*, 1958, **6**, 415.
7. Marziano, Montaudo and Passerini, *Ann. Chim. Rome*, 1962, **52**, 121.
8. Marziano and Montaudo, *Ric. Sci.*, 1961, **A1**, 87.
9. Marziano and Montaudo, *Gazz. Chim. Ital.*, 1961, **91**, 587.
10. Otting and Neuberger, *Chem. Ber.*, 1962, **95**, 540.
11. Hambly and O'Grady, *Austral. J. Chem.*, 1964, **17**, 860.
12. Holst and Fernelius, *J. Org. Chem.*, 1958, **23**, 1881.
13. Gillespie and Robinson, *Can. J. Chem.*, 1961, **39**, 2171.
14. Freeman and Hambly, *Austral. J. Chem.*, 1957, **10**, 227.
15. Geiseler and Bindernagel, *Zeit. Electrochem.*, 1959, **63**, 1140.
16. Geiseler and Bindernagel, *Zeit. Electrochem.*, 1960, **64**, 421.
17. Malewski and Weigmann, *Spectrochim. Acta*, 1962, **18**, 725; *Z. Chem.*, 1964, **4**, 389.
18. Momose, Ueda and Shoji, *Chem. Pharm. Bull. Japan*, 1959, **7**, 734.
19. Katritzky and Jones, *J. Chem. Soc.*, 1960, 4497.
20. Vandi, Moeller and Audrieth, *J. Org. Chem.*, 1961, **26**, 1136.
21. Tosolini, *Chem. Ber.*, 1961, **94**, 2731.
22. Kresze, Maschke, Albrecht, Bederke, Patzschke, Smalla and Trede, *Angew. Chem.*, 1962, **74**, 135.
23. Merian, *Helv. Chim. Acta*, 1960, **49**, 1122.
24. Simon and Kriegsman, *Chem. Ber.*, 1956, **89**, 1883, 2378, 2384.
25. Detoni and Hadzi, *Spectrochim. Acta*, 1957, **11**, 601.
26. Guthrie and Spedding, *J. Chem. Soc.*, 1956, 953.
27. Philbin, Stuart, Timoney and Wheeler, *J. Chem. Soc.*, 1956, 4414.
28. Lloyd, Tudhall and Dodgson, *Nature*, 1959, **184**, 548; *Biochem. and Biophys. Acta*, 1961, **52**, 413.
29. Lloyd and Dodgson, *Nature*, 1959, **184**, 548.
30. Norita, *Acta, Chem. fenn.*, 1959, **32**, 83.
31. Fujimori, *Bull. Chem. Soc. Japan*, 1959, **32**, 83.
32. Simon and Kunath, *Zeit. Anorg. Chem.*, 1961, **308**, 321.
33. Gillespie and Robinson, *Can. J. Chem.*, 1963, **41**, 2074.
34. Daasch, *Spectrochim. Acta*, 1958, **13**, 257.
35. Kartha, Jones and Robertson, *Proc. Ind. Acad. Sci.*, 1963, **58A**, 216.
36. Borek, *Naturweiss.*, 1963, **50**, 471.
37. Katritzky and Simmons, *Rec. Trav. Chim. Pays Bas.*, 1960, **79**, 361.
38. Conduit, *J. Chem. Soc.*, 1959, 3273.
39. Van Veen, Verkade and Wepster, *Rec. Trav. Chim. Pays Bas*, 1957, **76**, 801.
40. Yamaguchi, *J. Chem. Soc. Japan*, 1959, **80**, 155.
41. Sorygin and Il'Iceva, *Bull. Acad. Sci. U.R.S.S. Phys. Ser.*, 1958, **22**, 1058.
42. Urbanski and Dabrowska, *Bull. Acad. Polon. Sci.*, 1959, **7**, 235.

43. Baitinger, Schleyer, Murty and Robinson, *Tetrahedron,* 1964, **20,** 1635.
44. Danilova and Smakova, *Bull. Tech. Inst. Tomsk,* 1962, 91.
45. Cardinaud, *Bull. Soc. Chim. France,* 1960, 634.
46. Sloveckij, Sljapocnikov, Sevelev, Fajzil'berg and Novikov, *Bull. Acad. Sci. U.R.S.S. Ser. Chim.,* 1961, 330.
47. Sloveckij, Fajzil'berg, Gulevskaja and Novikov, *Bull. Acad. Sci. U.R.S.S. Ser. Chim.,* 1961, 683.
48. Novikov, Belikov, Fajzil'berg, Ershchova, Slovetskii and Shahevelov, *Izvest. Akad. Nauk. S.S.S.R. Otdel Khim. Nauk,* 1959, 1855.
49. Urbanski, *Roczniki Chem.,* 1957, **31,** 37.
50. Eckstein, Glucinski, Sobotka and Urbanski, *J. Chem. Soc.,* 1961, 1370.
51. Urbanski, *Bull. Acad. Polon. Sci. Cl III,* 1957, **5,** 533.
52. Urbanski, *Roczniki Chem.,* 1958, **32,** 241.
53. Pickering and Werbin, *J. Amer. Chem. Soc.,* 1958, **80,** 680.
54. Iogansen and Litovchenko, *Optics and Spectroscopy,* 1964, **16,** 380.
55. Lunn, *Spectrochim. Acta,* 1960, **16,** 1088.
56. Bellamy, in *Spectroscopy,* ed. Wells, Institute of Petroleum, 1962.
57. Carrington, *Spectrochim. Acta,* 1960, **16,** 1279.
58. Gatehouse, Livingstone and Nyholm, *J. Chem. Soc.,* 1957, 4222; *J. Inorganic and Nuclear Chem.,* 1958, **8,** 75.
59. Bannister and Cotton, *J. Chem. Soc.,* 1960, 2276.
60. Devlin and Hisatsune, *Spectrochim. Acta,* 1961, **17,** 206.
61. Devlin and Hisatsune, *Spectrochim. Acta,* 1961, **17,** 218.
62. Hisatsune, Devlin and Califano, *Spectrochim. Acta,* 1960, **16,** 450.
63. Nakamoto, Fujita and Murata, *J. Amer. Chem. Soc.,* 1958, **80,** 4817.
64. Puget and Duval, *Compt. Rendu. Acad. Sci. France,* 1960, **250,** 4141.
65. Beattie and Tyrrell, *J. Chem. Soc.,* 1956, 2489.
66. Chatt, Duncanson, Gatehouse, Lewis, Nyholm, Tobe, Todd and Venanzi, *J. Chem. Soc.,* 1959, 4073.
67. Morris and Busch, *J. Amer. Chem. Soc.,* 1960, **82,** 1521.
68. Jonathan, *J. Mol. Spectroscopy,* 1960, **4,** 75.
69. Spinner, *J. Chem. Soc.,* 1964, 4217.
70. Flett, *Spectrochim. Acta,* 1962, **18,** 1537.
71. Hargreaves and Stevinson, *Spectrochim. Acta,* 1965, **21,** 1681.
72. Vratny, Rao and Dilling, *Analyt. Chem.,* 1961, **33,** 1455.
73. Green, Kynaston and Lindsay, *Spectrochim. Acta,* 1961, **17,** 486.
74. Ellis and Pyszora, *Nature,* 1958, **181,** 181.
75. Nakamura, *J. Chem. Soc. Japan,* 1958, **79,** 1411, 1420.
76. Nakamoto, *The Infrared Spectra of Inorganic Coordination Compounds,* Wiley, New York 1963, pp. 197 *et seq.*
77. Nakamoto, Morimoto and Puxeddu, *Gazz. Chim. Ital.,* 1957, **87,** 885.
78. Ghersetti, *Boll. Sci. Fac. Chim. Ind. Bologna,* 1963, **21,** 237.
79. Ghersetti and Zauli, *Ann. Chim. Rome,* 1963, **53,** 710.
80. Birchall and Gillespie, *Spectrochim. Acta,* 1966, **22,** 681.
81. Uno, Machida, Hanai, Ueda and Saski, *Chem. Pharm. Bull. Japan,* 1963, **11,** 704.
82. Kingusa and Nakashima, *J. Chem. Soc. Japan,* 1963, **84,** 365.
83. Dabrowska and Urbanski, *Roczniki. Chem.,* 1963, **37,** 865.
84. Urbanski and Witanowski, *Trans, Faraday Soc.,* 1963, **59,** 1510.
85. Miller, Bernitt and Hisatune, *Spectrochim. Acta,* 1967, **23A,** 223.
86. Uhlich and Kresze, *Zeit. Analyt. Chem.,* 1961, **182,** 81.
87. Warrier and Narayanan, *Spectrochim. Acta,* 1967, **23A,** 1061.
88. Shinriki and Nambara, *Chem. and Pharm. Bull. Japan,* 1963, **11,** 178.

89. Exner, *Coll. Czech. Chem. Comm.,* 1963, **28**, 935.
90. Nagel, Stark, Fruwert and Geiseler, *Spectrochim. Acta,* 1976, **32A**, 1297.
91. Geiseler and Nagel, *J. Mol. Structure,* 1973, **16**, 79.
92. Christie, Schack and Curtis, *Spectrochim. Acta,* 1970, **26A**, 2367.
93. Goldstein, Russell and Willis, *Spectrochim. Acta,* 1969, **25A**, 1275.
94. Arcoria, Maccarone, Musumarra and Tomaselli, *Spectrochim. Acta,* 1974, **30A**, 611.
95. Thompson, *Spectrochim. Acta,* 1972, **28A**, 1479.
96. Miles, Doyle, Cooney and Tobias, *Spectrochim. Acta,* 1969, **25A**, 1515.
97. Green and Lauwers, *Spectrochim. Acta,* 1971, **27A**, 817.
98. Green and Harrison, *Spectrochim. Acta,* 1970, **26A**, 1925.
99. Diallo, *Spectrochim. Acta,* 1974, **30A**, 1505.
100. Diallo, *Compt. Rend. Acad. Sci. Paris,* 1971, **272**, 1777.
101. Loewenschuss, Yellin and Gabri, *Spectrochim. Acta,* 1974, **30A**, 371.
102. Nakamoto, *Infrared Spectra of Inorganic and Coordination Compounds,* Wiley Interscience, London, 1970, p. 220.
103. Oldham, *Progress in Inorganic Chemistry,* Vol. 10, Interscience London, 1968, p. 223.
104. Faniran, Patel and Mesubi, *Spectrochim. Acta,* 1975, **31A**, 117.
105. Patel and Faniran, *Spectrochim. Acta,* 1975, **31A**, 123.
106. Hovius, Zuidema and Engberts, *Rec. Trav. Chim. Pays Bas,* 1971, **90**, 633.
107. Engberts and Zuidema, *Rec. Trav. Chim. Pays Bas,* 1970, **89**, 1202.
108. Engberts and Zuidema, *Rec. Trav. Chim. Pays Bas,* 1970, **89**, 741.
109. Dallinga and Engberts, *Spectrochim. Acta,* 1974, **30A**, 1923.
110. Butcher, Charalambous, Frazer and Gerrard, *Spectrochim. Acta,* 1967, **23A**, 2399.

8

Associated XH Frequencies, the Hydrogen Bond

8.1. Introduction

Hydrogen bonds are formed in any XH ... Y system in which the XH bond has some polarity and the Y atom some basicity. The strength of the hydrogen bond formed depends upon both of these functions, so that for example, the vOH frequency shift in the dimer of phenol is little different from that of the dimer of methanol, the greater acidity of the one being counterbalanced by the greater basicity of the other. The ability of an XH bond to associate in this way is directly linked to its ionic character and so to the electronegativity of the X atom. The halogen acids, OH groups and to a lesser extent NH groups are strong donors, whereas SH, PH and CH links usually form only weak hydrogen bonds. The requirements of the proton acceptor are less well defined, but the bonding normally involves a lone pair of electrons or less usually a π cloud.

The phenomenon of hydrogen bonding is of such fundamental importance in chemistry, physics and biology that it is not surprising that an enormous volume of literature has built up around it in the last twenty years. Many lengthy reviews and books are available. General reviews have been given by Pimentel and McClellan [1, 2], and by others [3, 245], and the papers of the Hydrogen Bonding conference in Lubljana [4] contain much useful information. More specialist reviews cover such topics as the understanding of the very complex band shapes and substructures which can arise [246, 247], thermodynamic properties [248], hydrogen bonding by CH bonds [249], and matrix isolation methods [250]. The totality of data on just spectroscopic aspects of the hydrogen bond is such that it cannot be contained in a single chapter of this kind. The discussion which follows therefore concentrates on the changes in frequencies and band shapes which result from hydrogen bonding, and on their physical significance.

It is easy to recognize the occurrence of a hydrogen bond of moderate strength, but it is much more difficult to draw any kind of line which will define where weak hydrogen bonding ceases and dielectric and similar effects begin. A good example of this problem is provided by the monomeric vOH frequencies of the series acetic to trichloracetic acid. In the vapour phase all these frequencies are the same [5], whereas in acetone all are shifted to lower frequencies and there is now a difference of 266 cm^{-1} between the values for the first and last members of the series. This is clearly due to hydrogen bonds, and one can show that there is an excellent linear relation between $\Delta \nu$OH and the pK_a value of the acids. In less polar solvents such as cumene the differences are smaller (95 cm^{-1}) but still well defined. However, even in carbon tetrachloride, which is not normally regarded as an associating solvent, both the differences (31 cm^{-1}) and the linearity with the pK_a values still persist. This suggests that we are dealing with the same phenomenon in both acetone and carbon tetrachloride and that the differences between them are of magnitude and not of kind. There is other evidence to the same effect [6, 251], and it seems likely that the proton is attracted weakly to the polarizable chlorine atom in its immediate vicinity. The fact that this chlorine is attached to a carbon atom carrying three others symmetrically arranged, and that the molecule has no dipole moment, is therefore irrelevant. For the purposes of this review hydrogen bonds will be taken as including all cases where the νXH frequency falls significantly below the value in hexane, or in intramolecular cases where it is lower than would otherwise be expected.

(a) Frequency shifts and band shapes

The maximum shifts of the XH stretch are equally difficult to define, partly because of the impact of medium effects, and partly because the original XH stretch is replaced in some cases by symmetric and antisymmetric modes of the complete XH...Y system. However, the shifts of both OH and NH can be as large as 3000 cm^{-1} in extreme cases.

The low frequency shift of the stretching band on hydrogen bond formation is accompanied by an increase in intensity and a broadening of the band. The intensity increase derives in part from the increased polarity of the XH bond, but also from the charge redistribution within the whole of the XH...Y system. There is no corresponding intensity increase in the Raman spectra, and indeed Lautie and Novak have shown that whilst the NH intensity of pyrrole is doubled on self-association, the Raman intensity is nearly halved [252]. The band broadening and band shapes vary with the strengths of the hydrogen bonds. With small displacements the band broadens but remains reasonably symmetric. However, as the band moves to lower frequencies it broadens out on the lower frequency side, as for example in the liquid alcohols. With still stronger bonding as in the carboxylic acid dimers, the band shows a series of well defined submaxima which have been identified as overtone and combination bands of lower frequency fundamentals enhanced by Fermi resonance. Effects of this kind are found in both OH and NH systems. Further increases in hydrogen bond strength produce a more dramatic effect in that the single broad XH stretch is replaced by three separate bands, all of which are connected with the XH stretch and all of which are deuterium sensitive. These are known as the A, B and C bands and their origins are discussed in Section 8.2.6.

Finally with extremely strong hydrogen bonds involving very short X...Y distances, these three bands are replaced by a single very broad maximum which underlies the main fingerprint region, so that the normal spectrum is superimposed on a very broad absorption over the whole of the lower frequency region. In such cases it is possible for the XH deformation band (which rises in frequency as the stretch falls) to occur at higher frequencies than the stretch.

In some situations of very strong bonding proton transfer occurs (e.g. in ammonium chloride) the XH stretch is then that of the HY^+ ion and not that of XH so that for example on bonding HI in some systems the frequency appears to rise rather than fall. However, even in very short hydrogen bonds the XH bond can retain its identity. Thus in the complex H_3NHCl which has been studied by Ault and Pimentel [253], the potential function is not symmetric and the HCl stretch appears at the very low frequency of 630 cm^{-1}.

The origins of this band broadening have been much discussed. There is little doubt that a number of factors can be involved each contributing to differing extents in different situations. The earlier predissociation theories have been largely discarded, as have the ideas on proton tunnelling through a double potential energy minimum (except in a few very special cases). The major contributors are the presence of several components of different hydrogen bond strengths, as in the alcohols and phenols where the dimers, trimers and polymers absorb at separate frequencies, by variations in solvation, and particularly by interaction with the low frequency X...Y mode which effectively produces variations of the X...Y distances. The special cases of the very strong hydrogen bonds are discussed later.

The behaviour of intramolecular hydrogen bonds is rather different. There is again a very considerable broadening of the XH stretching band but this is not accompanied by the same degree of intensification. The result is that as the band broadens it becomes more and more difficult to detect, and in nickel dimethylglyoxime the band is detectable only at high concentrations. In an intermolecular hydrogen bond the X and Y atoms come to that natural distance which maximises the hydrogen bond energy. In many intramolecular bonds the X...Y distances are instead fixed by the molecular geometry, and the dipole changes in the XH bonds may well be much smaller. In consequence the intensification is reduced.

(b) Relationships between Δv and X...Y distances

As an increase in hydrogen bond strength results in both a frequency shift and a reduction in the X...Y distance it is natural to look for some relationship between these two parameters. The linear relationship for OH...O systems was first demonstrated by Lord and Merrifield and has since been studied by many workers [7–11, 254, 255]. This system gives essentially linear plots for O...O distances within the range 2.6–2.5 Å. At longer distances the curve becomes asymtotic, with the frequency shifts per unit of distance becoming smaller and smaller as the non-bonding separation is approached. Similarly at the other end of the scale, the relationship does not hold for very short hydrogen bonds [256], in the 2.5–2.4 Å range.

The proportionality between Δv and RX...Y, depends amongst other things on the properties of the X and Y atoms. It is not therefore reasonable to expect that it will apply to all systems in the same way. In practice it is found that separate curves, each with a useful linear portion, are given by each individual XH...Y system. In some papers this has been illustrated by plots showing the separate curves for the various systems on a single diagram. However, this is only practicable if R is plotted against the observed XH frequency rather than against the frequency shift. Such plots give a false impression of crossovers between the various lines because the asymtotic part of the curve for say NH...N falls in the frequency region of the linear part of the curve for OH...O. In reality, as Bellamy and Owen [255] have shown, all the curves have similar shapes but the slopes of the linear portions vary with the nature of the end atoms. The greatest changes of frequency with distance occurs in FH...F followed by OH...O, OH...N, NH...O and NH...N. They have therefore suggested that the lone pair electron repulsion between the end atoms is the dominant term in fixing the slopes of these lines, and they have been able to reproduce the differences between the various systems by calculations of this repulsion energy. If this is so it may well be that even the limited OH...O relationship might not hold for systems such as SiOH...O bonds which the back-donation of electrons from the silicon atom [15] could well have an important effect.

In intramolecular hydrogen bonds one has the additional complications that the bonds may be bent or may be artificially held at an otherwise abnormal distance. This is, for example, the case in 2-halophenols in which a direct comparison of Δv values led people to suppose that the strongest bonds were formed to iodine. This is not so, as equilibrium studies have shown [14]. In such systems there will be no relationship whatsoever between the frequency shifts and the internuclear distances.

(c) Frequency shifts and hydrogen bond energies

In principle a simple relationship should exist between vXH and ΔH, as exemplified by the Badger–Bauer relationship. However, there are many complicating factors. The frequency shift is essentially a measure of the extension of the XH bond whereas the hydrogen bond energy is affected by other factors such as the differences in solvation of the free and bonded molecules. A number of studies have been made in which relationships have been identified between Δv and ΔH but these are applicable only within very narrow limits in closely related systems [257].

There is of course no direct relationship between the hydrogen bond strengths themselves and the equilibrium coefficients. The latter are a function of the total free energy change of the system, and both the enthalpy and entropy terms are involved. In the 2-alkyl phenols associated with ether one finds very similar Δv values and widely different equilibrium coefficients. In such closely similar systems it is reasonable to suppose that Δv values run parallel to ΔH, and the changes in equilibrium coefficients are then attributable wholly to entropy effects [12, 13].

Similarly, in the series of intramolecularly bonded diols $HO(CH_2)_n OH$ the strongest hydrogen bonds as measured by the frequency shifts which occur in butane diol, but the entropy factor is such that at room temperature there is a greater proportion of bonded ethane diol molecules despite the fact that their hydrogen bonds are very weak [258].

(d) Deuterium substitution

Replacement of the hydrogen atom by deuterium should reduce the stretching frequency by $1/1.41$, and in practice the observed ratio for free XH bonds is 1.35. However, this ratio falls systematically as the strengths of any hydrogen bonds increase. This can be accounted for in terms of the differences in zero point energy of the H and D atoms. The vibration of the XH bond involves an anharmonic potential energy well, and the fact that the zero-point energy of hydrogen is greater than that of deuterium necessarily implies that the anharmonicity will be more strongly felt by the hydrogen atom. The observed ratios fall off quite steeply with hydrogen bond strength [5, 259] so that the NH/ND ratio of isothiocyanic acid falls from about 1.33 in carbon tetrachloride solution to 1.15 in trimethylphosphine oxide [259]. In some very short but unsymmetrical hydrogen bonds the ratio can actually fall to 1.0 and no shifts are seen on deuteration although there is some reduction in the band intensity [256, 260]. So large a change cannot be due entirely to the effect of anharmonicity on the OH frequency and it is likely that a second effect, also connected with the anharmonicity is responsible. Crystallographic data have previously suggested that there may be differences in the O...O distances of H and D bonded pairs, and this has been reinforced by microwave data. This has shown that the O...O distances in the dimer of $CF_3COOH/HCOOH$ are greater in the deuterated system [19]. These very low ratios therefore arise from a combination of both effects. Surprisingly these very low ratios are not observed in wholly symmetric hydrogen bonds. Here the hydrogen bond stretching band is effectively the anti-symmetric X...X stretch, and the OHO/ODO ratios vary somewhat erratically between 1.5 and 1.2 [256]. An exception to this is the compound CrO_2H which is thought to have a symmetric hydrogen bond but which has an OH/OD ratio of less than 1

[20, 261]. However, this is a special case in which the OD band is doubled, and will be discussed further in a later section.

(e) Ternary systems

It is generally recognised that when an XH bond associates with a base, the polarity of the X atom is increased, and with it its basicity. The result is that when this atom acts as a proton acceptor to another XH molecule to form a trimer, both the XH hydrogen bonds are stronger than that of the original dimer. For this reason, alcohol and phenol polymers absorb at substantially lower frequencies than the dimers. A similar effect is found in proton donating solvents. The hydrogen bonded OH frequency of phenol in a mixture of ether and chloroform is 56 cm^{-1} lower than it is in pure ether [16].

It is less generally realised that the inverse situation also arises. That is, in an XH_2 group the formation of one hydrogen bond results in a greater frequency shift than the formation of two if both involve proton donation from the same group. This is well shown by partial deuteration studies on primary amines and on water, which indicate that the XH frequency shifts are substantially reduced as one passes from a 1 : 1 to a 2 : 1 complex [262].

Exactly the same effect is found when more than one lone pair on a single atom is engaged in hydrogen bonding. When phenol associates with N-dimethylacatamide in a 1 : 1 complex the OH band appears at 3300 cm^{-1} but if the concentration of phenol is increased to allow the production of the 2 : 1 complex the frequency rises to 3390 cm^{-1} [263]. An atom which donated either one proton or one lone pair into a hydrogen bond is therefore less willing to donate a second and the resulting bonds are weaker than before. These findings have important implications for multiple bonded systems such as liquid water.

The complexes with phenol and N-dimethylacetamide are a good illustration of the dangers of considering frequencies in isolation. The carbonyl frequency of the 2 : 1 complex is substantially lower than that of the 1 : 1 complex, so that one might assume that the hydrogen bond strength had increased. However, this is simply the additive effect of two hydrogen bonds each of which is individually weaker than that of the 1 : 1 complex.

(f) Other characteristic frequencies of the hydrogen bond

(i) *XH deformation vibrations.* The XH deformation modes occur in the fingerprint region where they are often strongly coupled with other vibrations, and they have been less intensively studied. However all XH deformation bands show an increase in breadth on hydrogen bonding, although they do not show the large intensification which is such a feature of the stretching bands. Nevertheless the band width is a useful aid to identification in such cases as the NH band in secondary amines and amides near 700 cm^{-1}. All deformation bands move to higher frequencies on hydrogen bonding. This is the direct result of the increase in p character in the lengthened XH bond, making it easier to stretch but more difficult to bend. The frequency shifts are smaller than those of the stretching band in terms of wavenumbers but the relative shifts are even larger. The out of plane OH deformation in carboxylic acids occurs at 650 cm^{-1} in monomers and rises to about 960 cm^{-1} in dimers in which its characteristic breadth makes it a valuable group frequency. In acid salts with very strong hydrogen bonds it can rise to 1300 cm^{-1}. The corresponding in plane modes are strongly coupled and more difficult to identify, but in acid salts the frequencies can rise above those of the OH stretching frequencies themselves [264].

Provided the XH deformation is not strongly coupled one can expect to find a good linear relationship between the shifts of the stretching frequency and those of the bend, for any single XH...Y series, although the ratios for one system will not necessarily be the same as those of another. For the OH bond Novak [254] has derived a linear relationship with a slope of about 5.8.

Within a very close related series one can also expect to find a relation between the shifts of the deformation bands and the strengths of the hydrogen bonds which produce them, just as there is for the stretch. For acids and phenols Iogansen and Rosenberg [265, 266] have derived a relationship of this kind.

(ii) *The X...Y stretching mode.* With normal and medium strength hydrogen bonds this band occurs at very low frequencies in the far infrared. It is sensitive both to coupling with other modes and to the masses attached to the end atoms, and is therefore of little value as a group frequency. It has however been much studied as its position is of considerable theoretical importance in relation to the broadening of the XH stretching band. Jakobsen *et al.* [267, 268] have reviewed the data on acid dimers and give the frequency ranges of 185–100 cm^{-1} for monosubstituted acids, 125–95 cm^{-1} for disubstituted acids, and 105–80 cm^{-1} for trisubstituted acids. This of course refers to substitution on the α carbon atom, substitution on the β carbon makes only a small difference and the frequencies become essentially constant in acids with more than two methylene groups attached to the carbony. The frequency is in a similar range for hydrogen bonds between phenols and amides which fall in the 190–150 cm^{-1} region [269]. Here again the frequencies are sensitive to mass effects and change with the degree of substitution on the phenol ring.

As one passes to the very strong hydrogen bonds the X...Y mode shifts to higher frequencies until in the symmetric situation it is merged with the XH stretch, to give a broad band in the 1200–600 cm^{-1} range. A typical example is the $H_5O_2^+$ ion produced by proton transfer from HCl or HBr to the water dimer. The OHO antisymmetric mode appears as a broad band near 1000 cm^{-1} [270, 271].

(g) Solvent effects

(i) *Solvent interactions with XH monomers.* By far the largest contribution to the frequency shift of an XH bond on solution in a basic solvent is due to hydrogen bond formation. Even with solvents as non-polar as carbon disulphide and carbon tetrachloride, local association effects are important contributors to the shifts. This is not to say that dipolar and dielectric factors do not occur. Clearly hexane has no basic properties and the frequency shifts which occur on passing from the vapour to this solvent must be due to dielectric effects. However, with even small amounts of solvent polarity short lived collision complexes begin to make a significant contribution to the shift [251, 272, 273], and in stronger bases, normal hydrogen bonding takes over completely [274, 17]. In ternary systems in which the XH/solvent association is studied in a neutral medium, the shifts can be concentration dependent if it is possible to form 1 : 2 or 2 : 1 complexes (see below).

These conclusions have important implications for the measurement of hydrogen bond strengths through equilibrium coefficients. These necessarily involve concentration changes, and they will measure the differences in the hydrogen bond strengths between the monomer/solvent system and the monomer/base system rather than absolute values [22].

The ability of XH groups to form hydrogen bonds with a solvent will also influence the proportions of monomer to dimer in self-associated systems such as the carboxylic acids and secondary amides. Acids which are essentially dimeric in carbon tetrachloride are largely monomeric in benzene. The hydrogen bonds to the aromatic ring are of course much weaker than those of the acid dimer, but entropy effects determine that the solvent associations will be dominant.

(ii) *Tertiary and ternary systems.* The frequency changes in an existing XH...Y bond which follow a change in solvent can be considerably greater than the changes which occur when the monomer is dissolved in the solvent. The OH stretch of phenol falls by 23 cm^{-1} when the solvent is changed from hexane to chloroform, whereas the frequency of the hydrogen bonded complex of phenol and *N*-dimethylacetamide changes by 100 cm^{-1} following the same solvent change [263]. However, the order of solvent effectiveness is totally different in the two systems. Monomeric XH frequencies are sensitive to the proton accepting powers of the solvent whereas those of the bonded complexes are sensitive to the proton donating properties. The solvent sensitivity of these bonded frequencies therefore follows the pattern of the carbonyl and similar systems rather than that of the XH monomer.

These changes arise primarily from the formation of ternary or tertiary systems [263, 274] such as those below. In these the presence of an additional hydrogen bond strengthens that which already exists, just as the hydrogen bonds of phenol polymers are stronger than those of dimers. This effect can also operate in the reverse direction. With XH$_2$ groups a solution containing a

$$\begin{matrix} X \\ \diagdown \\ H \\ \vdots \\ O-H\cdots OR \\ \diagup \\ R \end{matrix}$$

high concentration of base will absorb at higher frequencies than one with a lower concentration as the 1 : 2 complexes form weaker bonds than the 1 : 1. A similar effect occurs in solutions with a high concentration of XH in relation to a base which has the capacity to form two hydrogen bonds at the same site. The concentration dependence of the OH bands of phenol in various concentrations of ether is illustrated in reference [274].

However, whilst proton donation is a major factor in suitable solvents, it is not the only one and dielectric effects must also play some part. In the complex between phenol and N-dimethylacatamide, a change of solvent from hexane to mesitylene reduces the hydrogen bonded frequency by 40 cm^{-1}. This is greater than the shifts which can be attributed to dielectric effects in the monomers, probably due to the increased polarity of the XH link when hydrogen bonded.

The solvent response of intramolecular bonds is similar, so that the OH frequency of *ortho*nitrophenol is lowered in proton donating solvents due to the formation of a ternary complex [23]. When the solvent is sufficiently basic to offer a stronger bonding site the original hydrogen bond is broken and replaced by an intermolecular bond to the solvent. In intermediate cases both forms occur. In *ortho*halophenols for example there are considerable changes in the ratios of *cis* and *trans* forms as the solvents are altered [24–26].

8.2. OH...X systems

8.2.1. OH interactions with π clouds

It is well established that OH groups can interact with π cloud systems to give well-defined hydrogen bonds and corresponding frequency shifts of up to 100 cm^{-1}. More usually the frequency shifts are small (15–50 cm^{-1}) and the measured bond energies are small also. Tentative suggestions that OH groups associate with π clouds can be found in the literature from about 1950 onwards, and one of the earliest definite observations is that of Trifan *et al.* [29], who found that νOH in 1-hydroxyferrocene is reduced to 3574 cm^{-1} and that 2-phenylphenol has twin bands at 3630 and 3601 cm^{-1}. Since that date examples have multiplied. Oki and Iwamura [27, 28] have been particularly active and have studied a wide variety of intramolecular hydrogen bonds to π clouds in aromatics. These include 2-phenyl-phenol, its substituted derivatives, substituted benzyl alcohols (in which the abnormally low νOH value of the monomers as compared with other primary alcohols is attributed to π-cloud bonding), aryl alcohols, alkenylphenols, hydroxy-biphenyl and phen-ethyl alcohols. They find that association effects persist in phenols in which a vinyl group is separated from the ring by up to two CH_2 groups, and that this is true also of compounds in which the vinyl group is replaced by an aromatic ring. The frequency shifts in all these cases are relatively small, and typical energy values are as follows: 2-allylphenol 0.46 kcal/mol. 2-benzylphenol 0.33 kcal/mol. and 2-phenylphenol 1.45 kcal/mol. Substitution effects follow the general pattern that the hydrogen bonds are strengthened by the attachment of nucleophyllic groups and weakened by electrophilic substitution.

Parallel results for other intramolecular bonds have been reported by several other groups. Baker and Shulgin [30] studied o-allylphenol, o-propenylphenol and compounds with more heavily substituted double bonds. In o-allylphenol the cis (associated) form absorbs 63 cm^{-1} below the value for the trans isomer, but the interaction is weaker in 2-propenylphenol, in which the OH...π cloud separation is increased. Substitution at the double bond resulted in a strengthening of the association. Comparable results were obtained by Beckering [31], and by Kuhn [32]. o-Substituted biphenyls have been studied by Schleyer et al. [40, 41], and o-tritylated phenols by Baker [33]. One particularly interesting feature of all this work is the general result that while the Δv values increase systematically as the basicity of the double bonds is increased, there does not appear to be any general relation between Δv and ΔH. Thus 2-allylphenol has ΔvOH 64 cm^{-1} and ΔH 0.46 kcal/mol, whereas 2-phenylphenol has Δv 43 cm^{-1} and ΔH 0.45 kcal/mol. Intramolecular bonds to π clouds in long-chain hydroxy unsaturated esters have been studied by Grundy and Morris [60]. Finally, mention should be made of an observation of Cairns and Eglinton [34] on an alkyl-substituted bis(hydroxy phenyl)alkane in which the steric arrangement is such that a particularly strong π cloud hydrogen bond is formed with a frequency shift of 123 cm^{-1}.

Intermolecular hydrogen bonding with π clouds has been less studied. The ability of phenol to associate with aromatic rings has, of course, been recognized, and the effects of substitution have been examined in some detail. Josien and Sourisseau [35] were able to show that the $\Delta v/v$ values for the OH stretching frequency of phenol in aromatic solvents gave a good linear relation with the corresponding ionization potentials. The hydrogen bonding strength increases as the ionization potential falls, as is to be expected, since this corresponds to a more diffuse π cloud and a greater area for orbital overlap. Berthelot et al. [27] have also shown that the OH frequency is related to the π electron density in substituted aromatics and have also shown that in halogenated benzenes the attachment is symmetric and is therefore to the ring rather than to the halogen atoms. Similar results are reported by Basila [36, 37] in studies on the association between aromatics and tert-butanol. A good linear relationship with the ionization potential was found and rationalized in terms of a charge transfer approach.

Work on the intermolecular association of OH groups with olefinic bonds is more limited. The main data are due to West [38], who has measured the Δv values for phenol and for p-fluorophenol on association with a variety of olefines, and to Kuhn [21], who has made extensive parallel studies with phenol. The frequency shifts are greater than those of aromatics and increase with the degree of substitution at the double bond. Typical values of Δv for phenol are benzene 47 cm^{-1}, hex-1-ene 69 cm^{-1}, hex-2-ene 65 cm^{-1}, 2-methylbut-1-ene 104 cm^{-1} and hex-1-yne 92 cm^{-1}. Data on associations with primary alcohols have been given by Schleyer *et al.* [39]. The frequency shifts are smaller, as is to be expected from the reduced polarity.

8.2.2. OH...halogen interactions

The nature of OH...Halogen interactions has been extensively studied in the intramolecular bonding in the halophenols and alcohols, and to a lesser extent of intermolecular bonding with alkyl halides. There is no doubt that the largest frequency shifts (ΔvOH) for halophenols and ethanols are for iodine as the proton acceptor, and the order is I > Br > Cl > F. The proportion of unbonded OH follows the same order. However, enthalpy measurements indicate a different situation. There are differences between various groups of workers on some points, but there is general agreement that ΔH is least for association with iodine, and the usual order is Cl > Br > F > I.

The 2-halophenols have been studied by Baker [14, 26, 30, 42, 45] and Banerjee [48, 49]. Two vOH bands are shown by 2-chloro-, bromo- and iodo-phenol, with separations ranging from 56 (Cl) to 95 cm^{-1} (I). 2-Fluorophenol has only a single band at 3591 cm^{-1}, but this is grossly asymmetric, and there is little doubt that it represents a similar situation in which the two bands are unresolved. A qualitative study on 2-fluorophenol by Sandorfy [46] concludes that fluorine is indeed involved in hydrogen bonding but that the energy involved is less than that of any other halogen. In contrast, studies of competitive hydrogen bonding with unsymmetrical 2,6-dihalophenols [2, 42] put the order of ΔH values as Cl > Br > F > I. Baker [42], and more recently Robinson *et al.* [275] have given useful summary tables listing the various data in the literature on both the frequency shifts and on the ΔH measurements. The variations in both the relative magnitudes and the order of the latter emphasise the difficulties of measurement of such small energy differences. Robinson's paper also covers data on halogenated alcohols and 2-cyclohexanols.

The situation with 2-haloethanols is very similar. The work of Mecke [50] and of Josien [51] showed that of the many possible rotational conformers, only two, corresponding to the *trans* (free OH) and *gauche* (bonded OH) could be identified by infrared spectroscopy. 2-Chloroethanol shows two bands at 3623 and 3597 cm^{-1} corresponding to these two forms. 2-Trifluoroethanol absorbs at 3620 cm^{-1}, and the fact that this band is asymmetric on the high-frequency side suggests that this compound also is associated internally [52]. The frequency shifts and thermodynamic properties have been measured by Kreuger [52, 53], and by Buckley *et al.* [276, 277]. Fujimoto *et al.* [278] have given corresponding data for the 2-halocyclohexanols. In both series the frequency shifts are substantially smaller than in the halophenols, and the same inconsistencies occur between the order of the frequency shifts and of the enthalpy measurements.

Intermolecular OH...Halogen bonds have been studied by West [54, 55], by Josien [56] and by Kreuger [53]. West studied the frequency shifts and measured the OH values for the association of phenols or methanol with aliphatic halides such as *n*-butyl halides. The frequency shifts again follow the pattern I > Br > Cl > F, whereas the ΔH values follow the reverse order F > Cl > Br > I. This second order is also reported by Josien using the association of phenol with cyclohexyl halides.

The apparent discrepancies between the order of bond shifts and of the enthalpy measurements has given rise to much controversy. However, the discrepancy only arises if the frequency shifts are a true measure of the relative strengths of the hydrogen bonds. It is by no means certain that this is so. The rate of change of νOH with the internuclear X...Y distance varies with the nature of the Y atom, so that a greater OH shift on bonding to iodine than to chlorine does not necessarily indicate a stronger hydrogen bond. In the cases of the intramolecular hydrogen bonds other factors also affect the frequency shifts. The terminal X and Y atoms are now held at an arbitrary distance determined by the molecular geometry and this is quite different from the intermolecular situation in which these atoms come to that distance which maximises the hydrogen bond energy. Bellamy and Pace [280] have pointed out that in *ortho*fluorophenol the O...F distance is only 0.02 Å less than the sum of the Van der Waals radii of the O and F atoms, so that only weak bonds are to be expected. In contrast the O...I distance in *ortho*iodophenol is about 0.4 Å lower than the sum of the radii, so that a large frequency shift is not surprising. This shift does not, however, reflect the hydrogen bond strength in the same way as it would if the O and I atoms were allowed to come to the distance appropriate to a normal intermolecular bond. These authors suggest that the larger frequency differences amongst the halogens found in *intra* as compared with intermolecular bonds may originate in this way. A second factor which may well contribute to this difference is the bending of the hydrogen bonds in the intramolecular cases. Robinson *et al.* [275] have made some calculations using the Schroeder–Lippincott potential function and have shown that this predicts that there will be no necessary relation between the OH stretching frequency and the strength of the hydrogen bond.

8.2.3. OH...O hydrogen bonds

These represent a very large class of hydrogen bonds, ranging from associations by alcohols which are almost devoid of acidity (Δv to ether 10–20 cm^{-1}) to the extreme cases, such as potassium hydrogen acetate, in which the hydrogen is symmetrically placed between the two oxygen atoms. Within this range in which the end atoms remain the same there seemed at one time to be a better possibility that the factors which controlled ΔvOH would also be those which controlled ΔH, and many authors have studied this possibility. Becker [58] found a reasonably good linear relation between Δv and ΔH for fifteen different OH...O bonds between methanol, ethanol and *tert*-butanol and bases such as dioxane, acetone, benzophenone and ethyl acetate. Gramstad [59] has similarly found that complexes of phenol with ketones, aldehydes, esters, ethers and amides can all be shown to follow at least reasonably closely, a linear relation between Δv and ΔH. However, while a good deal of latitude seems possible in variations of the proton acceptor, this is not so for changes in the donor. Major changes in the donor lead to wide variations [59, 61, 235]. Gramstad [59] himself finds that complexes of pentachlorophenol with the same series of bases will not fit this linear relation, and his earlier work on methanol [61] showed that this gave a different $\Delta v/\Delta H$ relationship from that given by phenol. West [55] has quoted parallel results.

Later work has fully confirmed these findings [2, 248, 257]. There are indeed many useful relationships between the frequency shifts and the bond energies within the confines of a very closely related series, and these can be valuable for example in studies on steric hindrance, but any change of proton donor, or a major change of acceptor will invalidate the relation.

(a) XOH...O *bonds to ethers*

Studies by Gramstad [59] on the association of phenol with a variety of bases indicate clearly that, in the absence of steric hindrance, the strength of the bond is directly related to the basicity as determined by the availability of the lone-pair electrons of the oxygen atoms. Thus normal ethers, such as diethyl ether, tetrahydrofuran, di-isopropyl ether and tetrahydropyran, all show Δv shifts for phenol in carbon tetrachloride in the range 271–290 cm^{-1}. In dibenzyl ether Δv falls to 233 cm^{-1}, and the value falls further as the structure alters to allow more and more delocalization of the ether oxygen lone-pair electrons. Thus phenyl methyl ether has Δv (phenol) of 137 cm^{-1}, while in furan and benzofuran the value falls further to 103 cm^{-1}. Gramstad claims a good linear relation between Δv and either k_{assN} or ΔH. There is no doubt that this is sound overall, but it is probably not sufficiently discriminating to detect small changes. Thus for a series of ethers giving Δv values between 282 and 290 cm^{-1} he quotes k_{assN} values ranging from 7.0 to 13.8. Bis(trimethylsilyl) ether, as expected, is considerably less basic than its alkyl counterpart [12].

The question of steric hindrance to the association of alcohols to ethers cannot be isolated from the nature of the proton donor, but Bellamy [12] concludes that even with di-*tert*-butyl ether there is little steric hindrance to hydrogen bonding with phenol itself, although the effect becomes more marked as the size of any *ortho* substituents on the phenol is increased. It has also been shown [17] that ΔvOH for a very wide range of different alcohols in dioxane can be plotted against the corresponding values in ether to give a good linear relationship, the slope of which is related to the relative basicities of the ethers. Hallam has extended such studies and measured the relative basicities of ethers and of amines by the measurement of the slopes of such lines.

The strengths of hydrogen bonds from phenol to ethers are of the order of 4.5–5.5 kcal, and for systems in which this is the sole proton donor, Joesten and Drago [64] propose the relationship $\Delta H \pm 0.5$ kcal $= 0.016\ \Delta v + 0.63$. However, this is sensitive to some extent on the nature of the solvent and of course it applies only to intermolecular bonds. Singh [235] *et al.* have studied this relationship in great detail. They show that it is valid for medium strength hydrogen bonds which are of roughly comparable strengths, but that a different relation is required for weaker hydrogen bonds. Rao *et al.* [73] and Huong *et al.* [94] have studied similar relationships with various types of X=O bonds.

Intramolecular hydrogen bonds are a special case because the terminal atoms are not allowed to come to that natural distance which would maximise the bond strengths but are fixed by the external geometry. There are thus major differences between inter and intramolecular bonds even when the end atoms have comparable acidities and basicities. Thus the intermolecular hydrogen bond between phenol and anisole shows a frequency shift of $281\ \mathrm{cm}^{-1}$, whereas the corresponding intramolecular bond in *ortho*methoxyphenol has a frequency shift of only $52\ \mathrm{cm}^{-1}$. In this second case the geometry prevents the oxygen atoms from coming close enough together to maximise the bond strength. However, for a constant O...O distance the Δv values can be expected to vary systematically with the basicity of the ether as before. One interesting case of intramolecular hydrogen bonding is that of monomethylated pyrogallol. The forms I and II are known, and in both vOH is the same, suggesting that the hydrogen bonds are of the same strength.

(I)   (II)

However, no free OH band is visible in the spectrum of the 1-methyl ether, whereas the intensity ratio of free/bonded OH bands in the 2-methyl isomer is 0.32. Clearly then, despite the similarity of Δv values, the isomer in which the hydrogen atoms are both bonded to the same oxygen is less stable than the other [63].

Ethers such as dioxane or diethyl ethers have been extensively employed as standard bases for the measurement of Δv values of different alcohols on association, and this affords some basis for the assessment of changes in the acidities of alcohols with changes in their chemical structure. It is immediately clear that there is no overall relationship between vOH and the acidity of the alcohol as measured in this way, although within a given class of alcohols such relations do occur. Thus on passing from *tert*-butanol to methanol both vOH and ΔvOH (ether) increase, and the two are linearly related. Equally, on passing from *p-N*-dimethylaminophenol to *p*-nitrophenol there is a linear relation between vOH and ΔvOH (ether), but the line is of opposite slope to that found previously, and vOH falls as ΔvOH rises. Some suggested reasons for this behaviour are given in the discussion of free OH frequencies in Chapter 4.

The attachment of the OH group to elements other than carbon can produce very dramatic effects. West [15, 66] has measured a number of such compounds and finds, for example, that the ΔvOH (ether) value for $(CH_3)_3SiOH$ is just about twice that of $(CH_3)_3COH$, although the basicity of the OH oxygen atom is not much changed. In general, it is true that the basicity of a hydroxyl group varies inversely with the acidity, so that anything which increases the acidity of an OH group reduces its basicity. However, while there may be some kind of quantitative relationship between these two properties so far as COH systems are concerned (and even this is not fully established) it is certain that it cannot be applied generally. Indeed, the data quoted above show that this is so.

Variations in the structure of the alcohol can also lead to abnormalities in hydrogen bonding through steric effects. The majority of studies of steric hindrance to association are concerned with phenol dimers or with associations with acetone, and these will be referred to in later sections. In associations with ethers the effect of steric hindrance is most clearly shown in complexes with 2,6-di-*tert*-butylphenol, as is to be expected. Bellamy [12, 13] suggests that phenols with smaller groups form hydrogen bonds with simple ethers of essentially similar strengths so far as Δv is concerned, although the equilibrium coefficients may change through alterations in the entropy terms. This is supported by the data of Singh and Rao [236]

(b) OH...OH bonds. Alcohol dimers and polymers: intramolecular OH...O bonds

Most alcohols associate intermolecularly to some extent in the vapour phase at normal temperatures, and in solutions in non-polar solvents. The vapour association of methanol has been studied by Inskeep *et al.* [69]. A study of the variations of the intensity of the whole vOH envelope with temperature and pressure, and a determination of the monomer absorption coefficient allowed them to deduce values for the absorption of the possible dimer, trimer and tetramer species. Barnes *et al.* have studied other alcohols in the vapour using very long path length cells and derived frequency shifts and ΔH values for the various species present. A more convenient approach is that of matrix isolation in which the alcohol is trapped on nitrogen or argon at very low temperatures. Such studies show very clearly a series of peaks which can be assigned to dimer, trimer, tetramer and higher polymers [57, 70]. The frequencies fall as the polymer chain grows, and at high resolution each of the individual peaks shows fine structure which is not yet fully understood. The band centers for methanol are as follows [57]: dimer $3520\ cm^{-1}$, trimer $3495\ cm^{-1}$, tetramer $3446\ cm^{-1}$ (open chain), $3369\ cm^{-1}$ (cyclic and pentamer) and high polymer $3254\ cm^{-1}$. These results raise the interesting problem of why the Δv values for dimers should be so much smaller than those of the higher polymers. The Δv value of a typical alcohol or phenol is about $120\ cm^{-1}$ for dimerization, and nearer to $300\ cm^{-1}$ for higher polymers. Since the dimer band disappears as the concentration is increased and the proportion of polymer grows, it must be concluded that the existing OH...OH link of the dimer had been very much strengthened by the addition of further units to either end of the chain, and there has been much discussion of why this should be so.

Two possibilities have been canvassed to explain these observations. The first suggests that dimers are cyclic (I) and that the hydrogen bonds are abnormally weak because of the acute angles involved. The polymers are then regarded as open-chain systems with normal hydrogen bonds (II). The second explanation inverts this and assumes that the dimers are open chain as in (III) and have normal hydrogen bonds, whereas the polymers are cyclic as in (IV).

This involves the requirement that the hydrogen bonds of cyclic polymers should be abnormally strong, and reasons why this should be so have been advanced by both Bellamy [71] and Kuhn [63]. Briefly, this implies that the oxygen atoms of an OH group which is donating its hydrogen atom in a hydrogen bond becomes more basic as a result. It can similarly be argued that the proton of the OH group which is accepting a hydrogen bond becomes more acidic. In the cyclic system, therefore, there is an overall increase in the acidity of the hydrogen atoms and in the basicity of the oxygen atoms as compared with the values for the original monomer.

Experimental studies to resolve this problem have not led to wholly decisive results, but the balance of evidence now appears to favour the second of these two explanations. A direct approach to this problem has been made by Bellamy [71] in the cases of mixed dimers. This appears to give the conclusive result that such dimers are open chain and that they do contain free endgroups, but unfortunately the approach is not applicable to homogeneous dimers. However, it seems likely that the same considerations will hold for these also. Bellamy [71] has pointed out that the free νOH bands of phenol and methanol are sufficiently well removed from each other to be observed independently and also that one might well expect the hydrogen bond between the two to be stronger than that of either of the homogeneous dimers. This is because the bond is between a strong acid and a strong base in the heterogeneous dimer and between a strong acid and weak base, or weak acid and strong base in the others. This is confirmed by the fact that association occurs between phenol and methanol at much lower concentrations than those at which normal dimers are found, and the frequency shift is also very much greater. Further, it can be shown that on mixing dilute solutions of methanol and phenol at equal concentrations there is no appreciable reduction in the intensity of the free OH band of methanol, whereas that of phenol falls sharply. This would be expected for the formation of the open-chain dimer $C_6H_5OH...OH$, in which only the phenolic OH group is involved

$$CH_3$$

in the hydrogen bond. Parallel results have been obtained for other heterogeneous dimers of this kind.

These studies, coupled with cancellation techniques using extremely dilute solutions in the reference beam, have allowed measurements of the real position of free OH frequencies of groups in which the oxygen atom is involved in a hydrogen bond. In agreement with Kuhn's [74] earlier findings on α-diols, it appears that the observed shifts are small and rarely exceed 10 cm^{-1} from the original frequency. However, in proton-accepting solvents such as benzene the increased acidity of the free OH of dimers as compared with the original monomer leads to larger shifts. The separation of the free OH of phenol in benzene (actually phenol associated with benzene) from that of the terminal OH of the phenol dimer (itself associated with benzene) is very markedly greater than in carbon tetrachloride. In the same way it has been shown that the OH...O hydrogen bond of alcohol dimers is responsive to solvents which are either proton donors or proton acceptors, whereas the OH...O ether bonds respond only to proton donor solvents [17].

The problems of the impact of steric hindrance effects on the association of alcohols has always been one that has interested spectroscopists, but it is not at all easy to disentangle real steric hindrance from other effects, such as entropy and acidity changes. Even in a comparison of the equilibrium constants of methanol and *tert*-butanol, there is clear evidence that the proportion of free alcohol at any given dilution is greater for the latter and calculation of ΔH based on this and on temperature effects lead to a difference of as much as 4.4 kcal between the two. However, the Δv values show only small differences, and it seems that the proportions of the free and associated forms are determined more by the change of entropy on passing from methanol to *tert*-butanol than by any real changes in the strengths of the hydrogen bonds. Similar difficulties arise in the interpretation of the spectra of 2,6-substituted phenols. Bellamy *et al.* [13] have argued from the fact that the liquid 2,6-di-alkylphenols with methyl, ethyl and isopropyl groups all show essentially the same Δv values, that the hydrogen bonds are all of similar strengths, and that entropy effects rather than enthalpy changes are responsible for the observed differences in the equilibrium constants. This is supported by indirect evidence from solvent studies on complexes with ether. Only in the case of *tert*-butyl-substituted phenols do they find any clear evidence for a true steric effect. It must be admitted, however, that the Δv values of the di-*ortho* alkyl phenols are smaller than those of the mono-alkylated compounds, which in turn are smaller than those of phenol, and it still remains something of an open question whether this is due, as Bellamy suggests, to changes in the OH polarity produced by the alkyl groups or to a steric effect resulting from longer O...O distances. Puttnam [94], for example, has also studied this problem and reached the opposite conclusion. He believes that there is a strong increase in the hindering effect of 2,6-dialkylphenols as the degree of branching at the α-carbon atom is increased. Other workers have reached similar conclusions for phenols associating with acetone (see following section). The question cannot therefore be finally resolved at this time. The shape of the proton acceptor molecule is obviously equally important in this, and even 2,6-di-*tert*-butylphenol can associate with some suitably shaped bases [12, 68].

Intramolecular OH...OH bonding is common in those diols in which the bond angles allow a sufficiently close approach of the two groups. In 1,2-diols the O...O distances are somewhat greater than those taken up in intermolecular bonds and the ΔvOH values are correspondingly smaller. Ethane diol has a frequency shift of only 35 cm^{-1} as compared with the 1 : 4 diol which shifts by 160 cm^{-1} [258]. Despite this ethane diol has the higher proportion of cyclic structures at room temperature due to the favourable entropy factors. Several attempts have been made to relate ΔvOH with the O...O distances in this special series, the latest being that of Brutcher and Bauer [76]. However, as Kuhn [77] points out, none are entirely successful. Most of the recent work in this area is given in references [76–80]. The factor of prime importance in determining ΔvOH is the azimuthal angle ϕ between the two C—O bonds on adjacent carbon atoms. This, of course, determines the O...O distance. In compounds such as cyclopentane-1,2-diol (ϕ between 90° and 120°) the oxygen atoms are too far apart for interaction to occur, whereas in *cis-exo*-norbornane-2,3-diol ($\phi = 0$) the Δv value is 103 cm^{-1}. Most 1,2-

diols have ϕ values near 60° and Δv's between 30 and 50 cm^{-1}. Kuhn [77] gives a table illustrating the way in which Δv values vary with ring size in 1,2-dihydroxycyclanes. A second factor which is of importance is the degree of substitution at the carbon atoms. Increasing substitution leads to larger Δv values, so that 1,1,2,2-tetra-*tert*-butylethylene glycol has the largest Δv value yet found in a 1,2-diol (170 cm^{-1}). This is probably also due to changes in the azimuthal angle arising from the distortion of the C—C—C angle (the Thorpe-Ingold effect). Essentially the same considerations of O...O distances as determined by the angles of the C—O bonds are operative in 1,3-diols, which have also been extensively studied [81–84]. The hydrogen bonds are now appreciably stronger, but the effect of substituents at the α position is of particular importance. Groups such as an isopropyl group in this position lead to substantial changes in Δv through the Thorpe-Ingold effect.

1,4-diols have been mainly studied by Kuhn [77] by Burfield [258] and by Stolow [84], and these show an interesting difference in behaviour from that of earlier members of the series. Whereas in 1,2-diols Δv increases monotonically with decreasing azimuthal angles between the OH groups, there is no parallel behaviour in the 1,4-series. Here a maximum Δv value appears to be achieved at angles of 90° and the value falls off on either side. Kuhn has rationalized this result in terms of the permitted conformers of the 1,4-diols. In this series a wide number of possible conformations could be adopted, and it is possible for the OH groups to take up intramolecular separations comparable with those found in intermolecular bonds. The Δv values are therefore significantly higher than in the 1,2-series. Butane-1,4-diol has a Δv of 157 cm^{-1} (CCl$_4$), which is closely similar to that of an alcohol dimer. Indeed, as the former must have an open structure OH...OH with a free hydroxyl group, this provides supporting evidence for the open form of intermolecular dimers rather than the cyclic form discussed earlier. Other factors which will optimize the hydrogen bond strength in addition to the O...O distance are the OH...O angle (optimum at 180°) and the C—O...H angle (optimum 110°). Kuhn shows that all three factors are optimized at an azimuthal of 90° (C—O bonds) and that if the angle is varied from this any gain which might be realized by an improvement in one parameter is more than offset by losses from the others. His paper covers some fifty-seven 1,4-diols and has data on cyclic, unsaturated and substituted systems. Significant increases in Δv OH...O are observed in chloroform solution as compared with carbon tetrachloride in just the same way as has been described for intermolecular hydrogen bonds.

Intramolecular bonding in triols has been investigated by Kuhn and Bowman [63]. An interesting finding is that acyclic trimers of the kind O—H···O—H···O—H, in which the hydroxyl groups are unable to form a

R———R———C—

completely closed ring of hydrogen bonds, give Δv values which, although greater than those of dimers, are still very much less than those of monohydric alcohol polymers. This provides some additional evidence that the latter are cyclic.

Intramolecular hydrogen bonding involving even larger numbers of OH groups can be realized in compounds such as the Novolaks, where the presence of a phenol in a polymeric chain can lead to cyclic forms involving the monomers with 4,5- and 6-phenol units. All give strong hydrogen bonds with vOH in the 3200-cm^{-1} region. Intermolecular associations which also lead to large hydrogen-bonded ring systems are equally possible in this series [85].

(c) OH...O=C systems

Intermolecular hydrogen bonds between alcohols or phenols and various types of carbonyl group have been extensively studied, and information is now available on the way Δv and ΔH vary with the nature of the proton acceptor, and to a lesser extent on the effects of changes in the donor alcohol. Most carbonyl groups form somewhat weaker hydrogen bonds than ethers, but the OH frequency shift is still substantial. Gramstad [59, 86] gives extensive data on Δv and ΔH values for the association of phenol with esters, ketones, aldehydes and amides. The bond strength within a series is a direct function of the basicity of the CO group, so that in p-nitrobenzaldehyde ΔvOH is 117 cm^{-1}, and this rises to 260 cm^{-1} in p-dimethylaminobenzaldehyde. The largest shifts of ΔOH occur with the most basic carbonyl systems, and amides give shifts of up to 340 cm^{-1}. Bellamy has pointed out that there is a reasonable parallelism between the ΔvOH values and vCO itself, provided certain classes of compounds, such as conjugated carbonyl groups, thioesters and strained rings, are excluded. This follows the general pattern that ΔvOH falls as vCO rises (see Chapter 5). There is, however, no overall relationship with vCO or with the carbonyl ionization potential. Gramstad suggests that the $\Delta v/\Delta H$ relation is reasonably well obeyed by all these systems, and some comment has already been made on this in Section 8.2.3. (a). A typical ΔH value suggested for the association of phenol with dimethylacetamide is 5.4 kcal/mol in carbon tetrachloride. This rises to 6.0 kcal/mol for the same complex in carbon disulphide [86]. Other measurements with phenol as donor have been made by Joesten and Drago [64] and by Dunken and Fritsche [87] using ethyl acetate and acetone as acceptors respectively. Powell and West [62], working on the first overtone band of phenol, give the following ΔH values for carbonyl association. Methyl ethyl ketone 5.34 kcal/mol, n-butyraldehyde 4.67 kcal/mol and ethyl acetate 4.45 kcal/mol. Heinen [88] has measured Δv and equilibrium constant values for the association of acetone and variously substituted phenols. If one omits 2-$tert$-butylphenol and 2,6-dialkylphenols (which will be discussed later) an excellent linear relation is obtained between $\log k$ and the sum of the Hammett σ values of the substituents (for $ortho$ substituents it is assumed that the $para$ value applies). A good relation also exists between ΔvOH and $\log k$.

Several workers have studied the simultaneous changes in the OH and C=O frequencies in hydrogen bonded systems. For a given carbonyl acceptor there is a good linear relationship between ΔvOH and ΔvC=O. This has been shown by Doral *et al.* [65] for the association of phenols with *NN*-dimethylacetamide, and Bellamy and Pace have shown that the same relationship holds good for alcohols other than those chlorinated at the α carbon atom. In the case of the phenols there is also a good relationship between ΔvOH and the acidities as measured by Hammett σ values. For any single 1 : 1 complex the frequency shifts of both bands following changes in solvation also follow a linear relationship [263].

Similar relationships have been found for associations between phenol and variously substituted *NN*-dimethylbenzamides and cinnamides [67] and the frequency shifts have been correlated with the substituent constants and with the carbonyl π electron density. However, these cases cover a common acceptor which is subject to relatively minor changes in the electron density at the oxygen atom. It is well established that whilst there is a reasonably good relationship between the frequency shifts of the OH and C=O groups when the donor is varied and the proton acceptor is held constant, there is no relationship whatsoever in situations in which the donor is constant and the type of carbonyl acceptor is changed. In this the behaviour is interesting in that it is a reversal of the behaviour found in studies on the relation between ΔvOH and ΔH. Here the relationships described show a good deal of tolerance to changes in the type of carbonyl group, but fail if one attempts to apply them to some other alcohol or phenol.

At some concentrations the OH stretching band of OH...O=C bonds appears to be asymmetric [87, 90, 91]. Various explanations have been offered but the most likely appears to be the possibility of the formation of 1 : 1 and 1 : 2 complexes. Kagarise [92] studied complexes of these kinds between phenol and acetone and deduced from the increased frequency shifts of the carbonyl group in the 1 : 2 complex that this had the stronger hydrogen bonds. However, Bellamy and Pace [263] have shown that as the phenol concentration is increased and the 1 : 1 complex passes over to the 1 : 2, the bonded OH stretching frequencies rise whilst the C=O frequency falls. The C=O is indeed more strongly bonded because it is attached to two OH groups, but the individual hydrogen bond strengths, at least as judged by the OH frequencies are weaker than in the 1 : 1 complex. This is consistent with the concept that a carbonyl group that has donated a lone pair into a hydrogen bond will be more reluctant to donate a second, so that if it is forced to do so both bonds are weaker. This result, together with solvent studies on similar systems shows that the 1 : 2 complex takes the form

$$\text{ROH...O...HOR} \quad \text{rather than} \quad \text{ROH...ROH...C=O}$$
$$\text{||}$$

as in the latter case both hydrogen bonds would be strengthened.

Steric hindrance effects on the association of *ortho*-substituted phenols with carbonyl groups have been studied by Takahashi and Li [93], and by Heinen [88]. It is generally accepted that there is considerable steric hindrance to solvation in 2,6-di-*tert*-butylphenols, but the position is less clear for smaller substituents, such as the isopropyl or ethyl groups. On the basis of solvent studies, Bellamy [13] has suggested that steric hindrance does not play a major role in determining the strengths of hydrogen bonds between phenols and ether unless the alkyl groups are as large as *tert*-butyl. He attributes the other variations in equilibrium constants to changes in the acidity and in entropy. However, Heinen's findings on associations with acetone are at variance with this. He finds that the ΔvOH values of 2,6-dialkyl phenols do not follow the Hammett σ relationship, and this does imply that the whole of the differences in hydrogen-bond strengths in the various phenols cannot be attributed to acidity changes alone. Measurements by Brookes *et al.* [237] on associations between hindered phenols and hindered ketones, generally support Bellamy's approach.

Intramolecular hydrogen bonds between OH and carbonyl groups which are not conjugated follow the pattern of bonds to ethers and to other OH groups. The strength depends not only on the acidity of the donor and the basicity of the acceptor but also on the molecular geometry, which determines the O...O distances. 1-Acetylethanol, for example, absorbs at 3481 cm^{-1}, corresponding to a reasonably strong intramolecular bond. However, the association in the 2-acetyl derivative is very much weaker. Similar intramolecular hydrogen bonds are found in alpha diketones at temperatures between 70 °C and 200 °C, when they partially enolise. A weak band then appears at 3480 cm^{-1} which disappears at lower temperatures [72].

The greatest interest in this type of association centres round the β-diketones, which can enolize, and on β-hydroxy-$\alpha\beta$-unsaturated ketones. Resonance effects can be very large in this series and lead to a considerable strengthening of the hydrogen bonds. There are correspondingly large shifts in vOH, vCO and vC=C. In these cases the hydrogen bonding does not result in the same degree of intensification of the OH stretching band as is normal for the intermolecular bonds. For this reason many studies of enols of this type have concentrated on the shifts of the C=C and C=O frequencies [95–97]. The difference in the OH intensities of *cis* and *trans* enols is well shown by the spectra of the two forms of methylphenylformylacetate, given by Matrosov and Kabachnik [223]. The *trans* form which is intermolecularly bonded has a very strong broad band centred about 2700 cm^{-1}, whereas the *cis* form has an extremely weak broad band in the same region. 3-methylthio-2 : 4-pentane dione [234], which has an enhanced enol contribution has a similar weak band near 2580 cm^{-1}. Detoni *et al.* [236] have compared the integrated intensities of *ortho* and *para* hydroxyketones and found that the intramolecular intensities are one fourth to one sixth of those of the intermolecular bonds. These systems have rather weaker hydrogen bonds than many β diketones.

and the intensity reduction is accentuated as the bond strength is increased. The *peri*hydroxyquinones show no OH band at normal concentrations, and in potassium hydrogen maleate no OHO antisymmetric band has been identified. This has a symmetrical hydrogen bond but the same result is found in picolinic-1-oxide-2 carboxylic acid which is not symmetrical [281].

The reduction in bond strength in the salicylates makes it a good deal easier to measure νOH with precision, and Brookes *et al.* [98] have observed an interesting example of the buttress effect in this series. In this effect, the presence of a bulky group on one side or other of the hydrogen bond leads to a contraction of the O...O distance and a strengthening of the association. Some typical values for compounds in their paper are:

νCO 1684 cm^{-1}
νOH 3210

νCO 1681 cm^{-1}
νOH 3195

νCO 1679 cm^{-1}
νOH 3180

νCO 1676 cm^{-1}
νOH 3110

νCO 1670 cm^{-1}
νOH 3080

Although there is a good deal of resonance stabilisation of the hydrogen bonds in the salicylates, it would seem that competitive bonding with nitro groups attached to the ring is still possible. Hoyer [99, 100] identifies OH...O_2N^- and OH...O=C bands corresponding to the rotational isomers in 3-nitrosalicylic esters and in 3,5-dinitrosalicylaldehyde.

(d) OH...O=X systems

X=O systems where X is an element other than carbon are usually considerably more basic than carbonyl groups and form stronger hydrogen bonds. Each X system produces a range of frequency shifts in the OH band of phenol, depending on how it is substituted. Generally, however, the As=O group appears to be the strongest proton acceptor, giving shifts of 500–600 cm^{-1} with substituted phenols. The N-oxides of the heteroaromatics are also strong bases with frequency shifts in the 500–400 cm^{-1} range. The shifts with P=O compounds are only a little smaller, followed by S=O and then N=O in nitrites and nitrosamines. A tabulation of the existing data on the association of these various systems with phenols is given by Bueno and Lucisano [101]. The order of effectiveness of the various X elements in forming hydrogen bonds appears to be broadly similar to their relative effectiveness in molecular complex formation [282].

The most extensively studied systems are the sulphoxides and the phosphoryl compounds. Gramstad [102] measured Δv, ΔH and K values for the association of ten different sulphoxides with phenol. The ΔvOH values ranged from 154 cm^{-1} in covalent sulphites to 350–370 cm^{-1} in dialkyl sulphoxides. As with the carbonyl compounds, he finds a good linear relation between log k_{assN} and both ΔH and ΔvOH. In the sulphoxides there is a general trend for the largest OH shifts to correspond to the lowest S=O frequencies. The inverse study in which variously substituted phenols are associated wide diphenyl sulphoxide has been made by Ghersetti and Lusa [103]. Again they find a linear relationship between ΔvOH and ΔH and ΔF. The values of ΔS were almost constant in the series. The ΔH values suggested are large, and range from 7.0 to 9.0 kcal/mol.

The phosphoryl band has been studied by Gramstad and his associates [61, 104–107]. This group is also an excellent proton acceptor, and in triethyl phosphine oxide the OH frequency shift on association with phenol is as much as 510 cm^{-1}. Within a given class of organophosphorus compounds there is a linear relation between ΔvOH and ΔH for any given donor. However, separate relationships need to be worked out for each donor. The relations are valid for trialkyl or trialkoxy compounds and for mixed systems with both residues, but it becomes invalid if an electron-attracting group such as CH$_2$Cl, N(CH$_3$)$_2$, or even S-alkyl, is introduced. Overall there is a tendency for the strength of the hydrogen bond, as assessed by either ΔvOH or the equilibrium constant, to increase as the unassociated P=O frequency falls. The values opposite, taken from Gramstad's various papers, give a picture of the changing basicity of the P=O group with substitution.

It will be seen that there is no general parallelism between the behaviour of ΔvOH, ΔvP=O and K. In compounds 2 and 7 the ΔvP=O shifts are about the

	Proton acceptor	ΔvOH, cm^{-1}	ΔvP=O, cm^{-1}	$k_{assN_{20}}$
1.	(C$_2$H$_5$O)$_3$P=O	345	30	350
2.	(C$_2$H$_5$)$_3$P=O	510	23	2522
3.	(C$_6$H$_5$)$_3$P=O	430	—	1055
4.	[(CH$_3$)$_2$N]$_3$P=O	450	—	1500
5.	(C$_2$H$_5$S)$_3$P=O	280	17	74.5
6.	(C$_6$H$_5$O)$_3$P=O	210	6	41
7.	(C$_6$H$_5$S)$_3$P=O	250	22	68.7
8.	(CCl$_3$)(C$_2$H$_5$O)$_2$P=O	260	32	73.2
9.	(C$_2$H$_5$O)$_3$P=S	172	—	45

same, but the equilibrium constants differ by a factor of nearly forty, and the ΔvOH values by a factor of two. In compounds 3 and 4 the ΔvOH values are similar, but the K values are widely apart. Changes in the donor give even more extraordinary results. With pentachlorophenol, for example, one finds that in compound 2 the ΔvOH value has risen to 685 cm^{-1}, but the equilibrium constant has fallen by an order of magnitude to 209.5.

Only a limited amount of work has been done on the association of N=O groups in hydrogen bonds. From the geometry one would expect the behaviour to be similar to that of the carbonyl group, but there are a few differences. Gramstad [102] has reported a small number of measurements of ΔvOH, ΔH and equilibrium constants for the association of phenol with a few N=O compounds. The results are too few for any general trends to be found, but as one would expect, the largest OH shifts occur with the heteroaromatic oxides. These have been studied by several workers [94, 101, 283, 284]. The pyridinic nucleus plays a part in the resonance with the N=O bond and so plays a part in stabilising the hydrogen bonds. The hydrogen bond strengths do not therefore vary in any systematic fashion with the pK values of the proton donor molecules [101]. Intramolecular hydrogen bonding to the N=O group is well established. Boll [108] has shown that the OH group in 1-nitroso-2-naphthol is completely chelated, and there is no absorption corresponding to a free OH group.

(e) OH...O$_2$X systems

Some measurements have been made on hydrogen bonds to groups such as NO$_2$, SO$_2$, CO$_2$$^-$, etc. The nitro group has received the most attention, and the recent literature is well documented by Schleyer [109]. Intramolecular hydrogen bonding in o-nitrophenol is, of course, well established and is revealed by the large OH shift and by the smaller, but well marked, change in $v(sym.)$NO$_2$. However, this is a special case, and in intermolecular hydrogen bonds the OH shifts are small, and the changes in the NO$_2$ frequencies are virtually undetectable. Thus while vOH in 2-nitrophenol is 3243cm^{-1}, the value for the association of phenol with nitrobenzene is only 3521 cm^{-1}. Schleyer [109] gives ΔvOH values for the association of both methanol and phenol with a range of alkyl and aryl nitro compounds. The differences between these last two classes are small, so that the whole range of OH shifts for methanol is no larger than 26–42 cm^{-1}. Even then, this includes the nitroanisoles, which may well be special cases. The shift for nitromethane is within 1 cm^{-1} of that for nitrobenzene. With phenol as donor, somewhat larger shifts occur, in the range 83–101 cm^{-1}, and again there is little distinction between alkyl and aryl compounds. However, the shifts in the alkyl nitro compounds appear to follow Taft σ values.

Few authors have bothered to record the shifts in the nitro group stretching frequencies. These are usually very small, but some data are available in a paper by Iogansen and Litovchenko [116]. Intramolecular hydrogen bonding has given rise to some controversy. While this is well established in 2-nitrophenol, 1-nitro-2-naphthol [108] and other nitronaphthols [99, 100], the **shifts in non-resonant systems are so much smaller that doubts have been cast** on the reality of the effect [110, 111]. However, the balance of evidence from the studies on nitro alcohols by Kuhn, Robinson [113], Urbanski [114, 115] and Schleyer [109] indicates that internal association does occur, but that it is no stronger than is the intermolecular bond between methanol and nitro compounds. The association band of the OH group is therefore always accompanied by a free OH band due to the rotational isomer, and the two are not resolved. A broad unsymmetrical band is found, and it is difficult to measure $\Delta \nu OH$ with precision. There is also the possibility of competitive OH...OH association in compounds such as 2-methyl-2-nitropropane-1,3-diol and this then gives an abnormal spectrum.

The ability of the sulphonyl group to form hydrogen bonds has been studied by Kartha, Jones and Robertson [117], who measured $\Delta \nu OH$, ΔH and equilibrium constants for the association of p-chlorophenol with a range of sulphonyl compounds from methanesulphonyl chloride to diethyl sulphone. The OH frequency shifts for these two compounds were 58.5 and $176 \ cm^{-1}$ respectively. Over the range studied there was a linear relation between $\Delta \nu OH$ and the log k values. The strengths of the hydrogen bonds, as far as they are reflected in the $\Delta \nu$ values, relate to the availability of the lone-pair electrons of the oxygen atoms, and are therefore related to the νSO_2 frequencies, and in the cases of aromatic compounds to the Hammett σ values of the substituents. Similar results have been reported by Dallinga and Engberts [118]. In measurements on the association of phenol with twenty two sulphones, they have shown that OH is a good linear function of the antisymmetric stretching frequencies. The equation is as follows:

$$\nu SO_2{}^{as} = -0.499 \Delta \nu + 1398$$

As with the carbonyl series the basis strength of the S=O bonds increases as the frequencies fall and the polarity is increased. As the antisymmetric frequency has been shown to be wholly dependent upon the inductive properties of the substituents, it follows that the basicity is determined by these factors also. The corresponding relationship with the symmetric stretching frequencies is less good, perhaps due to some coupling in this mode in some of the compounds studied. This seems likely as a good relationship can be found within the limited series of the dialkyl sulphones in which any such coupling will be reasonably constant.

The association of the ionized carboxyl group has been discussed by Pimentel in the special case of the trifluoroacetic acid/sodium trifluoroacetate association. This is discussed in the following section dealing with the associations of acids. Apart from this, there is little information available, although the $CO_2{}^-$ ion would be expected to be a strong acceptor.

(ƒ) OH...O *bonds in acids*

The intermolecular association of acids gives rise to very broad diffuse bands with a large number of minor peaks. The interpretation of these very characteristic spectra has been discussed by Sheppard [119, 120], and the whole problem has been dealt with at some length in reference [247]. There has been much discussion on the origins of the great breadth of the OH stretching bands in acids. A number of different mechanisms contribute to the band shape and its substructure but most theoretical studies concentrate on one or another alone, so that they lack generality. It is well established that a major factor is the anharmonic coupling between the O...O stretching vibration which occurs near 100 cm^{-1}, and the νOH stretch. This might be expected to give rise to a series of submaxima on either side of the main band with this separation. Although peaks of this kind have been identified for associations of halogen acids with ether in the vapour phase they have not been clearly identified in the carboxylic series, even in matrix isolation studies when the bands are sharpened up. Nevertheless there is little doubt that this is a major contributor to the band width. The quantitative theory of Marechal and Witkowski [285] using this assumption does enable them to reproduce with good precision the observed band contour for deuteroacetic acid dimer.

The submaxima are clearly recognisable as overtone and combination bands of lower frequency fundamentals, and the earlier assignments based on this assumption have been fully confirmed by matrix isolation studies when the overlapping of bands which occurs in the vapour phase is much reduced and the individual peaks can be more clearly identified [286, 287]. Another factor which can contribute to the band width is the presence of more than one hydrogen bonded species. Although carboxylic acids are generally thought to associate as cyclic dimers, some can take the open chain polymer form, and in solution there can be contributions from both. Bellamy has shown [123, 124] that the two polymorphic forms of oxalic acid form bonds of widely different strengths, and this has been confirmed by Villepin and Novak [122]. The *alpha* form is associated in chains with an O...O distance of 2.70 Å whereas the *beta* form is a cyclic dimer with significantly stronger hydrogen bonds and an O...O distance of 2.674 Å. The cyclic resonance structure therefore allows the formation of stronger bonds. In a solution in which both forms are present there will clearly be an important contribution to the overall breadth of the OH band.

There have been many measurements of the hydrogen bond energies of carboxylic acid dimers and much of this data is summarized in reference [248]. The measure of agreement amongst different workers is relatively poor reflecting the experimental difficulties. Guilleme *et al.* [121] have found a simple linear relation between the log K values for dimerisation of alkyl and conjugated acids and their pK_a values. As the latter are linked to the free OH values within this limited series there is also a linear relation between the free OH frequencies and log K.

Intermolecular bonding between carboxyl groups and other basic groups is, of course, common. The equilibrium constant and enthalpy [238] for the dimerization of acids are much reduced in benzene solution because of the competition of the ring. In dioxane, acids are monomeric, at least in the sense that they are wholly bonded to the solvent and not to each other. The effects on vOH of the formation of strong hydrogen bonds with other acceptors has been studied by Hadzi et al. [125], and by Odinokov et al. [137] using basic groups such as P=O and S=O.

As the strengths of the hydrogen bonds are progressively increased beyond those found in acid dimers, by changes either in the acid or basic strengths, the OH band is broadened even further on the low-frequency side, and two or sometimes three broad subminima appear. The position of the sub-minima varies with the strength of the hydrogen bond, and it is not possible to say whether they represent entirely new peaks or are simply the corresponding bands of the dimer shifted to lower frequencies. However, as the strength of the hydrogen bonds increase further, two of these peaks take on an appearance very like that of the A and B bands of the very strong hydrogen bonds discussed in Section 8.2.5. At the same time, with very strong acids and bases, a new band similar to band C appears in the 1900–1800-cm^{-1} region, and there is a general elevation of the background of the low-frequency region of the spectrum. Some special cases of very strong associations between acids and pyridine have been discussed in detail by Hadzi [126] and by Barrow [127] in connexion with the problems of quantum mechanical proton tunnelling. The discussion on effects of this kind is given in Section 8.2.5 below.

Intramolecular hydrogen bonds are less common in acids, but do occur when the acids contain suitable basic sites. Pyruvic acid is such a case [128], and it is very likely that the per acids are intramolecularly bonded. The frequency shifts are small compared with the shifts on dimerization, and the OH bands are sharp and well defined. 0 Aminobenzoic acid is interesting in that it can exist in more than one form. In two of its crystalline forms the OH stretching bands are typical of those of a normal carboxylic acid dimer and the NH stretching bands are close to those of free NH groups. However, in a third crystalline form the NH bands are at low frequencies (3338 and 3250 cm^{-1}), and the center of the broad OH band is also displaced downwards. In this case the association is in chains through OH...N and NH...O=C bonds. A related chain form can also be observed in the para substituted compound. In the case of the meta derivative there is actual proton transfer in the chain form to give bands corresponding to the NH$_3^+$ structure [288]. It would seem that the expected effects of intramolecular bonds are not shown in the ortho compounds of molecules of this type.

8.2.4. OH...N systems

Hydrogen bonds of this type form readily between OH groups and amine nitrogen atoms, and with unsaturated or heterocyclic nitrogen atoms. In any comparison between intramolecularly bonded pairs of compounds such as 3-methoxy- and 3-amino-propanol it is usually found that the OH frequency shift is much greater for the association with the nitrogen compound. In nearly all the systems of this type that have been compared [129] the geometry requires that the O...O and O...N distances should be the same, and Freedman has therefore concluded that the hydrogen bonds to nitrogen are the stronger. In intermolecular bonds the O...O and O...N distances are unlikely to be the same, and comparisons are more difficult. Gramstad [130] has compared the $\Delta\nu$OH and equilibrium constants for the association of phenol with triethylamine and with a phosphoryl derivative which gives a closely similar $\Delta\nu$OH value. The equilibrium constants differ very widely (90 and 518 respectively), and he concludes that the latter forms the stronger hydrogen bonds. However, as the entropy terms will almost certainly be widely different in the two cases, this is not necessarily a valid conclusion.

(a) OH...amines

The main body of data on the association of hydroxyl groups with amine nitrogen atoms is concerned with intramolecular bonds and the relation of the frequency shifts to the molecular geometry. The most exhaustive study is that of Sicher, Horak and Svoboda [131], who measured $\Delta\nu$OH for the *cis* and *trans* forms of cyclic amino alcohols of the type

$$(CH_2)_n \begin{array}{c} CH_2 \\ \diagup \quad \diagdown CHNH_2 \\ \quad \quad \quad | \\ \diagdown \quad \diagup CHOH \\ CH_2 \end{array}$$

with various ring sizes from five to twenty members. As is to be expected, the strongest hydrogen bonds are found in the *cis* five-membered ring, in which the OH and NH_2 group lie in the same plane. The corresponding *trans* form is not associated. However, as the ring size is increased and the ring departs more and more from a planar structure, hydrogen bonding becomes possible in the *trans* form also. Even when the ring has reached eight members, the buckling is such that the *trans* form actually forms a stronger hydrogen bond than does the *cis*. This trend continues with ring size, although the maximum difference between the two is found at a ring size of twelve. This result, which demonstrates a very simple and elegant way of studying the changes of ring geometry as the size is increased, is parallel to the earlier findings of Kuhn on cyclic α-diols, but the effects of ring size are considerably magnified by the larger OH...N frequency shifts.

Large numbers of *cis* and *trans* pairs of other amino alcohols have been studied by Drefahl and Heublein [132], including 1-amino-2-hydroxyindane and 1-amino-2-hydroxytetralin. They note that hydrogen bonding does not occur if the bond to a substituent is inclined at an angle greater than 60° to the C—C axis. They have also studied [133] *tert*-1,2-amino alcohols with very similar results. Other useful papers on this topic are those of Hite *et al.* [134] (3-piperidinols), De Roos and Bakker [135] (amino alcohols of trihexyphenidyl*), Igonin and Bass [136] (hydroxy benzylamines) and of Freedman [129]. Intramolecular OH...N bonding also occurs in suitably substituted acids with nitrogen atoms in the chain. The carboxyl groups then take a *trans* conformation and link to the nitrogen. The frequency shifts of vOH are not large, and are much smaller than in dimer formation. However, the carbonyl frequency rises sharply, and this is discussed more fully in Chapter 5.

Fewer data are available on OH...N bonds to amines in intermolecular situations, probably because the association is usually so strong that the bands are very broad and difficult to define. It is therefore easier to study associations to nitrogen with less active donors, such as chloroform or phenyl acetylene. However, Gramstad [130] has tabulated ΔvOH, ΔH, K and ΔF values for the association of phenol, methanol and α-naphthol with a variety of tertiary bases. He also gives some values for pentachlorophenol. The frequency shifts are large, but it is very surprising to find that although the ΔH values for α-naphthol complexes are larger than those from the methanol adducts, the ΔvOH values are greater in the latter. Findlay and Kidman [112] have also given some data on the association of alcohols with pyridine.

The association of phenols and of acids with strong bases gives rise to very strong hydrogen bonds and the appearance of the OH band varies according to the bond strength, ranging from spectra which are similar to those of acid dimers but broader and moved to lower frequencies, to examples of very strong hydrogen bonds such as those discussed in Section 8.2.5.

(b) OH...N═C and —C≡N *bonds*

Intramolecular association with the nitrogen atom of C═N— double bonds occurs readily in Shiff's bases and related compounds. Baker and Shulgin [138] have studied many compounds of type (I) with different R substituents. The OH frequencies range from 3466 to 3421 cm^{-1} and vary systematically with the Hammett σ values of the R groups. These are clearly related to the basicity of the nitrogen atom. In the cases of compounds to type (II) a more stable six-membered ring arrangement leads to larger frequency shifts, and the OH bands occur near 2730 and 3549 cm^{-1}. The first represents the association to the nitrogen, and the second the much weaker association to the π cloud. The greater stability of the six-membered ring systems is also well shown in the tabulations of Freedman [129], using both his own data and those of others.

* Trihexyphenidyl is 1-(3-cyclohexyl-3-hydroxy-3-phenylpropylpiperidine.

(I)   (II)

He quotes many examples of very low OH frequencies in such compounds as N-salicylideneaniline (2850 cm^{-1}) and comments at the same time that these strong associations have only a minor influence on the N=C stretching absorptions.

Work on intermolecular bonds to C=N links is largely confined to the oxime series, which has been intensively studied by Califano and Luttke [140]. They showed that the bonding is bifunctional and can give cyclic rings with OH...O or OH...N bonds of about the same energies. Further studies on oximes have since been made by Luck [141] and by Reiser [142].

Hadzi and Premru [239] have recently found some interesting differences between syn and anti aldoximes in the crystalline state. In the liquid both forms exist as cyclic dimers or trimers, and both show the same associated OH frequencies. However, in the crystal the syn compounds form dimers, whereas the anti derivatives exist as long-chain complexes. In contrast to the behaviour of the carboxylic acids, it would seem that the open-chain systems form the stronger hydrogen bonds, so that there is a regular and systematic difference of about 100 cm^{-1} between the associated OH bands of the two forms.

Intermolecular bonds to nitriles have been studied by Mitra [143] using phenol and methanol as proton donors. The frequency shift range found with phenol lay between 160 cm^{-1} (acetonitrile) and 102 cm^{-1} (BrCN). ΔH was approximately linear with $\Delta\nu$OH. Similar results were obtained by Allerhand and Schleyer [139]. The bonding of phenol to thiocyanates has been studied by Igarashi et al. [289]. The shifts are of the same order as with the nitriles and the bonding appears to be to the nitrogen atom.

(c) OH...N bonding to heterocyclics

Intramolecular bonding in 8-hydroxyquinolines has been studied by Rossotti and Rossotti [144] and by Badger and Moritz [145]. νOH in the five-membered ring formed is between 3420 and 3465 cm^{-1}, but there is no simple relation between this frequency and the pK value. The compound (V) below should give very much stronger hydrogen bonds corresponding to the more stable six-membered ring arrangement. However, Gill and Morgan [146] who have examined this material, were unable to detect any OH bands between 5000 and 1650 cm^{-1}. This behaviour is similar to that in nickel dimethylglyoxime, and to a lesser extent in acetylacetone, in which the OH bands have a much lower intensity than one would expect. It may well be, therefore, that

(III)

compound (III) is another such case and is in fact strongly hydrogen bonded. Reference [147] has given some data on OH...N bonds in pyrazolones.

Most of the work on intermolecular OH...N (heterocyclic) bonds has been done with pyridine [126, 127] but Gramstad has also examined the bonding of various alcohols and phenols to collidine, lutidine and the various picolines. He lists ΔvOH, ΔH, ΔF and ΔS values for each of these [130].

8.2.5. Very strong hydrogen bonds

The behaviour of the OH stretching band as the hydrogen bond strength is increased progressively beyond that in carboxylic acid dimers has been described by Hadzi [125] and by Odinokov [137, 290, 294, 295]. With complexes only slightly stronger than the acid dimers, the band remains single and shows overtone and combination band peaks similar to the acids but with the band center at lower frequencies. However, as the bond strength is increased further this band splits into two separate well defined peaks designated the A and B bands. With further increases in bond strength a new band C begins to appear near 1900 cm^{-1}, and this grows in intensity at the expense of band A as the bonding becomes even stronger. In some situations the band B can double giving four well defined peaks. Finally the intensity of bands A and B diminish and band C grows and moves to yet lower frequencies, so that it appears as an exceptionally broad band between 1300 and 600 cm^{-1} upon which are superimposed the normal fingerprint bands of the remainder of the spectrum. These last cases with no absorption due to OH above 1700 cm^{-1} are essentially symmetric or near symmetric hydrogen bonds of very short length and the OH stretching bands have then become the antisymmetric OHO stretching mode. An excellent general review of the data on strong hydrogen bonds is given in reference [247] and there is much useful data in the papers of Hadzi [125, 148–153, 264, 296], Sheppard [154, 261, 291], and Odinokov [137, 290, 294, 295].

There has been a great deal of discussion on the origins of these multiple bands and many different theories have been advanced. Deuteration shows that bands A and B are mainly OH absorptions, but give indecisive results on band C, mainly because the higher-frequency bands move into this same region on deuteration. The first suggestion, which initially received a good deal of support, was that the A and B bands originated in a quantum mechanical tunnelling phenomenon leading to band splitting in the same way as the well-known splitting in the inversion band of ammonia. However, the magnitude of the splitting does not agree with calculation and it is now generally accepted that this is not a major factor. Hadzi [155] then suggested that the A and B bands originated in the occurence of Fermi resonance interactions with the OH in plane deformations which are raised in frequency as the hydrogen bond strength increases. The C band would then arise from a similar interaction with the OH torsion mode. This view is supported by the observation that there is a steady growth in the integrated intensities of the A, B and C bands as the hydrogen bond strength increases [125] and this correlates with the frequency shift of the centre of gravity of the three bands [259]. Further support for this view has been given by Odinokov [137, 290], who calculated the Fermi interaction constants for a number of systems using the frequencies and intensities of the A, B and C bands, and found good agreement with the observed spectra and the deformation frequencies.

However, there is no simple overall explanation which will account adequately for all the data. In particular, some compounds such as the phosphinic and arsinic acids show no relationship between the ABC bands and the positions of the OH deformations [291]. In fact the apparent opposite appears to occur as the wavenumbers of the overtones fall at the minima between the bands rather than at the expected maxima. This is interpreted by Clayton and Sheppard [291] in terms of a different type of Fermi resonance interaction previously reported by Evans as the source of transmission windows in spectra [156]. The OH band is regarded as initially a single very broad band stretching over the whole region of the ABC bands. The breadth is derived from a number of unresolved bands arising from interactions between the OH stretch and the O...O stretch. If an overtone falls at the frequency of one of these unresolved bands and interacts with it the original band will be displaced. Its contribution to the intensity at its original frequency is then removed and a transmission window appears at this point. Similar transmission windows have been observed in the broad lower frequency OH bands of acid salts with symmetrical or near symmetrical hydrogen bonds. A valuable feature of this explanation is that it removes the difficulty of the multiple bands from a single OH stretch and replaces it by the single broad band which would be expected; this is then split by the mechanism described. A similar mechanism has been proposed to explain the otherwise anomolous spectra of $HCrO_2$ and $DCrO_2$ in which the OD stretching bands appear to occur at higher frequencies than the OH [261].

Fermi resonance can therefore lead either to intensity enhancement at or near the overtone value or to intensity reduction giving the appearance of a band minimum. Which of these occurs will depend in part on whether the overtone falls near the centre or near the tail of a band, but as Bratos has pointed out [247] these two apparently different descriptions of the ABC bands are closely related to each other. The occurrence of either mechanism is adequately covered by his theoretical treatment of hydrogen bonds of this kind.

The spectra with no OH bands above 1700 cm^{-1} represent the strongest hydrogen bonded group. These are all symmetric or near symmetric bonds. The simplest cases are XHX^- or XHX^+ ions where X is a polyatomic molecule. With OHO and NH...O bonds the bands are very broad, beginning around 1300 cm^{-1} and finishing about 400 cm^{-1}, but in a few other systems such as the hydrogen dihalides, the bands are quite sharp. The broad OH...O bands become much more clearly recognisable for what they are if the temperature is lowered sufficiently. In sodium dihydrogen acetate for example the OHO $as.$ band narrows to about 50 cm^{-1} wide at 20 K, and shows some splitting into different components. It then rises well above the other low frequency bands in intensity and is no longer just a broad continuum on which they are superimposed. These systems have been much studied for their theoretical interest. Typical examples are the work of Hadzi on sodium hydrogen diacetate, potassium hydrogen di-trifluoroacetate, and potassium hydrogen succinate, [264, 157, 159], and of Speakman [158]. Interestingly the sodium salt of potassium hydrogen phthalate has weaker non-symmetric hydrogen bonds and shows typical ABC bands, with the B band split into a doublet [240]. In symmetric hydrogen bonds the H/D ratio can rise above 1.4 whereas in some strong but unsymmetrical bonds the ratio can lie close to 1.0 [264].

Although most of the observations on exceptionally strong hydrogen bonds of this type relate to OH...O systems, or to OH...N, very similar results are given by NH...O and NH...N bonds in a suitable situation. Thus the as NHN vibration in the ion $H(C\equiv N)_2^-$ in $H_3CO(C\equiv N)_6$ occurs in the 1000 cm^{-1} region [18], and other similar examples are given by Beck and Smedal [161] and Evans [292]. In contrast, the NHN^- ion in the pyridine hydrogen pyridine ion, and in the bis-trimethyl ammonium ion [293] has its as NHN band in the 2100 cm^{-1} region.

8.2.6. OH deformation vibrations

The in plane OH deformation is very strongly coupled with other modes so that its position gives no information on the strength of the bond. Both the in plane and out of plane frequencies rise as the bond strength increases and in extreme cases both can rise above the value of the OH stretch. In the metal glyoximates for example, the band near 1700 cm^{-1} which was earlier thought to be the OH stretch has now been identified as the in plane bend [297].

In contrast the OH and NH out of plane deformations are relatively free from coupling which makes them useful both for recognition and for the assessment of bond strength. Fischmeister [162] has listed the positions of this band in many carboxylic acids and correlated the frequencies with the O...O distances which are themselves related to the bond strength. The frequencies range from about 650 cm^{-1} for monomers, to 960 cm^{-1} for dimers and to about 1300 cm^{-1} in some acid salts. As the bands are not coupled some relationship is to be expected between their frequencies and those of the corresponding OH stretch. This was first studied by Tarte [163] with some success and has since been extended by Huong [297] and by Novak [254]. The relation is linear as expected. There is some intensification and broadening of these bands on bonding but on a much smaller scale than that which occurs with the OH stretch.

8.3. NH...X hydrogen bonds

Less data are available on NH...X systems than on OH hydrogen bonds. However, pyrrole has been widely used as a standard donor for the assessment of base strengths, and there have been numerous studies on the association of amides and of nucleotides. The NH shifts are usually smaller than those shown by the OH groups of most alcohols or phenols, and the intensification and broadening is correspondingly smaller. It is not legitimate to compare the shifts of OH...O bonds with those of NH...N for the reasons given earlier, but it is likely that the hydrogen bonds are weaker than those of alcohols and acids simply because the NH bonds are usually less acidic and are therefore poorer donors. There are however situations in which the NH bond can gain considerable polarity and strong, and even very strong hydrogen bonds result. The strong bonds occur in systems in which the polarity is increased by resonance. In polymers of pyrazole or imidazole for example the broad NH bands are split into a number of multiple peaks, similar to the bands of acid dimers except that in the amines the individual sub peaks are more clearly differentiated.

The very strong NH...N bands occur in XHX^+ ions such as the pyridine/hydrogen/pyridine complex. This shows two broad bands near 2500 and 2000 cm^{-1} and which is one of the few cases in which there is good evidence that the band splitting arises from proton tunnelling through a double minimum potential with a low barrier [298]. Other examples of very strong bonds are the *bis*-trimethyl ammonium ion which absorbs near 2100 cm^{-1} [293], and the $H(CN)_2$ system which absorbs near 1000 cm^{-1} [18]. The NH_3^+ system in amino acid hydrohalides also forms strong hydrogen bonds showing many multiple peaks between 3000 and 2000 cm^{-1}.

8.3.1. Hydrogen bonding in alkyl and aryl amines

Primary amines are very weak proton donors, but there is little doubt that thay can form hydrogen bonds. Cutmore and Hallam [164] give v_s and v_{as} values for a series of substituted anilines in a variety of solvents, including acetone, ether and pyridine. The shifts are relatively small (v_{as} for *p*-chloroaniline, for example, shifts by only 25 cm^{-1} in acetone), but they can be plotted directly against the corresponding NH values of pyrrole in the same solvents to give a straight line. Similar studies by Josien [165] confirm the weakly associative properties of anilines. Solvent associations can involve either 1 : 1 or 1 : 2 complexes and this will influence the behaviour of the two NH stretching bands. Dyall [299] has studied the changes which occur on passing from one complex to the other. In a 1 : 1 complex the antisymmetric band moves only slightly whilst the symmetric band is moved considerably more. On going to the 1 : 2 complex the symmetric band remains almost stationary and the antisymmetric band shows the major shift. One result of this is that the separation of the two bands is markedly greater in the 1 : 1 complex, and this can be used as a pointer for the occurrence of hydrogen bonding [299, 301]. However, it must be used with caution as major changes in the NHN angles will also affect the separation. The reasons for the differing behaviour of the symmetric and antisymmetric bands on complex formation are set out in Chapter 4. Brink and Bayles [300] and Bellamy and Pace [262] have used the alternative technique of partial deuteration to detect non equivalence in the NH bonds. Brink finds the NH bands remain equivalent in most solvents but that two NH bands appear in partially deuterated aniline in butyl ether. This may well indicate that the latter solvent forms a 1 : 1 complex whilst the other solvents have the 1 : 2 form. Whetsel et al. [166] have reported on solvent effects in aniline, in the near infrared region, and Hambly et al. [167] discuss the association of amines with carbonyl compounds. Intramolecular bonding in o-nitroaniline has been the source of some controversy, as the small shift due to association is masked by the somewhat larger shift due to the electronic effects of the nitro group. However, there is no doubt that intramolecular bonding occurs [168, 173, 262]. Secondary amines form slightly stronger bonds, but unless the nitrogen atom is part of a heterocyclic ring, the frequency shifts remain small. Data on N-substituted anilines in various bases are given by Cutmore and Hallam [164] and by Perrier, Saumagne and Josien [169]. With acetone, N-methylaniline gives a $\Delta\nu$NH value of 40 cm^{-1}, and with pyridine 158 cm^{-1} as compared to the value in hexane. Piperidine is a weaker proton donor, and the corresponding shift in acetone is only 12 cm^{-1}. In N-benzylamines there is some evidence of intramolecular bonding between the NH link and the π cloud of the ring [170]. Very much stronger bonds are found in $\alpha\beta$-unsaturated β-aminoketones, in which resonance gives a greatly enhanced acidity. Dabrowski [174] has given data on a number of compounds of this kind. An extreme case of this bond strengthening is found in NN-dimethylanthranilic acid. In the solid state this exists in the zwitterion form I below, with the $\overset{+}{N}$H absorption in the region of 1660 cm^{-1}, whereas in solution it occurs in form II with an OH hydrogen bond absorbing at about 2540 cm^{-1} [302].

Imines have not been extensively studied, but some preliminary data [171, 172] suggest that =NH groups are able to form stronger hydrogen bonds than simple secondary amines. This would be expected by analogy with pyrrole.

I   II

8.3.2. Hydrogen bonding by heterocyclic amines

Cyclic NH groups in systems such as pyrrole are substantially more acidic than normal amines, because the partial delocalization of the lone-pair electrons of the nitrogen atom increases the charge at this point and so alters the NH polarity. Thus the ΔvNH of pyrrole in ether is the same as the ΔvOH value of methanol in the same solvent. However, the similarity vanishes when [175] the acceptor is changed to triethylamine. The Δv value of pyrrole is then about 100 cm^{-1} smaller than the corresponding value for methanol. This illustrates very well the dangers of attempting to compare hydrogen bonds of different types. Such limited enthalpy measurements as are available indicate that for a given shift in vNH the corresponding ΔH values are significantly greater than those for a corresponding shift of vOH [176].

Pyrrole has, of course, been much studied, and vNH values are available for the association with many different bases. Bellamy [6] lists the shifts for solvent associations and uses these as a standard for the comparison of other systems. Fuson et al. [177] give values for a number of acceptors in inert solvents, and Gomel and Pineau [178] for association with substituted pyridines. Bellamy and Pace [181] give ΔvNH values for the association with a wide range of carbonyl compounds, as do Paoloni et al. [303]. These latter workers have found a relationship between the frequency shifts of the NH and C=O bonds which is given a theoretical basis in terms of Hückel theory and CNDO/2 calculations. Pyrrole-aldehydes are also strongly bonded, and these have been studied by Mirone [179, 180].

Indole also forms relatively strong hydrogen bonds, and Katritzky [182] has tabulated and commented on some sizeable frequency shifts which occur on passing from solution to the solid phase. Gramstad [176] has used indole as a standard donor for the assessment of the relative basicities of phosphoryl compounds, and lists a number of ΔvNH and equilibrium constant values. He finds that the ability of methanol to associate with pyridine (as judged by either ΔvOH or K values) is greater than that of pyrrole, indole or carbazole, but that the reverse is true for associations with the phosphine oxides. This is similar to the earlier findings of Pimentel [175]. Comparable results are quoted by Fritzsche and Dunken [201].

The self-association of pyrazole has been examined in some detail by

Anderson *et al.* [183], who find that, even in 10^{-4}M concentrations in carbon tetrachloride solution, monomers, dimers and trimers coexist. These give rise to a very broad peak between 3400 and 2000 cm^{-1} with six major maxima. Of these, a band at 3175 cm^{-1} is attributed to the dimer absorption. Imidazole has also been studied by Anderson *et al.* [184], Zimmerman [185] and by Wolff and his coworkers [304, 305, 313] who have also studied some derivatives. The bonding is strong so that for example 4-methylimidazole shows no free NH bands even at a dilution of 0.1 mol l^{-1}, and the polymer bands are in the region of 2800 cm^{-1}. The spectra show multiple peaks which are much more clearly differentiated from each other than the corresponding bands in acid dimers, and at one time it was thought that these arose from structure due to interactions with the low frequency NH...N vibrations. However, although the latter do contribute to the overall broadening and so allow Fermi resonance to occur, it is now accepted that the actual subpeaks originate wholly in Fermi resonance interactions. Wolff *et al.* [304] have shown for example that variations in the nature of the acceptor molecule in hetero-association in imidazole, which must cause changes in the NH...X frequencies does not affect the positions of the sub maxima which remain unchanged. The band centre sharpens and moves markedly to lower frequencies on cooling to low temperatures [306]. The shifts are greater than those shown under similar conditions by cyclic dimers and Rice and Wood have explained this in terms of the additional factors which can contribute to band broadening in chains [307].

The self-association of pyrazole has also been studied by Wolff and Muller [308]. This shows two main NH band areas, one at 3260 cm^{-1} and another at 3170 cm^{-1} which is accompanied by as many as eleven sharp peaks on the low frequency side. As with imidazole, they were able to show that, apart from the CH bands all of these originate in Fermi resonance effects, four of them with combinations involving a ring mode at 1543 cm^{-1} and the remainder with interactions with the NH deformation. As before, changing the nature of the acceptor molecule did not alter the position of these subpeaks although there were of course intensity changes related to the shift of the main 3170 cm^{-1} band with which they interact. The Fermi resonance interpretation is therefore well substantiated for compounds of this type.

Strong NH...N bonds are also found in the self-association of compounds such as *iso*cytosine [309] and guanine [310]. This last compound shows a large number of subpeaks spread over a broad band extending from about 3350–2700 cm^{-1}. The main peaks from the two differently bonded NH groups have been identified as at 2908 cm^{-1} and 2696 cm^{-1}. Lowering the temperature increases the intensity and narrows the bands, but in contrast to imidazole, most of them move to higher frequencies. There is no doubt that many of these subpeaks originate in Fermi resonance interactions, just as they do in the azole series. Similar multiple peaks originating in the same way are found in compounds such as purine and adenine [311, 312].

8.3.3. Hydrogen bonding in amides

(a) νNH *stretching frequencies*

Amides self-associate strongly, and unless they are examined in dilute solutions in polar solvents, the NH bands found correspond to the associated form. As the number of units involved in the hydrogen bonded complex itself affects the strength of the bonds, one finds that νNH varies considerably with the concentration. It tends to drift systematically towards lower frequencies as the concentration rises. There is an additional complication arising from the fact that δNH shows a corresponding steady rise. In the *trans*-amides the overtone of this band then approaches increasingly closely to the stretching frequency. Fermi resonance effects then increase.

Alkyl primary amides show the associated NH bands in the solid state near 3300 and 3185 cm^{-1}. In benzamide, which has been studied in more detail by Luttke [186] using polarized radiation, the frequencies fall at 3546 and 3436 cm^{-1} in the vapour, at 3472, 3333 and 3185 cm^{-1} in the melt, and at 3372, 3290 and 3175 cm^{-1} in the crystal. The differences between the melt and the crystal are attributed to the fact that the association in the former is primarily to dimers comparable with those of carboxylic acids, while in the crystal the bonds are further strengthened by a chain association of the dimer units.

Secondary amides have been further studied by several workers. Two bands appear due to Fermi resonance interactions, the main band being slightly displaced towards higher frequency by the combination band which always appears near 3080 cm^{-1}. Data on the positions of these bands in a large series of *trans* secondary amides have been given by Beer *et al.* [187], for liquids and dilute solutions, and by Nyquist for 10 per cent solutions in carbon tetrachloride [188]. The shorter-chain secondary amides all show the bonded νNH absorption near 3280 cm^{-1} in the liquid phase or in concentrated solution, but with halogen, methoxy or phenoxy groups attached to the N-alkyl group the frequency rises to about 3360 cm^{-1}, and on occasion to 3390 cm^{-1}. The drift in position as the concentration changes is well shown by the values given by Nyquist for N-methylacetamide. At low concentrations (below 0.01M) the frequency of the associated band is no longer concentration dependent and only a single bonded species is present. This is the dimer form with νNH at 3366 cm^{-1}. As the concentration is increased, the frequency diminishes rapidly, and in this case reaches a stable value of 3305 cm^{-1} at a concentration of 0.3M. At this point the average size of the aggregated units is seven. In the crystal the frequency falls further still to 3250 cm^{-1}. However, in N-*tert*-butylpivalamide steric hindrance to extensive hydrogen bonding occurs and limits the fall in νNH to 3364 cm^{-1} [208]. Steric effects in this series are largely confined to compounds in which the hydrogen atoms of an NCH$_3$ group are replaced by methyl substituents [241].

The position of this band is also influenced by Fermi resonance with the overtone of the amide II band, and Nyquist gives values which have been corrected for this [188]. The frequency is also affected by α-halogen or alkoxy substitution, as intramolecular bonds then alter the degree of association. The frequencies are then higher than those of normal systems. The NH bands of urea are very complex. Four bands appear in crystals and interstitial compounds. These are discussed by Mecke et al. [195], and by Jose [314]. The spectra of oxamides and of thio-oxamides are described by Spinner [196] and by Nyquist et al. [315]. The NN'-disubstituted oxamides always take the trans form and show two NH stretching bands due to the in phase and out of phase stretching. In dialkyl oxamines in the solid state these bands occur as a doublet in the 3300 cm^{-1} region with a band separation of about 30 cm^{-1}. They are accompanied by combination bands near 3200 and 3080 cm^{-1}. The spectrum of dipropionamide is interesting in that X-ray work has confirmed that the hydrogen bonds are bifurcated and directed towards two equivalent oxygen atoms, in the trans/trans form in the crystal. The hydrogen bond appears to be a little stronger than in normal secondary amides. Two bands appear at 3270 and 3175 cm^{-1}, giving a value of 3320 cm^{-1} after correction for Fermi resonance [317].

Cyclic amides exist in the cis configuration in rings of up to eight members. With nine-membered rings the cis form persists in solution, but the trans form is preferred in the solid. Larger rings all have the amide group in a trans arrangement. This is well shown by Huisgen et al. [190], who show that the amide II band, which is absent from cis lactams, reappears when the ring size is sufficiently large for the trans form to be taken. Large ring systems therefore behave in the same way as open chains, and in the solid state the associated NH band occurs near 3280 cm^{-1}. The cis arrangement of the smaller ring systems allows the NH groups to form stronger hydrogen bonds. νNH in five-, six- or seven-membered rings occurs in the range 3180–3210 cm^{-1}, and is accompanied by subsidiary peaks. These have also been shown to originate in the dimer system. Caprolactam has been extensively studied by Lord and Porro [191], and γ-butyro-lactam by Affsprung [192]. Caprolactam has bands at 3303, 3217 and 3088 cm^{-1}.

In unsaturated cyclic amides there is often the possibility of enhanced resonance, and this greatly strengthens the hydrogen bonds. In pyrid-2-ones and pyrid-4-ones [316], for example, νNH appears as a very broad band, with many sub-maxima, extending over the range 3200–2300 cm^{-1}. This is attributed to the additional strength derived from the resonance, and possibly also from the symmetry in relation to proton transfer. Compounds of this kind have been studied by Bellamy [316], by Shindo [193] and by Price and Willis [194].

The association of amides with other compounds has been less studied. In benzene solutions νNH appears at a value well below that of the normal free NH band, and the proportion of monomer is much increased as compared with non-polar solvents. This is similar to the behaviour of carboxylic acid dimers in this solvent, and can be ascribed to the same cause, that is to association between the polar hydrogen atom and the π cloud of the ring. More general solvent effects in acetanilides have been examined by Dyall and Kemp [199]. These are very complex, because there are two active centres in these compounds and solvents associate either with the carbonyl oxygen or with the NH hydrogen according to their type. These authors have also considered intramolecular bonds in acetylamino compounds and concluded that the ability of a solvent to break such a bond is partly dependent on the energy required to rotate the acetyl amino group into a position where solvent access is possible. Other examples of intramolecular hydrogen bonding in amides are given in references [334] and [340]. Suzi [200] has studied the self-association of amides in dioxane solution. He finds that the hydrogen bond energies of the dimers are about the same as those of the amide/dioxane complexes, so that ΔH for dimerization is zero in this solvent.

Primary thioamides have been studied by Walter [318, 319]. In dilute solution these give free NH bands at about 3500 and 3380 cm^{-1} with a reasonably constant separation of about 115–120 cm^{-1}. In solution at higher concentrations they self-associate and two different species have been observed.

In the presence of bases, 1 : 1 and 1 : 2 complexes are formed, but the splitting of the symmetric stretch due to Fermi resonance makes it difficult to measure the separation of the main bands. In the NHD compounds the frequency shift of thioacetamide on association with dioxane is 127 cm^{-1} and with pyridine 234 cm^{-1}. Primary dithioxamides have been examined by Desseyn *et al.* [323] and shown to be rather weakly intramolecularly hydrogen bonded. This contrasts with the oxamides which form intermolecular bonds. Selenoacetamide has been studied by Devi *et al.* [207].

Secondary thioamides have been studied by Hallam [320, 321], who has compared the associated NH frequencies of *cis* and *trans* forms of amides, thioamides and selenoamides. He quotes values of 3300 (O), 3200 (S) and 3180 cm^{-1} (Se) for the *trans* forms and 3200 (O), 3170 (S) and 3145 cm^{-1} (Se) for the *cis* form. In both conformers there are subsidiary Fermi resonance bands. It must not be concluded from these results that the hydrogen bond strengths follow the order Se > S > O. Gramstad [322] has studied the association of phenol with thioamides and has concluded that the hydrogen bonds are significantly weaker than in the amides themselves.

(b) The amide II band

The amide II band is a well-defined absorption which appears in primary and in *trans* secondary amides. It is a complex vibration in which the in-plane NH deformation mode is strongly coupled with the C—N stretch. In *N*-methylacetamide a normal coordinate treatment suggests that these modes are mixed in the proportions of 60 δNH : 40 C—N stretch [202]. In contrast to the behaviour of the stretching vibration, hydrogen bonding shifts the amide II band to higher frequencies. As the NH bond becomes longer and easier to stretch the orbitals of the nitrogen atom take on more p character, which makes the bond more directional and harder to bend. However, because of the extensive coupling, no relation is to be expected between the shifts of vNH and those of the amide II band. Substantial changes in vNH of more than 100 cm^{-1} can occur without any corresponding shifts in the latter. This is particularly well shown in the data of Geiger [203] on N-substituted phenylbenzamides. Nevertheless, the amide II band always appears at lower frequencies in unassociated compounds, and like vNH its position is liable to drift depending on the degree of polymerization. For these reasons, and because of the impact of coupling, there has been little discussion of the position of this band in relation to hydrogen bonding.

The fact that this absorption is very dependent on the physical state and on the concentration, which is not always given by some authors, makes it impracticable to draw up any tables showing typical frequencies. However, some useful tables of experimental data are available. Flett lists the position of this band in a large number of primary and secondary amides studied in the solid state in potassium bromide discs [204]. Under these conditions most primary amides absorb in the 1640–1620-cm^{-1} range, but there are exceptions, such as o-cyanobenzamide, in which the frequency rises to 1667 cm^{-1}. Flett attributes this to the prevention of amide association by the bulky cyano group. In secondary amides the band appears between 1565 and 1525 cm^{-1}, but its position bears no obvious relation to the chemical structure. Other valuable compilations of data on this absorption are those of Beer et $al.$ [187] (a homologous series of monosubstituted amides), Katritzky and Jones [205] (urethanes) and of Nyquist [188] (α-halogen or alkoxy substituted amides), [315] (oxamides). In the last series the degree of association is influenced by the possibility of competitive intramolecular bonding between the NH group and the halogen or oxygen atom. In addition, Huisgen et $al.$ [190] report the position of this band in large ring systems with the $trans$ configuration. These are normal and show absorption between 1547 and 1538 cm^{-1} in the solid state. In cis amides the corresponding band is thought to have more of a true δNH character. It has been identified near 1440 cm^{-1} in a small number of compounds [189, 197].

Secondary thioamides [206, 196, 323] also show a band in the 1550–1500-cm^{-1} region, which is deuterium sensitive and is assigned as the amide II band. In primary thioamides this rises to the 1600 cm^{-1} region [319].

8.4. Hydrogen bonding in thiols

The frequency shifts in vSH on change of phase are very small. However, it has been recognized that thiols can form hydrogen bonds, as for example, in the association of thiophenol with pyridine, when vSH shifts by 80 cm^{-1}. Studies at higher resolution, using a range of different concentrations, have shown that self-association does occur in thiols. Josien [209, 210] has shown that there are doublets in vSH in thiophenol and in some of its halogenated derivatives, which vary in their relative intensities with the concentration. The free SH band is located near 2591 cm^{-1}, and this is displaced in strong solutions to 2574 cm^{-1}. This result has been confirmed by Spurr and Byers [211] for both thiophenol and for five alkyl mercaptans, the displacement in all cases being about 20 cm^{-1}.

David and Hallam [212] have extended this work, and shown that in nine different thiophenols self-association occurs at concentrations greater than 1 M in carbon tetrachloride solution. The self-association of thiols is very clearly shown in the matrix isolation studies of Barnes et al. [324, 325] on methane and ethane thiols. Methane thiol has a monomer band at 2603 cm^{-1} accompanied by broadened bands at 2576 cm^{-1}, and a doublet at 2552 and 2550 cm^{-1}. It was initially suggested that the first bonded band was due to the dimer and the others from the cyclic tetramer, but it now appears more likely that they all derive from the dimer structure. In the solid, the SH band is considerably broadened and moves to about 2520 cm^{-1}. With suitable *ortho* substituents, intramolecular bonding occurs. With *ortho*, OH or NH$_2$ groups this leads to somewhat stronger hydrogen bonds. In the former, vSH appears at 2547 and 2535 cm^{-1}. These are associated with inter- and intramolecular bonds. In the amino compound vSH appears at 2547 cm^{-1}.

In the ethyl thiosalicylate ΔvSH is again small (23 cm^{-1}) [214]. The energy of the hydrogen bond has been measured by Ginsburg and Loginova [215]. Bulanin et al. [216] have also tabulated some useful data on hydrogen bonds in thiols, and Mathur et al. [217] have investigated their association with N-methylacetamide.

Somewhat stronger hydrogen bonds can be formed in resonant systems. Randhawa and Rao [213] have shown that the bonds of HCOSH dimers are weaker than those of HCSOH and that those of HCSSH are weaker still. Nevertheless the SH shifts in dithioacids are of the order of 80 cm^{-1}. Shifts of over 100 cm^{-1} occur in SH bonds to alkyl sulphoxides [214], in trithiocarbonic and related acids [220] and in dithiophosphoric acids [218]. In alkyl thiophosphonic acid, the shift on intermolecular bonding is about 140 cm^{-1}, but these compounds exist in dilute solution in two rotamers, one of which is weakly hydrogen bonded intramolecularly [219]. The shift from the free frequency is then only 38 cm^{-1}.

8.5. CH...X hydrogen bonds

8.5.1. Hydrogen bonding by haloforms

The ability of the acidic hydrogen atom of chloroform to form a hydrogen bond has been recognized for many years. This is the origin of the heat of mixing with many solvents, and of the frequency shifts in vCO of ketones when they are dissolved in this solvent. These can be as large as $20 \, \text{cm}^{-1}$. Examples of the strengthening of existing bonds by the further association of chloroform have already been discussed. However, there is often little change in vCH as a result of hydrogen-bond formation. In diethyl ether the CH stretching band of chloroform is displaced by only $10 \, \text{cm}^{-1}$, and in acetone it is not displaced at all. This, despite the clear evidence for hydrogen bond formation from the heat of mixing, from the intensity changes both in the fundamental and in the first overtone, and from the changes in vCO. Following the early studies of Lord, this problem has been investigated by many workers who have tried to establish the equilibrium constants and hydrogen bond energies. Studies on this topic have been reported by Bulanin [221], Josien [222, 223] and Kagarise [224, 225]. Becker [226] has shown that chloroform is itself associated in the liquid phase, and suggested that for this reason measurements on the ΔH of association with a base should be made in an inert solvent.

Kagarise [225] has made a number of measurements of this kind using deuterochloroform and bromoform in association with acetone. From equilibrium measurements at different temperatures he arrives at a value of ΔH of 3.5 kcal/mol for the former, and of 2.7 kcal for the latter. The acetone-chloroform association has also been studied by McGlashan and Rastogi [227], and that between haloforms and pyridine by Allerhand [242]. The whole of the data on hydrogen bonding in chloroform and related compounds has been extensively reviewed by Green [249].

8.5.2. Hydrogen bonds with acetylenic and other acidic CH bonds

There is little evidence from infrared spectra of the formation of hydrogen bonds by the $\equiv$CH groups of vinyl compounds, although there is some evidence from other techniques that these may exist. Hydrogen bonding has been observed with trihalo-ethylenes [242], and there is good evidence from Raman spectra of association in 1 : 5 hexadiene [326]. Similarly, there is only slight evidence for hydrogen bonding by active methylene groups, although in the special cases of the onium compounds there is evidence of a progressive fall in vCH accompanied by an increase in intensity as the basicity of the acceptor is increased. This has been regarded as evidence for the formation of hydrogen bonds by the methylene groups [228]. There is also some evidence of hydrogen bonding by methyl groups in methyl sulphonyl compounds. The presence of an adjacent SO_2 group does increase the acidity ($HC(SO_2CH_3)_3$ has a pK_a value of 2), so that this is not unreasonable. Robinson and Aroca [327] find small systematic frequency shifts of the CH stretch in CH_3SO_2F on passing from carbon tetrachloride to d_6 dimethyl sulphoxide as solvent. The shifts are of the order of $26 \, \text{cm}^{-1}$ but they are accompanied by a noticeable band broadening.

Terminal acetylenes show frequency shifts of vCH in electron donor solvents which have long been recognized as arising from hydrogen bonds [229–231, 235, 243]. In mixtures of the acetylene and an acceptor group, in an inert solvent, two bands appear, due to the equilibrium between the free and associated forms, and the relative intensities of these two bands vary with the concentration. The shifts are not large but are well defined, and the very sharp band shape makes them easy to measure with precision. The shifts of vCH in various solvents are exactly paralleled by the nuclear resonance chemical shifts of the acetylenic proton [232]. When acetylene itself associates with acetone in a 1 : 1 complex the symmetry of the C≡C bond is altered, and the stretching band now appears in the spectrum. In the 2 : 1 complex the symmetry is restored and the band vanishes again [244].

Self-association involving the CH link and the π cloud also occurs [75] and results in shifts of the order of 12–14 cm^{-1} in alkyl acetylenes and of 22 cm^{-1} in phenylacetylene. Self-association involving CH...O links also occurs, as in o-bromobenzoylacetylene [160]. The most extensive compilations of data on the frequency shifts of acetylenic hydrogen atoms are those of West [75], Baker [230], Cook [44] and Steen [249].

West [75] has examined both the acidity and basicity of monosubstituted acetylenes, using for the last the ΔvOH values for the association of phenol with the π cloud. In general, electronegative substituents increase the CH acidity and reduce the basicity of the π cloud. The largest CH shift found by West was 123 cm^{-1} for the association of ethyl propiolate with dimethylacetamide.

A particularly interesting acetylenic hydrogen bond is that to the isocyanide group. This is observed in benzyl isocyanide/phenylacetylene complexes, and must be the only known example of a CH...C hydrogen bond [43]. The frequency of the phenyl acetylene CH band is reduced by 26 cm^{-1} on association, and on dilution in inert solvents the monomer band also appears. The shift is comparable with that for the associations with benzyl cyanide (32 cm^{-1}). The assumption that the point of association is the isocyanide carbon atom rather than the π cloud is based on the corresponding OH shift of amyl alcohol bonding to the same compound. This is as much as 158 cm^{-1}, and the fact that the shifts in vOH on association with the π clouds of aromatic rings is very small certainly suggests that in this instance the point of attachment is the carbon atom of the isocyanide group.

8.6. Hydrogen bonding by inorganic acids

(a) Halogen acids

The hydrogen bonding of the halogen acids to ethers has been studied in the vapour phase, and the results are of considerable theoretical interest. These are the only examples in which the interaction with the low frequency hydrogen bond stretching modes results in well defined sub bands whose spacing corresponds to the low stretching frequencies. The bands appear as a broad maximum with sub-bands on either side which are attributed to sum and difference bands [328–330].

In the solid state the acidities of these acids is such that proton transfer usually occurs so that the individual identities of the acids is lost. Some early matrix work [331] suggested that normal hydrogen bonds might persist between the halogen acids and ether, but later studies have shown that in the solids the main feature is a broad band between 1700–700 cm^{-1} derived from the bonded OH$^+$ structure [332]. Similar very strong hydrogen bonds are found in the halogen acid dihydrates. Here proton transfer forms the H$_5$O$_2{}^+$ ion in which the OHO as frequency falls near 1000 cm^{-1} [270, 271]. With weaker bases such as aromatic rings or π clouds, normal hydrogen bonding occurs. Barnes *et al.* [333] have studied the association of HI with alkenes by matrix methods and have been able to determine the configuration of the complex by reference to the changes in the alkene vibrational modes.

One particularly interesting case of hydrogen bonding to a strong base without proton transfer taking place, has been reported by Ault and Pimentel [253]. This is the association of HCl with hydrazoic acid. A very strong hydrogen bond is formed with a shift of the HCl frequency to 630 cm^{-1}.

(b) Other inorganic acids

The pseudohalogen acids, isocyanic acid and isothiocyanic acid have been studied by several workers. Both are considerably stronger proton donors than pyrrole, and isothiocyanic acid is a stronger donor than *iso*cyanic acid. Nelson has given some useful tables listing the shifts of these two acids with various acceptors [336] and also with the shifts of hydrazoic acid in the same solvents [337]. Typical values for the relative shifts in tetrahydrofuran are HNCS 550 cm^{-1}, HNCO 361 cm^{-1} and HN$_3$ 207 cm^{-1}. There was no evidence of proton transfer in any of these systems. Novak [254] has also made a detailed study of the association of H and D isothiocyanic acid with various bases and has commented on the steady fall in the NH/ND ratio as the bonding strength is increased.

The association of HCN has also been studied. The bonding is relatively weak, but the 1 : 1 complex with ether can be detected in the gas phase [338]. In the solid state a 2 : 1 complex is found with the structure

$$R_2O...HCN...HCN$$

Sheppard has also studied the gas phase association of HCN and HN$_3$, and the HCN dimer [339].

Bibliography

1. Pimentel and McClellan, *The Hydrogen Bond,* Freeman, San Francisco, 1960.
2. Pimentel and McClellan *Ann. Reviews Phys. Chem.,* 1971, **22**, 347.

3. Joesten and Drago, *Hydrogen Bonding,* Dekker, New York, 1974.
4. *Hydrogen Bonding,* ed. Hadzi and Thompson, Pergamon Press, 1959.
5. Bellamy, Osborne and Pace, *J. Chem. Soc.,* 1963, 3749.
6. Bellamy, Hallam and Williams, *Trans. Faraday Soc.,* 1958, **54**, 1120.
7. Rundle and Parasol, *J. Chem. Phys.,* 1952, **20**, 1487.
8. Pimentel and Sederholm, *J. Chem. Phys.,* 1956, **24**, 639.
9. Lippincott and Schroeder, *J. Chem. Phys.,* 1955, **23**, 1099.
10. Feilchenfeld, *Spectrochim. Acta,* 1958, **12**, 280.
11. Schwarzmann, *Naturwiss.,* 1962, **49**, 103.
12. Bellamy and Williams, *Proc. Roy. Soc.,* 1960, **A244**, 119.
13. Bellamy, Eglinton and Morman, *J. Chem. Soc.,* 1961, 4762.
14. Baker and Kaeding, *J. Amer. Chem. Soc.,* 1959, **81**, 5904.
15. West, Banay and Powell, *J. Amer. Chem. Soc.,* 1960, **82**, 6269.
16. Allerhand and Schleyer, *J. Amer. Chem. Soc.,* 1963, **85**, 371.
17. Bellamy, Morgan and Pace, *Spectrochim. Acta,* 1966, **22**, 535.
18. Gudel, *J. Chem. Phys,* 1972, **56**, 4984.
19. Costain and Srivastava, *J. Chem. Phys.,* 1961, **35**, 1903.
20. Snyder and Ibers, *J. Chem. Phys.,* 1962, **36**, 1356.
21. Kuhn and Bowman, *Spectrochim. Acta,* 1967, **23A**, 189.
22. Cole and Mitchell, *Austral. J. Chem.,* 1965, **19**, 102.
23. Bellamy and Hallam, *Trans. Faraday Soc.,* 1959, **55**, 220.
24. Brown, Eglinton and Martin-Smith, *Spectrochim. Acta,* 1963, **19**, 463.
25. Ingold, *Can. J. Chem.,* 1962, **40**, 111.
26. Baker and Shulgin, *Spectrochim. Acta,* 1966, **22**, 95.
27. Oki and Iwamura, *Bull. Chem. Soc. Japan,* 1959, **32**, 567, 955, 1135; 1960, **33**, 681, 717, 1600.
28. Oki, Iwamura and Urushihara, *Bull. Chem. Soc. Japan,* 1958, **31**, 769.
29. Trifan, Weinmann and Kuhn, *J. Amer. Chem. Soc.,* 1957, **79**, 6566.
30. Baker and Shulgin, *J. Amer. Chem. Soc.,* 1958, **80**, 5358.
31. Beckering, *J. Phys. Chem.,* 1961, **65**, 206.
32. Moriconi, O'Connor, Kuhn, Keneally and Wallenberger, *J. Amer. Chem. Soc.,* 1959, **81**, 6472.
33. Baker and Shulgin, *Spectrochim. Acta,* 1963, **19**, 1611.
34. Cairns and Eglinton, *J. Chem. Soc.,* 1965, 5906.
35. Josien and Sourisseau, *Hydrogen Bonding,* cf. reference [4], p. 129.
36. Basila, *J. Chem. Phys.,* 1961, **35**, 1151.
37. Basila, Saier and Coggeshall, *J. Amer. Chem. Soc.,* 1965, **87**, 1665.
38. West, *J. Amer. Chem. Soc.,* 1959, **81**, 1614.
39. Schleyer, Trifan and Bacskai, *J. Amer. Chem. Soc.,* 1958, **80**, 6691.
40. Baitinger, Schleyer and Mislow, *J. Amer. Chem. Soc.,* 1965, **87**, 3168.
41. Schleyer, Wintner, Trifan and Bacskai, *Tetrahedron Letters,* 1959, **14**, 1.
42. Baker and Shulgin, *Can. J. Chem.,* 1965, **43**, 650.
43. Ferstandig, *J. Amer. Chem. Soc.,* 1962, **84**, 3553.
44. Cook, *J. Amer. Chem. Soc.,* 1958, **80**, 49.
45. Baker, *J. Amer. Chem. Soc.,* 1958, **80**, 3598.
46. Bourassa-Bataille, Savageau and Sandorfy, *Can. J. Chem.,* 1963, **41**, 2240.
47. Barnes, Hallam and Jones, *Proc. Roy. Soc.,* 1973, **A355**, 97.
48. Banerjee and Chakraborty, *Ind. J. Phys.,* 1961, **35**, 151.
49. Sirkar, Deb and Banerjee, *Ind. J. Phys.,* 1958, **32**, 345.
50. Kuhn, Luttke and Mecke, *Zeit. Anal. Chem.,* 1959, **170**, 106.
51. Josien and Pineau, *Compt. Rend. Acad. Sci. France,* 1960, **250**, 2359.
52. Kreuger and Mettee, *Can. J. Chem.,* 1964, **42**, 326.
53. Kreuger and Mettee, *Can. J. Chem.,* 1964, **42**, 340.
54. Schleyer and West, *J. Amer. Chem. Soc.,* 1959, **81**, 3164.

55. West, Powell, Whatley, Lee and Schleyer, *J. Amer. Chem. Soc.*, 1962, **84**, 3221.
56. Josien, *Pure and Applied Chem.*, 1962, **4**, 33.
57. Barnes and Hallam, *Trans Faraday Soc.*, 1970, **66**, 1920.
58. Becker, *Spectrochim. Acta*, 1961, **17**, 436.
59. Gramstad, *Spectrochim. Acta*, 1963, **19**, 497.
60. Grundy and Morris, *Spectrochim. Acta*, 1964, **20**, 695.
61. Gramstad, *Acta Chem. Scand.*, 1961, **15**, 1337.
62. Powell and West, *Spectrochim. Acta*, 1964, **20**, 983.
63. Kuhn and Bowman, *Spectrochim. Acta*, 1961, **17**, 650.
64. Joesten and Drago, *J. Amer. Chem. Soc.*, 1962, **84**, 3817.
65. Dorval and Zeegers-Huyskens, *Spectrochim. Acta*, 1973, **29A**, 1805.
66. West and Banay, *J. Amer. Chem. Soc.*, 1959, **81**, 6145.
67. Spaargaren, Kruk, Molenaar–Langeveld, Korver, Van der Haak and de Boer, *Spectrochim. Acta*, 1972, **28A**, 965.
68. Wren and Lenten, *J. Chem. Soc.*, 1961, 2557.
69. Inskeep, Kelliher, McMahon and Somers, *J. Chem. Phys.*, 1958, **28**, 1033.
70. Thiel, Becker and Pimentel, *J. Chem. Phys.*, 1957, **27**, 95.
71. Bellamy and Pace, *Spectrochim. Acta*, 1966, **22**, 525.
72. Juarez, Martin-Lomas and Bellanato, *Spectrochim. Acta*, 1976, **32A**, 1675.
73. Rao and Dwivedi *J. Chem. Soc. Faraday Trans* 1975, **11**, 955.
74. Kuhn, *J. Amer. Chem. Soc.*, 1952, **74**, 2492.
75. West and Kraihanzel, *J. Amer. Chem. Soc.*, 1961, **83**, 765.
76. Brutcher and Bauer, *J. Amer. Chem. Soc.*, 1962, **84**, 2236.
77. Kuhn, Schleyer, Baitinger and Eberson, *J. Amer. Chem. Soc.*, 1964, **86**, 650.
78. Kuhn, *J. Amer. Chem. Soc.*, 1958, **80**, 5950.
79. Schleyer, *J. Amer. Chem. Soc.*, 1961, **83**, 1368.
80. Malysev and Murzin, *Bull. Acad. Sci. U.R.S.S. phys. ser.*, 1958, **22**, 1107.
81. Julia, Varech, Burer and Gunthard, *Helv. Chim. Acta*, 1960, **43**, 1623.
82. Buc and Néel, *Compt. Rend. Acad. Sci. France*, 1961, **252**, 1786.
83. Stolow, *J. Amer. Chem. Soc.*, 1964, **86**, 2170.
84. Stolow, McDonagh and Bonaventura, *J. Amer. Chem. Soc.*, 1963, **86**, 2165.
85. Cairns and Eglinton, *Nature*, 1962, **196**, 535.
86. Gramstad and Fuglevik, *Acta Chem. Scand.*, 1962, **16**, 1369.
87. Dunken and Fritsche, *Zeit. Chem.*, 1961, **1**, 249; 1962, **2**, 379.
88. Heinen, Thesis, University of Amsterdam, 1964.
89. Grunwald and Coburn, *J. Amer. Chem. Soc.*, 1958, **80**, 1322.
90. Fritzche, *Spectrochim. Acta*, 1965, **21**, 799.
91. Fritzche, *Acta Chim. Acad. Sci. Hung.*, 1964, **40**, 31.
92. Whetsel and Kagarise, *Spectrochim. Acta*, 1962, **18**, 315.
93. Takahashi and Li, *J. Phys. Chem.*, 1965, **69**, 1622.
94. Huong and Graja, *Chem. Phys. Letters*, 1972, **13**, 162.
95. Campbell and Gilow, *J. Amer. Chem. Soc.*, 1960, **82**, 5426; 1962, **84**, 1440.
96. Nejland and Vanag, *Adv. Chem. Moscow*, 1959, **28**, 436.
97. Martin, Fernelius and Shamma, *J. Amer. Chem. Soc.*, 1959, **81**, 130.
98. Brookes, Eglinton and Morman, *J. Chem. Soc.*, 1961, 661.
99. Hoyer and Hensel, *Zeit. Electrochem.*, 1960, **64**, 958.
100. Hoyer and Macdonald, *Zeit. Electrochem.*, 1962, **66**, 269.
101. Bueno and Lucisano, *Spectrochim. Acta*, 1979, **35A**, 381.
102. Gramstad, *Spectrochim. Acta*, 1963, **19**, 829.
103. Ghersetti and Lusa, *Spectrochim. Acta*, 1965, **21**, 1067.
104. Aksnes and Gramstad, *Acta Chem. Scand.*, 1960, **14**, 1485.
105. Gramstad and Fuglevik, *Acta Chem. Scand.*, 1962, **16**, 2368.
106. Blindheim and Gramstad, *Spectrochim. Acta*, 1965, **21**, 1073.
107. Gramstad and Snaprud, *Acta Chem. Scand.*, 1962, **16**, 999.

108. Boll, *Acta Chem. Scand.*, 1958, **12**, 1777.
109. Baitinger, Schleyer, Murty and Robinson, *Tetrahedron*, 1964, **20**, 1635.
110. Ungnade and Kissinger, *Tetrahedron*, 1963, **19**, Suppl. I, 121.
111. Ungnade, Loughran and Kissinger, *J. Phys. Chem.*, 1962, **66**, 2643.
112. Findlay and Kidman, *Austral. J. Chem.*, 1965, **18**, 521.
113. Robinson, Quoted in ref. [101].
114. Urbanski, *Tetrahedron*, 1959, **6**, 1.
115. Eckstein, Gluzinski, Sobotka and Urbanski, *J. Chem. Soc.*, 1961, 1370, and references therein.
116. Iogansen and Litovchenko, *Optics and Spectroscopy*, 1964, **16**, 380.
117. Kartha, Jones and Robertson, *Proc. Ind. Acad. Sci.*, 1963, **58A**, 216.
118. Dallinga and Engberts, *Spectrochim. Acta*, 1974, **30A**, 1923.
119. Bratoz, Hadzi and Sheppard, *Spectrochim. Acta*, 1956, **8**, 249.
120. Sheppard, in *Hydrogen Bonding* (ref. 4), p. 85.
121. Guilleme, Chabanel and Wojtkowiak, *Spectrochim. Acta*, 1971, **27A**, 2355.
122. Villepin and Novak, *Spectrochim. Acta*, 1978, **34A**, 1009, 1019.
123. Bellamy and Pace, *Spectrochim. Acta*, 1963, **19**, 435.
124. Bellamy, Lake and Pace, *Spectrochim. Acta*, 1963, **19**, 443.
125. Hadzi and Kobilarov, *J. Chem. Soc.*, 1966, A439.
126. Hadzi, *Bull. Slovene. Chem. Soc.*, 1958, 21.
127. Bell and Barrow, *J. Chem. Phys.*, 1959, **31**, 300. 1158.
128. Josien, Jussot Dubien and Vizet, *Bull. Soc. Chim. France*, 1957, 1148.
129. Freedman, *J. Amer. Chem. Soc.*, 1961, **83**, 2900.
130. Gramstad, *Acta Chem. Scand.*, 1962, **16**, 807.
131. Sicher, Horak and Svoboda, *Coll. Czech. Chem. Comm.*, 1959, **4**, 950.
132 Drefahl and Heublein, *Chem. Ber.*, 1961, **41**, 915.
133. Drefahl and Heublein, *Chem. Ber.*, 1961, **41**, 922.
134. Hite, Smissman and West, *J. Amer. Chem. Soc.*, 1960, **82**, 1207.
135. De Roos and Bakker, *Rec. Trav. Chim.*, 1962, **81**, 219.
136. Igonin and Bass, *Doklady Akad. Nauk. S.S.S.R.*, 1958, **121**, 652.
137. Odinokov, Maximov and Dzizenko, *Spectrochim. Acta*, 1969, **25A**, 131.
138. Baker and Shulgin, *J. Amer. Chem. Soc.*, 1959, **81**, 1523.
139. Allerhand and Schleyer, *J. Amer. Chem. Soc.*, 1963, **85**, 866.
140. Califano and Luttke, *Zeit. Physikal. Chem.*, 1955, **5**, 240.
141. Luck, *Zeit. Electrochem.*, 1961, **65**, 355.
142. Reiser, *Chem. Listy.*, 1958, **52**, 397.
143. Mitra, *J. Chem. Phys.*, 1962, **36**, 3286.
144. Rossotti and Rossotti, *J. Chem. Soc.*, 1958, 1304.
145. Badger and Moritz, *J. Chem. Soc.*, 1958, 3437.
146. Gill and Morgan, *Nature*, 1959, **183**, 248.
147. Refn, *Spectrochim. Acta*, 1961, **17**, 40.
148. Baker and Harris, *J. Chem. Phys.*, 1957, **27**, 991.
149. Blinc, Hadzi and Novak, *Zeit. Electrochem.*, 1960, **64**, 567.
150. Blinc and Hadzi, *Spectrochim. Acta*, 1960, **16**, 853.
151. Detoni and Hadzi, *Spectrochim. Acta*, 1964, **20**, 949.
152. Hadzi, *J. Chem. Soc.*, 1962, 5128.
153. Hadzi and Novak, *Proc. Chem. Soc.*, 1960, 241.
154. Braunholtz, Hall, Mann and Sheppard, *J. Chem. Soc.*, 1959, 868.
155. Hadzi, *Pure Appl. Chem.*, 1965, **11**, 435.
156. Evans and Wright, *Spectrochim. Acta*, 1960, **16**, 352. Evans, *ibid*, 994.
157. Orel and Hadzi, *Spectrochim. Acta*, 1976, **32A**, 1731.
158. Speakman, *Structure and Bonding*, 1972, **12**, 141.

159. Angeloni, Marzocchi, Hadzi, Orel and Sbrana, *Spectrochim. Acta*, 1977, **33A**, 735.
160. Ferguson and Tyrrell, *Chem. Comm.*, 1965, 195.
161. Beck and Smedal, *Z. Naturforsch.*, 1964, **20B**, 109.
162. Fischmeister, *Spectrochim. Acta*, 1964, **20**, 1071.
163. Tarte, in *Hydrogen Bonding* (ref. 4), p. 115.
164. Cutmore and Hallam, *Trans. Faraday Soc.*, 1962, **58**, 40.
165. Lauransan, Pineau and Josien, *Ann. Chim.*, 1964, **9**, 213.
166. Whetsel, Robertson and Krell, *Analyt. Chem.*, 1960, **32**, 1281.
167. Hambly and Bonnyman, *Austral. J. Chem.*, 1958, **11**, 529.
168. Farmer and Thompson, *Spectrochim. Acta*, 1960, **16**, 559.
169. Perrier, Saumagne and Josien, *Compt. Rend. Acad. Sci. France*, 1964, **259**, 1825.
170. Oki and Mutai, *Bull. Chem. Soc. Japan*, 1960, **33**, 784.
171. Prevorsek, *Compt. Rend. Acad. Sci. France*, 1957, **244**, 2599.
172. Grivas and Taurins, *Can. J. Chem.*, 1959, **37**, 795.
173. Moritz, *Spectrochim. Acta*, 1962, **18**, 671.
174. Dabrowski, *Spectrochim. Acta*, 1963, **19**, 475.
175. Huggins and Pimentel, *J. Phys. Chem.*, 1962, **60**, 1615.
176. Gramstad and Fuglevik, *Spectrochim. Acta*, 1965, **21**, 503.
177. Fuson, Pineau and Josien, *J. Chim. Phys.*, 1958, **55**, 454.
178. Gomel and Pineau, *Compt. Rend. Acad. Sci. France*, 1961, **252**, 2870.
179. Mirone and Lorenzelli, *Ann. Chim. Roma*, 1958, **48**, 72.
180. Mirone and Lorenzelli, *Ann. Chim. Roma*, 1959, **49**, 59.
181. Bellamy and Pace, *Spectrochim. Acta*, 1963, **19**, 1831.
182. Katritzky and Ambler, in *Physical Methods in Heterocyclic Chemistry*, Academic Press, 1963, p. 212.
183. Anderson, Duncan and Rossotti, *J. Chem. Soc.*, 1961, 140.
184. Anderson, Duncan and Rossotti, *J. Chem. Soc.*, 1961, 2165.
185. Zimmerman, *Zeit. Electrochem.*, 1961, **65**, 821.
186. Weckherlin and Luttke, *Zeit. Electrochem.*, 1960, **64**, 1228.
187. Beer, Kessler and Sutherland, *J. Chem. Phys.*, 1958, **29**, 1097.
188. McLachan and Nyquist, *Spectrochim. Acta*, 1964, **20**, 1397.
189. Miyazawa, *J. Mol. Spectroscopy*, 1960, **4**, 168.
190. Huisgen, Brade, Walz and Glogger, *Chem. Ber.*, 1957, **90**, 1437.
191. Lord and Porro, *Zeit. Electrochem.*, 1960, **64**, 672.
192. Affsprung, Christian and Worley, *Spectrochim. Acta*, 1964, **20**, 1415.
193. Shindo, *Chem. Pharm. Bull. Japan*, 1959, **7**, 407.
194. Price and Willis, *Austral. J. Chem.*, 1959, **12**, 589.
195. Kutzelnigg, Mecke, Schrader, Nerdel and Kresse, *Zeit. Electrochem.*, 1961, **65**, 109.
196. Milligan, Spinner and Swan, *J. Chem. Soc.*, 1961, 1919.
197. Miyazawa, *J. Mol. Spectroscopy*, 1960, **4**, 155.
198. Suzuki, Tsuboi, Shimanouchi and Mizushima, *J. Chem. Phys.*, 1959, **31**, 1437.
199. Dyall and Kemp, *Spectrochim. Acta*, 1966, **22**, 483.
200. Suzi, *J. Phys. Chem.*, 1965, **69**, 2799.
201. Fritzsche and Dunken, *Acta Chim. Acad. Sci. Hung.*, 1964, **40**, 37.
202. Miyazawa, Shimanouchi and Mizushima, *J. Chem. Phys.*, 1958, **29**, 611.
203. Geiger, *Spectrochim. Acta*, 1966, **22**, 495.
204. Flett, *Spectrochim. Acta*, 1962, **18**, 1537.
205. Katritzky and Jones, *J. Chem. Soc.*, 1960, 676.
206. Hadzi, *J. Chem. Soc.*, 1957, 847.
207. Devi, Sathyanararana and Volka, *Spectrochim. Acta*, 1978, **34A**, 169.

208. Jones, *Spectrochim. Acta,* 1964, **20**, 1879.
209. Josien, Dizabo and Saumagne, *Bull. Soc. Chim. France,* 1957, 423.
210. Josien, Castinel and Saumagne, *Bull. Soc. Chim. France,* 1957, 648.
211. Spurr and Byers, *J. Phys. Chem.,* 1958, **62**, 425.
212. David and Hallam, *Spectrochim. Acta,* 1965, **21**, 841.
213. Randhawa and Rao, *J. Mol. Structure,* 1974, **21**, 123.
214. Wagner, Becher and Kottenhahn, *Chem. Ber.,* 1956, **89**, 1708.
215. Ginsburg and Loginova, *Doklady Akad. Nauk. S.S.S.R.,* 1964, **156**, 1382.
216. Bulanin, Denisov and Pushkina, *Optics and Spectroscopy,* 1959, **6**, 49.
217. Mathur, Wang and Li, *J. Phys. Chem.,* 1964, **68**, 2140.
218. Allen and Colcough, *J. Chem. Soc.,* 1957, 3912.
219. Nyquist, *Spectrochim. Acta,* 1969, **25A**, 47.
220. Tice and Powell, *Spectrochim. Acta,* 1965, **21**, 835.
221. Bulanin, Denisov and Shehepkin, *Optica i Spectroskopiya,* 1959, **7**, 119.
222. Lascombe, Devaure and Josien, *J. Chim. Phys.,* 1964, **61**, 1271.
223. Josien, Leicknam and Fuson, *Bull. Soc. Chim. France,* 1958, 188.
224. Whetsel and Kagarise, *Spectrochim. Acta,* 1962, **18**, 329.
225. Kagarise, *Spectrochim. Acta,* 1963, **19**, 629.
226. Becker, *Spectrochim. Acta,* 1959, **15**, 743.
227. McGlashan and Rastogi, *Trans. Faraday Soc.,* 1958, **54**, 496.
228. Aksnnes and Songstad, *Acta Chem. Scand.,* 1964, **18**, 655.
229. Wojtkowiak and Romanet, *Compt. Rend. Acad. Sci. France,* 1960, **250**, 3980.
230. Baker and Harris, *J. Amer. Chem. Soc.,* 1960, **82**, 1923.
231. Murahashi, Ryutani and Hatada, *Bull. Chem. Soc. Japan,* 1959, **32**, 1001.
232. Whipple, Goldstein, Mandell, Reddy and McClure, *J. Amer. Chem. Soc.,* 1959, **81**, 1321.
233. Matrosov and Kabachnik, *Spectrochim. Acta,* 1972, **28A**, 313.
234. Ogoshi and Yoshida, *Spectrochim. Acta,* 1971, **27A**, 165.
235. Singh, Murthy and Rao, *Trans. Faraday Soc.,* 1966, **62**, 1056.
236. Detoni, Hadzi and Juranji, *Spectrochim. Acta,* 1974, **30A**, 249.
237. Brookes, Eglinton and Hanaineh, *Spectrochim. Acta,* 1966, **22**, 161.
238. Allen, Watkinson and Webb, *Spectrochim. Acta,* 1966, **22**, 807.
239. Hadzi and Premru, *Spectrochim. Acta,* 1967, **23A**, 35.
240. Orel, Hadzi and Cabassi, *Spectrochim. Acta,* 1975, **31A**, 169.
241. Jones, *Spectrochim. Acta,* 1966, **22**, 1555.
242. Allerhand and Schleyer, *J. Amer. Chem. Soc.,* 1963, **85**, 1715.
243. Boobyer, *Spectrochim. Acta,* 1967, **23A**, 321.
244. Creswell and Barrow, *Spectrochim. Acta,* 1966, **22**, 839.
245. Vinogradov and Linnell, *Hydrogen Bonding,* Van Nostrand/Reinhold, London, 1971.
246. Wood, in *Spectroscopy and Structure of Molecular Complexes,* Ed Yarwood, Plenum Press, London, 1973.
247. Hadzi and Bratos, in *Hydrogen Bonding, Recent Developments in Theory and Experiment,* Eds Schuster, Zundel and Sandorfy, Amsterdam, North Holland, Vol. 2, p. 567.
248. Murthy and Rao, *Applied Spectroscopy Reviews,* 1969, **2**, 69.
249. Green, *Hydrogen bonding by CH groups,* Macmillan, London, 1974.
250. Hallam, as reference [247], Vol. 3, p. 1065.
251. Horak, Moravec and Pliva, *Spectrochim. Acta,* 1965, **21**, 919.
252. Lautie and Novak, *J. Chem. Phys,* 1972, **56**, 2479.
253. Ault and Pimentel, *J. Phys. Chem.,* 1973, **77**, 1649.
254. Novak, *Structure and Bonding,* 1974, **18**, 177.
255. Bellamy and Owen, *Spectrochim. Acta,* 1969, **25A**, 329.

256. Hadzi and Orel, *J. Mol. Structure*, 1973, **18**, 227.
257. Stymne, Stymne and Watermark, *J. Amer. Chem. Soc.*, 1973, **95**, 3490.
258. Busfield, Ennis and McEwan, *Spectrochim. Acta*, 1973, **29A**, 1259.
259. Detoni, Hadzi, Smerkolj, Hawarnek, and Sobczyk, *J. Chem. Soc. A*, 1970, 2851.
260. de Villepin and Novak, *Spectrochim. Acta*, 1971, **27A**, 1259.
261. Clayton, Sheppard, Stace and Upfield, *Chem. Comm.* 1975, **31**.
262. Bellamy and Pace, *Spectrochim. Acta*, 1971, **27A**, 1869.
263. Bellamy and Pace, *Spectrochim. Acta*, 1971, **27A**, 705.
264. Hadzi, Orel and Novak, *Spectrochim. Acta*, 1973, **29A**, 1745.
265. Iogansen and Rosenberg, *Doklady, Akad. Sci. USSR*, 1971, **197**, 117.
266. Rosenberg and Iogansen, *Spectrosc. Letters*, 1972, **5**, 75.
267. Jakobsen, Brasch and Mikawa, *Appl. Spectrosc.*, 1968, **22**, 641.
268. Jakobsen and Katon, *Spectrochim. Acta*, 1973, **29A**, 1963.
269. Doral and Zeegers-Huyskens, *Spectrochim. Acta*, 1974, **30A**, 1757.
270. Rosiere and Potier, *J. Mol. Structure*, 1972, **13**, 91.
271. Gilbert and Sheppard, *J. Chem Soc. Faraday Trans.* II, 1973, **69**, 1628.
272. Horak and Pliva, *Spectrochim. Acta*, 1965, **21**, 911.
273. Osawa and Yoshida, *Spectrochim. Acta*, 1967, **23A**, 2029.
274. Huong and Lassegues, *Spectrochim. Acta*, 1970, **26A**, 269.
275. Robinson, Schreiber and Spencer, *Spectrochim. Acta*, 1972, **28A**, 397.
276. Buckley, Giguere and Yamamoto, *Can. J. Chem.*, 1968, **46**, 2917.
277. Buckley, Giguere and Schneider, *Can. J. Chem*, 1969, **47**, 901.
278. Fujimoto, Takeoka and Kosima, *Bull. Chem. Soc. Japan*, 1970, **43**, 991.
279. Berthelot, Laurence and Wojtkowich, *J. Mol. Structure*, 1973, **18**, 43.
280. Bellamy and Pace, *Spectrochim. Acta*, 1969, **25A**, 319.
281. Brzezinski, Dziembowska, and Szafran, *Roczniki Chem.*, 1973, **47**, 155.
282. Reynolds, in *Progress in Inorganic Chemistry*, Ed Lippert, Wiley, New York, 1970, Vol. 12, p. 1.
283. Herlocker, Drage and Merk, *Inorganic Chem.*, 1966, **5**, 2009.
284. Nelson, Nathan and Radsdale, *J. Amer. Chem. Soc.*, 1968, **90**, 5754.
285. Marechal and Witkowski, *J. Chem. Phys.*, 1968, **48**, 3697.
286. Redington and Lin, *J. Chem. Phys.*, 1971, **54**, 4111.
287. Grenie, Cornut and Lassegues, *J. Chem. Phys*, 1971, **55**, 5844.
288. Theoret, *Spectrochim. Acta*, 1971, **27A**, 11.
289. Igarashi, Watari and Aida, *Spectrochim. Acta*, 1969, **25A**, 1743.
290. Odinokov and Iogansen, *Spectrochim. Acta*, 1972, **28A**, 2343.
291. Clayton and Sheppard, *Chem. Comm.* 1969, 1431.
292. Evans, Jones and Wilkinson, *J. Chem. Soc.* 1964, 3164.
293. Marsi and Wood, *J. Mol. Structure*, 1972, **14**, 201, 217.
294. Odinokov, Iogansen and Dzizenko, *Zh. Prikl. Spektroskopiya*, 1971, **14**, 418.
295. Odinokov, Mashkovsky, Glazunov, Iogansen and Rassadin, *Spectrochim. Acta*, 1976, **32A**, 1355.
296. Detoni, Diop, Gunde, Hadzi, Orel, Potier and Potier, *Spectrochim. Acta*, 1979, **35A**, 443.
297. Huong, Couzi and Lascombe *J. Chim. Phys*, 1967, **64**, 1056.
298. Clements, Dean, Singh and Wood, *Chem. Commun.*, 1971, 1125, 1127.
299. Dyall, *Spectrochim. Acta*, 1969, **25A**, 1423.
300. Brink and Bayles, *Spectrochim. Acta*, 1974, **30A**, 835.
301. Dyall, *Spectrochim. Acta*, 1969, **25A**, 1727.
302. Rao and Jose, *Spectrochim. Acta*, 1974, **30A**, 859.
303. Paoloni, Patti and Mangano, *J. Mol. Structure*, 1975, **27**, 123.
304. Wolff and Muller, *J. Chem. Phys.*, 1974, **60**, 2938.
305. Wolff and Wolff, *Spectrochim. Acta*, 1971, **27A**, 2109.

306. Foglizzo and Novak, *Advances in Raman Spectroscopy*, Heyden, London, 1972, p. 515.
307. Rice and Wood, *J. Chem. Soc. Faraday Trans*, II, 1973, **69**, 91.
308. Wolff and Muller, *Spectrochim. Acta*, 1976, **32A**, 561.
309. Delabar, *Zeit. Naturforsch*, 1974, 296, 343.
310. Delabar and Majoube, *Spectrochim. Acta*, 1978, **34A**, 129.
311. Lautie and Novak, *J. Chim. Phys.*, 1974, **71**, 415.
312. Lautie and Novak, *J. Chim. Phys*, 1968, **65**, 1359.
313. Wolff, Muller and Muller, *Ber. Bunsen Gesellschaft*, 1974, **78**, 1241.
314. Jose, *Spectrochim. Acta*, 1969, **25A**, 111.
315. Nyquist, Chrisman, Putzig, Woodward and Loy, *Spectrochim. Acta*, 1979, **35A**, 91.
316. Bellamy and Rogasch, *Proc. Roy. Soc.*, 1960, **A257**, 98.
317. Kuroda, Machida and Uno, *Spectrochim. Acta*, 1974, **30A**, 47.
318. Walter and Kubersky, *J. Mol. Structure*, 1972, **11**, 201.
319. Walter and Vinkler, *Spectrochim. Acta*, 1977, **33A**, 205.
320. Hallam and Jones, *J. Chem. Soc.*, 1969, 1033.
321. Hallam and Jones, *J. Mol. Structure*, 1970, **5**, 1.
322. Gramstad and Sandstrom, *Spectrochim. Acta*, 1969, **25A**, 31.
323. Desseyn, Jacob and Herman, *Spectrochim. Acta*, 1969, **25A**, 1685.
324. Barnes and Howells, *J. Chem. Soc. Faraday Trans.*, II, 1972, **68**, 729.
325. Barnes and Murto, *J. Chem. Soc. Faraday Trans.*, II, 1972, **68**, 1642.
326. Binet and Romanet, *J. Raman Spectroscopy*, 1976, **5**, 243.
327. Robinson and Aroca, *Spectrochim. Acta*, 1978, **34A**, 1249.
328. Bertie and Millen, *J. Chem. Soc.*, 1965, 497, 514.
329. Bertie and Falk, *Can. J. Chem.*, 1973, **51**, 1713.
330. Lascombe, Lassegues and Huong. *Int. Conf. on H bonding, Ottawa*, 1972.
331. Steel and Sheppard, *Spectrochim. Acta*, 1969, **25A**, 1287.
332. Lassegues, Cornut, Houng and Grenie, *Spectrochim. Acta*, 1971, **27A**, 73.
333. Barnes, Davies, Hallam and Jones, *J. Chem. Soc. Faraday Trans.*, II, 1973, **69**, 246.
334. Oki and Mutai, *Spectrochim. Acta*, 1969, **25A**, 1941.
335. Barakat, Nelson, Nelson and Pullin, *Trans. Faraday Soc.*, 1969, **65**, 41.
336. Nelson, *Spectrochim. Acta*, 1970, **26A**, 109.
337. Nelson, *Spectrochim. Acta*, 1970, **26A**, 235.
338. Steel and Sheppard, *Spectrochim. Acta*, 1969, **25A**, 1287.
339. Jones, Steel and Sheppard, *Spectrochim. Acta*, 1969, **25A**, 385.
340. Chiron and Graff, *Spectrochim. Acta*, 1976, **32A**, 1303.